AN INTRODUCTION TO THE
THEORY OF SEISMOLOGY

AN INTRODUCTION TO THE
THEORY OF SEISMOLOGY

BY

K. E. BULLEN
M.A., Sc.D., F.R.S.

Professor of Applied Mathematics
in the University of Sydney

THIRD EDITION

CAMBRIDGE
AT THE UNIVERSITY PRESS
1965

PUBLISHED BY

THE SYNDICS OF THE CAMBRIDGE UNIVERSITY PRESS

Bentley House, 200 Euston Road, London, N.W. 1
American Branch: 32 East 57th Street, New York, N.Y. 10022
West African Office: P.M.B. 5181, Ibadan, Nigeria

THIS EDITION

©

CAMBRIDGE UNIVERSITY PRESS

1963

First edition   1947
Second edition 1953
Reprinted   1959
Third edition   1963
Reprinted   1965

Printed in Great Britain at the University Printing House, Cambridge
(Brooke Crutchley, University Printer)

CONTENTS

TO
SIR HAROLD JEFFREYS

PREFACE TO THIRD EDITION

This book emerged from courses of lectures in Applied Mathematics given some time ago in the Universities of Auckland, Melbourne and Sydney. The present edition preserves the form of the more mathematical parts of the previous editions, but contains a number of major changes and much new matter, especially in the second half of the book.

The earlier chapters give essential background theory on the mechanics of deformable media, including the transmission of waves subject to various boundary conditions. The theory in chapters 2 to 8 has been set down in a form which, it is hoped, will be found helpful to the general student of physics and applied mathematics, as well as to the student specialising in geophysics. Chapters 9 to 11 are concerned with the gathering and treatment of instrumental data on earthquakes. In the remaining chapters, the theory and observational results are brought to bear on a variety of problems.

In the second edition (1953), apart from the addition of lists of references, there had throughout the whole book been only minor changes from the first edition. In the present edition, small but significant additions or replacements of material have been made in chapters 1, 2 and 4, and some sections of chapter 7 have been re-written in the light of the author's recent work on seismic ray theory. Alterations to the first eight chapters have, however, been kept to a minimum because of the extent to which the form of presentation in this part of the book has been found useful in centres where the theory of seismology is currently taught. Some new sections have been added in chapters 9 and 10, and an account of recent trends in the international organisation of seismology has been included in chapter 11.

From chapter 12 on, the changes have been considerable, resulting in a substantially larger book. Large portions of chapter 12 on near-earthquake seismology have been re-written or extended. In chapter 13, the account of the variation of density and other physical properties of the Earth's deeper interior is much more detailed, and the properties of the Earth Models A and B are set down explicitly. Chapter 14 on long-period oscillations of the Earth is entirely new. Chapter 15 (which replaces the previous chapter 14) on conditions near the earthquake focus, and related topics, contains much new material. Chapters 16 and 17, on nuclear-explosion seismology and extra-terrestrial seismology, are new. Further new topics have been included in the final chapter 18.

I wish to thank my former Sydney colleague, Professor B. A. Bolt, for helpful comments on several points, and Miss Lillian Robbins for valued assistance in preparing the manuscript for the printer. I wish also to thank the staff of the Cambridge University Press for their continued great help.

K. E. BULLEN

SYDNEY
May 1963

Advantage has been taken of the present reprinting to make a number of small improvements throughout the book.

K. E. B.

TOKYO
March 1965

CHAPTER 1

INTRODUCTION

1.1. Historical. The observations of geologists make it probable that the Earth has suffered earthquakes for at least some hundreds of millions of years.

Early historical records contain references to earthquakes as far back as 1800 B.C. The ancients attributed earthquakes to supernatural causes; indeed, a writer in the *Philosophic Transactions of the Royal Society of London* as late as A.D. 1750 deemed it expedient to apologise to 'those who are apt to be offended at any attempts to give a natural account of earthquakes'.

It is worthy of note, however, that Aristotle gave a classification of earthquakes into six types, according to the nature of the earth movement observed; for example, those which caused an upward earth movement, those which shook the ground from side to side, etc. Also, in the year A.D. 132, the Chinese philosopher Chang Heng devised an artistic instrument for indicating the direction of the first main impulse due to an earthquake; this instrument is reputed to have detected some earthquakes not felt locally, and Chang Heng was appointed as official earthquake observer.

About the middle of the eighteenth century A.D., useful observations of earthquake effects began to accumulate. In 1760, John Michell in England published a notable memoir on earthquakes, and showed some understanding of the association of earthquakes with wave motion in the Earth. Most work on earthquakes during the late eighteenth and the early nineteenth century was concerned with appraisals of geological effects of earthquakes, and of effects on buildings. It was noted, for instance, that, in the main, buildings on soft ground were more damaged by earthquakes than those on hard rock. Early in the nineteenth century, earthquake lists were being regularly published, and in 1840 von Hoff published an earthquake catalogue for the whole world.

About the middle of the nineteenth century, the foundations of instrumental seismology were laid when Robert Mallet suggested the setting up of a chain of observatories over the Earth's surface, and Palmieri in Italy devised a seismograph capable of detecting distant earthquakes and of recording some features of the consequent local earth movements. The history of seismology of this period includes the names of Nöggerath and Schmidt (Germany), who introduced the use of isoseismal lines to estimate the epicentre of an earthquake and the apparent speed of travel of the ensuing disturbance; of Perrey and Montessus de Ballore (France), who compiled notable earthquake records; and of de Rossi (Italy) and Forel (Switzerland), who together produced the Rossi–Forel intensity scale, the first well-known scale for estimating surface effects of earthquakes and determining isoseismal lines.

In 1892, a major step forward was taken when John Milne in Japan (aided by his association with Knott, Ewing and Gray) developed a seismograph which was sufficiently compact and simple in operation to enable it to be installed and used in many parts of the world. From this time onwards, precise instrumental data on earthquakes began to accumulate, and seismology began to develop from the qualitative towards the quantitative side.

Meanwhile a great deal of progress had been taking place independently on the mathematical 'front'. Studies of wave motion were fashionable among applied mathematicians throughout the nineteenth century, and much mathematical theory relevant to seismology was produced. As early as 1828, Cauchy and Poisson determined the equations of motion of a disturbance in a perfectly elastic substance, and Poisson showed that there could be two distinct types of waves (the seismological P and S waves) transmitted with different speeds through the interior of such a substance. Stokes showed that the P and S waves were of dilatational and rotational types, respectively, and Green studied the reflection and refraction of elastic waves. Later came the work of Kirchhoff, Kelvin and Rayleigh, including Rayleigh's theory of waves on the boundary of a homogeneous elastic substance.

The close of the nineteenth century saw the identification (1897) by Oldham of the three main types of seismic waves—P, S and surface—on actual records from seismographs—nearly 70 years after the mathematical theory of P and S waves had been formulated.

In 1904, Lamb attacked the problem of the generation of surface seismic waves. In his monumental Adams Prize Essay of 1911, Love explained the occurrence of a type of surface wave not included in the theory of Rayleigh and made a comprehensive study of the vibrations of a compressible gravitating planet.

1.2. Developments since 1911. The period from 1911 to 1940 saw the application of seismological data to problems of the Earth's internal structure to a quite remarkable degree. The period started with the vaguest notions about a molten central core and finished with well-determined values of the density, pressure, compressibility, rigidity and gravity throughout practically the whole Earth.

On the instrumental side, there were notable developments in seismographs, with new types developed by Omori and Wiechert, and outstandingly the Galitzin type introducing galvanometric recording. Later there were the elegant contributions of Benioff.

The period saw the rise of the *International Seismological Summary* and the development of an international co-operation that has not been excelled in any other branch of study. There was the evolution of travel-time tables from crudest beginnings, through the Zöppritz–Turner tables, to the 1940 J.B. and Gutenberg–Richter tables, in which errors of the order of minutes had been reduced to errors of the order of seconds.

There was the work of Herglotz and others enabling P and S velocities to be deduced from the travel-time data, with the consequent furnishing of information on compressibility-density and rigidity-density ratios throughout much of the Earth.

In 1914, Gutenberg published his very accurate determination of the depth of the boundary of the central core, one of the early results of a long and distinguished career.

Jeffreys became interested in seismology around this time and brought to bear elegant mathematical and statistical methods and a great knowledge of wider geodynamical problems. His attention to scientific method and statistical detail has been one of the main forces through which seismology has attained its present level of precision, and this book will give some indication of the extraordinary extent of his contributions.

In 1936, Miss Lehmann produced the first evidence of the existence of the Earth's inner core.

By 1940, it had become possible to classify the Earth's interior broadly into a number of regions occupying ranges of depth from the surface to the centre. The regions are denoted A, B, C, D', D″, E, F and G (see § 13.1.4). The essential work for Earth Model A was completed around this time.

Important attacks were made on the problem of the Earth's outer layers by near-earthquake studies, by surface-wave studies and, later, by the methods of explosion seismology. Starting from the work of A. Mohorovičić in 1909, the overall thickness of layers down to the discontinuity that bears his name came to be well determined, and much information derived on the P and S velocities inside the layers. It was also well established that crustal thickness is much less under oceans than continents.

Another important development was the experimental and theoretical investigation, especially by Bridgman, Adams, Williamson and Birch in the United States, of the behaviour of matter at pressures and temperatures of the order prevailing in the outer mantle of the Earth.

The period also saw many other important developments, both theoretical and practical, in various countries, notably Japan.

1.2.1. The period since 1940. Following World War II, there was a remarkable increase of effort put into seismological study. Large new schools, for example, the Lamont and the Moscow schools, rose from zero to considerable eminence, and the total output of results has been enormous. The stimulus of the International Geophysical Year of 1957–8 led to a great increase in the number of first-class seismological observatories.

Most notable among the achievements which can as yet be assessed has been a great extension in the spectrum of recorded seismic waves. At one end, the methods of prospecting seismology have enabled periods of order 0·001 sec to be measured in ground movements. At the other end, new instruments have enabled not only surface waves with periods extending up to 10 min to be observed, but free oscillations of the whole Earth with periods in excess of an hour. The spectral gap between surface wave oscillations of the order of 1 or 2 min and tidal oscillations of the order of hours has now been bridged.

The methods of explosion seismology have been greatly developed and nuclear explosions have been turned towards the study of the Earth's deeper interior. Already practical steps have been taken on planetary seismology.

1.3. The plan of this book. We have in § 1.1 indicated that a fundamental characteristic of earthquake phenomena is the passage of waves through the Earth. Hence some knowledge of the mechanics of a deformable body such as the Earth and of the theory of wave motion is a necessary preliminary to the more detailed study of seismology. Accordingly, the two immediately following chapters, 2 and 3, are concerned with the mathematical theories of elasticity and of vibrations and waves. In both these chapters the aim has been to set down fairly tersely the main results relevant to the broader problems of seismology. In the interests of terseness, use is made of cartesian tensors and the summation convention, though it not necessary for the reader to have previous knowledge of tensors.

In the next five chapters, 4–8, the wave theory is applied to problems on wave motion in an elastic body. The problems treated are those of direct importance to seismology, but most of the theory contained in the book up to chapter 8 is of fairly general interest in mathematical physics. These chapters give the theory of longitudinal and transverse waves, including reflection and refraction theory, with accompanying energy discussions; and introductory surface wave theory, including that of Rayleigh and Love waves.

Chapters 9–11 are more particularly concerned with the derivation of results special to seismology. In chapter 9, the essential principle of the seismograph is discussed; in chapter 10, methods of treating the instrumental data are described; and in chapter 11, a short account is given of the organisation of seismological observatories.

In chapters 12 and 13 it is shown how seismological data may be applied to the determination of properties of the Earth's interior. In chapter 12, studies of both bodily and surface seismic

waves are used to throw light on crustal structure; reference is made
to experiments carried out at high pressures and temperatures. In
chapter 13, values of the P and S velocities are set down for the
whole of the Earth below the crust, and are made the basis of a
broad classification of the interior of the Earth into the eight regions
mentioned in § 1.2. The density, pressure, elasticity and gravity
variations in the Earth, and to some extent the composition, are
examined in relation to the seismic data. The properties of Earth
Models A and B are discussed.

Chapter 14 is concerned with the theory of fundamental free
oscillations of the Earth and recent important observational results.

In chapter 15 questions of the conditions at the focus of an
earthquake are discussed. Such questions necessarily occupy a
late place in inferences from seismological data, since the initial
disturbance at the focus of an earthquake is more removed in time
from the instrumental observations than are the subsequent earth
movements. The discussion includes reference to related questions
such as the quantity of energy released in an earthquake, the geographical distribution of earthquake foci, the occurrence of aftershocks, etc.

Chapters 16 and 17 contain introductory accounts of two new
developments, nuclear-explosion seismology and planetary seismology.

The final chapter 18 touches on a number of topics that lie on the
border of theoretical seismology: large-scale, or 'macroscopic',
effects of earthquakes and effects on seas; small ground movements,
or 'microseisms', not caused by the usual type of earthquake; the
problem of designing structures which will resist earthquakes;
seismic prospecting and determination of ice-cap thicknesses; and
some special topics such as model seismology and ocean-bottom
seismographs.

CHAPTER 2

ELASTICITY THEORY

The theory of elasticity is concerned with the strain experienced by deformable matter when subjected to stress. In the present chapter, the theory is developed so far as is necessary for presentation of the basic theory of seismology. It will be assumed that media are made up of particles which are sufficiently closely packed for the various functions which appear in this chapter to be taken as continuous and differentiable.

2.1. Analysis of stress. Let P be any particle in the interior of a given body, and at any given instant of time draw through P a unit vector ν in any direction. Let δS be a small plane element of area inside the body, containing P and normal to ν. Consider the forces across δS between two separate portions of the body which have a common boundary at δS; in particular, consider the forces exerted on that portion for which ν is the outward normal. These forces are statically equivalent to a certain single force acting at P together with a couple. This single force is called the *traction* across δS. If δS be indefinitely diminished, the limit of the ratio of the traction across δS to the area δS is called the *stress* at P corresponding to the direction ν; in ordinary problems this limit is taken to be finite and significant, while the couple (whose moment involves an additional dimension of length) is disregarded.

2.1.1. The stress tensor. The stress at P in general varies with the direction of the normal ν to the small area considered, and is in general inclined to that normal. We proceed to show that the stress at P across any small plane area containing P is expressible in terms of nine components.

Take two sets of orthogonal axes, which we shall call the 1-, 2- and 3-, and the 1'-, 2'- and 3'-axes, respectively. Components of any vector parallel to the axes of the first set will be styled the 1-, 2- and 3-components; and similarly with the other set of axes. Consider the matter inside a small tetrahedron (Fig. 1) enclosing

P, and having the inward normals of three of the faces parallel to the 1-, 2- and 3-axes, respectively, and the outward normal of the fourth face parallel to the $1'$-axis. Let the corresponding areas of the four faces be δS_1, δS_2, δS_3 and $\delta S_{1'}$. Denote the 2-component of the stress across the face normal to the 1-axis by p_{12}; and similarly with other cases. Let $a_{12'}$ be the cosine of the angle between the 1- and the $2'$-axes, etc.

The matter inside the tetrahedron is in equilibrium under the action of body forces (such as gravity), the tractions across the

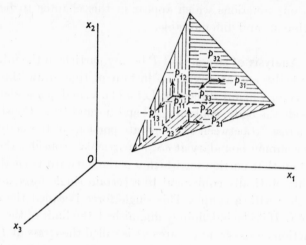

Fig. 1

boundary faces, and the reversed mass-accelerations of the constituent particles. In Fig. 1, the stresses on this matter across three of the four boundary faces are shown. Consider resolved parts parallel to say the $2'$-axis. All but the boundary forces are ultimately proportional to the volume of the tetrahedron. Hence, if l be a linear dimension of the tetrahedron, we have

$$p_{1'2'}\delta S_{1'} - p_{11}\delta S_1 a_{12'} - p_{12}\delta S_1 a_{22'} - p_{13}\delta S_1 a_{32'}$$
$$- p_{21}\delta S_2 a_{12'} - p_{22}\delta S_2 a_{22'} - p_{23}\delta S_2 a_{32'}$$
$$- p_{31}\delta S_3 a_{12'} - p_{32}\delta S_3 a_{22'} - p_{33}\delta S_3 a_{32'} = O(l^3).$$

Dividing through by $\delta S_{1'}$ and letting $l \to 0$, we have

$$p_{1'2'} = p_{11}a_{11'}a_{12'} + p_{12}a_{11'}a_{22'} + p_{13}a_{11'}a_{32'}$$
$$+ p_{21}a_{21'}a_{12'} + p_{22}a_{21'}a_{22'} + p_{23}a_{21'}a_{32'}$$
$$+ p_{31}a_{31'}a_{12'} + p_{32}a_{31'}a_{22'} + p_{33}a_{31'}a_{32'}$$
$$= \sum_{i=1}^{3} \sum_{j=1}^{3} a_{i1'}a_{j2'}p_{ij}.$$

It is clear that a similar result will hold for the l'-component of the stress across a small area normal to the k'-axis, where k and l may each be 1, 2 or 3. It is convenient, moreover, to introduce the *summation convention*, whereby if any suffix occurs twice in a single term, it is to be put equal to 1, 2 or 3 in turn and the results added. This convention will be employed regularly in the sequel. (A reader who finds trouble at first in the use of this 'adding demon' is advised to write out any of the subsequent equations in full when in difficulty.) The set of relations may thus be written as

$$p_{k'l'} = a_{ik'}a_{jl'}p_{ij}. \tag{1}$$

The reader will perceive that the suffixes i, j on the right-hand side of (1) are *dummy suffixes*, and could each be replaced by any other suffix not already present. (In order to make the summation convention work, the same suffix must of course never appear more than twice in a single term.)

Hence there have emerged nine components p_{ij} (associated with any particular point and instant of time) in terms of which the stress across any small plane area containing the point may be completely determined. An array p_{ij} which obeys a transformation law of the type (1) is a *cartesian tensor* of the second order. This is a simple extension from the tensor of the first order, or *vector*, v_i say ($i = 1, 2, 3$), which has three components and obeys a transformation law of the form

$$v_{k'} = a_{ik'}v_i, \tag{2}$$

and the tensor of zero order, or *scalar*, which is fully determined by a single component whose value is unchanged on transformation of axes. The set of nine elements p_{ij} constitutes the *stress tensor* at P.

2.1.2. Symmetry of the stress tensor. Now consider the matter inside a small parallelepiped which has three edges, PA, PB, PC, passing through P, parallel to the 1-, 2-, 3-axes, of lengths δx_1, δx_2, δx_3, say. In Fig. 2, the stresses across the pair of faces normal to Ox_2 are shown. From this figure, the resultant moment about PC of the corresponding tractions is seen (neglecting higher-order terms) to be $-p_{21}\delta x_1 \delta x_3 . \delta x_2$. The resultant moment about PC of the tractions across the pair of faces normal to Ox_1 is found to be $+p_{12}\delta x_2 \delta x_3 . \delta x_1$. The resultant moment about PC of all other forces (including body forces and reversed mass-accelerations) is

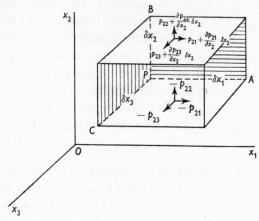

Fig. 2

found to be of higher order. It follows that $p_{12} = p_{21}$. Similarly $p_{23} = p_{32}$ and $p_{31} = p_{13}$. Hence, for all i, j,

$$p_{ij} = p_{ji}. \tag{3}$$

Thus the stress tensor is symmetrical, and only six of its nine components are independent.

The components p_{ij} $(i \neq j)$ are called *shear components of stress* on account of relations like (31) to be given later.

2.1.3. Use of the Kronecker δ. It will be convenient in parts of the subsequent argument to invoke the use of a special second-order tensor δ_{ij}, the *Kronecker δ*, which is represented by the array

$$\begin{pmatrix} 1 & 0 & 0 \\ 0 & 1 & 0 \\ 0 & 0 & 1 \end{pmatrix},$$

i.e. $\delta_{ij} = 1$ if $i = j$, and $= 0$ if $i \neq j$. It may be verified that this set of values of δ_{ij} is preserved on transforming the axes. (We use only orthogonal cartesian axes in this chapter.)

The set of direction-cosines a_{ij}, where a_{12} denotes the cosine of the angle between the 1- and the 2-axes, etc., constitutes the tensor δ_{ij}. We note also the *substitution property* of δ_{ij}, namely,

$$\delta_{ij} T_i = T_j, \tag{4}$$

where T_i denotes a tensor of any order which has i as one of the suffixes in its representation; this property is verified on giving to j in (4) the particular values 1, 2, 3.

If in (1) we replace the suffix l' by l, the result is still true (this would correspond to resolving parallel to, say, the 2-axis instead of to the 2'-axis as in § 2.1.1). Thus $p_{k'l} = a_{ik'} a_{jl} p_{ij} = a_{ik'} \delta_{jl} p_{ij}$. Using (4) and then replacing l by j, we obtain $p_{k'j} = a_{ik'} p_{ij}$. We may write this result in the form

$$p_j(\nu) = \nu_i p_{ij}, \tag{5}$$

which gives the stress $p_j(\nu)$ at P corresponding to the direction ν_i, in terms of ν_i and the stress tensor p_{ij}; the traction across the small area δS whose normal has the direction ν_i is $p_j(\nu)\,\delta S$, or $\nu_i p_{ij}\,\delta S$. The relation (5) is, of course, directly obtainable independently of (1); but the derivation just given is useful both in showing the connection between (1) and (5), and as a simple exercise in the use of δ_{ij}.

2.1.4. The stress quadric. Let y_i be the current coordinates, referred to the position of P as origin and to axes parallel to the 1-, 2- and 3-axes, of any point of the (central) quadric surface

$$p_{11}y_1^2 + p_{22}y_2^2 + p_{33}y_3^2 + 2p_{23}y_2 y_3 + 2p_{31}y_3 y_1 + 2p_{12}y_1 y_2 = \text{constant};$$

this may, by the summation convention and (3), be written as

$$p_{ij} y_i y_j = \text{constant}. \tag{6}$$

Let the current coordinates become $y_{i'}$ when axes are taken (still with P at the origin) parallel to the 1'-, 2'- and 3'-axes. Then by (2)

$$y_i = a_{ik'} y_{k'}, \tag{7}$$

and the equation of the quadric becomes

$$p_{ij} a_{ik'} y_{k'} a_{jl'} y_{l'} = \text{constant},$$

i.e. by (1), $\qquad p_{k'l'} y_{k'} y_{l'} = \text{constant}. \tag{8}$

The quadric (6) is the *stress quadric* at P. By (8), the coefficients in its equation referred to any set of orthogonal cartesian axes through P give the components of stress across small plane surfaces through P normal to these axes. It then follows from the theory of quadrics that at any given point there exist three mutually perpendicular planes the stress across each of which is in the direction of the normal. A knowledge of the magnitudes of these three stresses, called the *principal stresses* at P, and of the directions of the corresponding axes, called the *principal axes of stress* at P, is sufficient to determine fully the stress tensor at P.

2.1.5. Equations of motion. At any given time t, let x_i be the coordinates of the position of P referred to a fixed set of rectangular cartesian axes, and f_i the acceleration of P; and consider the matter contained inside the parallelepiped shown in Fig. 2. Let X_i be the components of body force per unit mass acting on this matter.

The resultant component parallel to the 3-axis of the tractions across the two faces normal to the 2-axis is (neglecting higher-order quantities)

$$-p_{23}\delta x_1\delta x_3 + \left(p_{23} + \frac{\partial p_{23}}{\partial x_2}\delta x_2\right)\delta x_1\delta x_3,$$

i.e.

$$\frac{\partial p_{23}}{\partial x_2}\delta x_1\delta x_2\delta x_3.$$

Hence the 3-component of the resultant of the tractions across all six faces is

$$\frac{\partial p_{j3}}{\partial x_j}\delta x_1\delta x_2\delta x_3.$$

The corresponding equation of motion therefore becomes, on dividing through by $\delta x_1\delta x_2\delta x_3$,

$$\rho f_3 = \frac{\partial p_{j3}}{\partial x_j} + \rho X_3,$$

where ρ is the density at x_i at time t. Using (3), we may hence write the set of three equations of motion in the form

$$\rho f_i = \frac{\partial p_{ij}}{\partial x_j} + \rho X_i \quad (i = 1, 2, 3). \tag{9}$$

2.2. Analysis of strain. Consider the same body again, and take axes as in § 2.1.5. Suppose that at the instant under consideration the body has undergone a change of configuration such that the displacement of the typical particle P now at x_i has been u_i. For the present we assume that such displacements are measured from a theoretical standard configuration in which the body forces and the stresses are zero at all points.

Let Q be the particle at a neighbouring point $x_i + y_i$, where y_i is infinitesimal. Then its displacement must (to sufficient accuracy for our purpose) have been

$$u_i + \frac{\partial u_i}{\partial x_j} y_j, \tag{10}$$

i.e.

$$u_i - \xi_{ij} y_j + e_{ij} y_j, \tag{11}$$

where

$$\xi_{ij} = \frac{1}{2} \left(\frac{\partial u_j}{\partial x_i} - \frac{\partial u_i}{\partial x_j} \right) \tag{12}$$

and

$$e_{ij} = \frac{1}{2} \left(\frac{\partial u_j}{\partial x_i} + \frac{\partial u_i}{\partial x_j} \right). \tag{13}$$

In elementary problems in elasticity, the relative displacements of the particles of a body are such that the components of $\partial u_i / \partial x_j$ are sufficiently small for their second powers to be neglected in equations containing significant first-order terms; the theory developed on this basis has been called *infinitesimal strain theory* and will apply in what follows, except where special mention is made (as in § 2.6).

In (11), each of the three terms denotes a vector, while each of ξ_{ij}, e_{ij} denotes a tensor of the second order; these results are verified by transforming axes and finding that laws of the forms (2) and (1) are satisfied. Substitution of particular values of i, j shows further that ξ_{ij} is antisymmetrical (i.e. $\xi_{ij} = -\xi_{ji}$; thus if $i = j$, $\xi_{ij} = 0$) and so has just three independent components, while e_{ij} is symmetrical and has just six independent components.

We leave it as an exercise to the reader to show that if α_{ij}, β_{ij} denote symmetrical and antisymmetrical tensors, respectively, then $\alpha_{ij} \beta_{ij} = 0$. This property will be used several times later on in the chapter.

We now proceed to interpret separately the three terms in (11). The first term u_i is equal to the displacement of P, and so corresponds to a pure translation (of the portion of matter near P) without rotation or deformation. The second term $-\xi_{ij} y_j$ will be shown to correspond to a pure rotation without translation or deformation, and the third term $e_{ij}y_j$ to a deformation. In §§ 2.2.1, 2.2.2, 2.2.3, the origin of axes will be taken at the position of P whenever the coordinates y_i are involved.

2.2.1. The rotation tensor. The contribution to the displacement (11) arising from the particular pair of elements ξ_{23} and ξ_{32} of (12) has components $(0, -\xi_{23}y_3, \xi_{23}y_2)$. The associated change in the square of the distance between P, Q must therefore have been

$$y_1^2 + y_2^2 + y_3^2 - \{y_1^2 + (y_2 + \xi_{23}y_3)^2 + (y_3 - \xi_{23}y_2)^2\}, \qquad (14)$$

which is zero to the first order in ξ_{23}. But the plane containing PQ and the 1-axis must have been rotated about the 1-axis through an angle

$$\tan^{-1}\left(\frac{y_3}{y_2}\right) - \tan^{-1}\left(\frac{y_3 - \xi_{23}y_2}{y_2 + \xi_{23}y_3}\right), \qquad (15)$$

i.e.

$$\tan^{-1}q - \tan^{-1}\left(\frac{q - \xi_{23}}{1 + q\xi_{23}}\right),$$

where $q = y_3/y_2$,   i.e. $\tan^{-1}\xi_{23}$.

This angle is independent of the coordinates y_i of Q's position relative to P, and is equal to ξ_{23} to sufficient accuracy. The pair of elements ξ_{23} and ξ_{32} is thus associated with a (local) pure rotation (as of a rigid body) about the 1-axis; and similarly for the other two pairs of non-zero elements of ξ_{ij}. The complete tensor ξ_{ij} thus corresponds to a small pure rotation about some axis through P, and is called the *rotation tensor* at P. The rotation may alternatively be represented as a vector of components $(\xi_{23}, \xi_{31}, \xi_{12})$; the vector whose components are double the latter, namely,

$$\left(\frac{\partial u_3}{\partial x_2} - \frac{\partial u_2}{\partial x_3}, \quad \frac{\partial u_1}{\partial x_3} - \frac{\partial u_3}{\partial x_1}, \quad \frac{\partial u_2}{\partial x_1} - \frac{\partial u_1}{\partial x_2}\right),$$

is called the *curl* of the vector u_i. We shall sometimes denote this vector as curl (u_i).

2.2.2. The strain tensor. It will now be shown that the components of e_{ij} as given by (13) are all associated with some internal deformation of the material, i.e. with *strain*; hence e_{ij} is called the *strain tensor* at P.

The contribution to (11) due to the element e_{11} has components $(e_{11}y_1, 0, 0)$. This clearly constitutes a strain in which all small lengths parallel to the 1-axis must have been increased by the small fraction e_{11}. Such a strain is an *extension*. The elements e_{11}, e_{22}, e_{33} thus give three mutually perpendicular extensions parallel to the 1-, 2-, 3-axes, respectively.

The contribution to (11) due to the pair of elements e_{23} and e_{32} has components $(0, e_{23}y_3, e_{23}y_2)$. On forming an expression analogous to (14), we find that the corresponding increase to the square of the distance PQ must (to sufficient accuracy) have been

$$4e_{23}y_2y_3. \tag{16a}$$

This is also the increase to the square of the distance PQ_1, where Q_1 is the projection of Q on the 2-3 plane through P. The proportionate increase in PQ_1^2 will therefore have been

$$2e_{23}\sin 2\alpha, \tag{16b}$$

where α is the angle between the 2-axis and PQ_1 (see Fig. 3). On forming the analogue of (15), we find further that the direction of PQ_1 must have been turned about the 1-axis through the angle

$$e_{23}(y_2^2 - y_3^2)/(y_2^2 + y_3^2), \quad \text{i.e.} \quad e_{23}\cos 2\alpha. \tag{17}$$

Both (16) and (17) vary with α; thus the elements e_{23}, e_{32} correspond to another type of deformation in the vicinity of P.

From (16) and (17), we can deduce the various properties of this second type of deformation. As an instance of this, let Q be taken to coincide with particles R, S, respectively, initially on the 2-, 3-axes (through P), respectively. By (17), it follows that during the deformation, PR must have turned through the (small) angle e_{23}, and PS through $-e_{23}$; thus the angle RPS (initially precisely a right angle) must have decreased by the small amount $2e_{23}$ (see Fig. 4). By (16), the lengths of PR, PS will, however, not have been changed. (This set of circumstances corresponds to a well-known elementary experiment wherein a prism of section initially rectangular is distorted without change of side-lengths into a prism whose section is a parallelogram.) A deformation possessing the features just described is a *shear*, the angle $2e_{23}$ being the *angle of shear.* Similar results are of course relevant to e_{31}, e_{13} and to e_{12}, e_{21}. We call e_{ij} $(i \neq j)$ the *shear components of strain.*

For use in a later section (§ 2.6), it will be convenient to note here that $(16a)$ may be derived in a more general way, directly from (10). By (10), the excess, $d(PQ)^2$ say, of the square of the distance between P, Q after strain over that before is given by

$$d(PQ)^2 = y_i^2 - \left(y_i - \frac{\partial u_i}{\partial x_j}y_j\right)\left(y_i - \frac{\partial u_i}{\partial x_k}y_k\right), \tag{18}$$

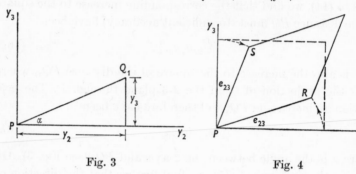

Fig. 3   Fig. 4

where y_i^2 denotes $y_i y_i$, i.e. $y_1^2 + y_2^2 + y_3^2$. As we are here neglecting powers beyond the first in the components of $\partial u_i/\partial x_j$, we may write (18) as

$$d(PQ)^2 = \frac{\partial u_i}{\partial x_j}y_j y_i + \frac{\partial u_i}{\partial x_k}y_i y_k$$

$$= \left(\frac{\partial u_j}{\partial x_i} + \frac{\partial u_i}{\partial x_j}\right)y_i y_j,$$

on rearranging suffixes. Hence, by (13),

$$d(PQ)^2 = 2e_{ij}y_i y_j. \tag{19}$$

From (19), the result $(16a)$ follows as a particular case.

We now introduce the *strain quadric* at P given by the equation

$$e_{ij}y_i y_j = \text{constant}. \tag{20}$$

By argument similar to that used in the case of the stress quadric, it follows that at any given instant there is one particular set of orthogonal axes through P with respect to which the shear components of strain at P vanish. A knowledge of the directions of these axes, called the *principal axes of strain* at P, and of the corresponding values taken by e_{11}, e_{22}, e_{33}, called in this case the *principal extensions*, is sufficient to determine completely the deformation in the neighbourhood of P. The deformation in the neighbourhood of any point is thus always expressible as the resultant of simple extensions in a certain three mutually perpendicular directions.

The theory of quadric surfaces gives the further result that $e_{11} + e_{22} + e_{33}$ is invariant for changes in the directions of the axes (the frame remaining orthogonal), i.e. e_{ii} is a scalar. This result may, of course, be directly established by noting that $e_{ii} = \partial u_i / \partial x_i$ and applying transformation formulae based on (2).

2.2.3. Cubical dilatation. Consider a small portion of matter, enclosing P, which undergoes deformation. Then the cubical dilatation at P is defined as the limit, as the area of the boundary surface approaches zero, of the proportionate increase in the volume of this matter. If e_{11}, e_{22}, e_{33} are the principal extensions at P (associated with this deformation), the dilatation θ at P is thus equal to

$$1 - (1 - e_{11})(1 - e_{22})(1 - e_{33}).$$

Thus
$$\theta = e_{11} + e_{22} + e_{33} = e_{ii}, \tag{21}$$

neglecting higher-order terms. By the preceding paragraph, it follows, moreover, that (21) is true even if e_{11}, e_{22}, e_{33} are other than the principal extensions.

From (13) and (21) we have

$$\theta = \frac{\partial u_1}{\partial x_1} + \frac{\partial u_2}{\partial x_2} + \frac{\partial u_3}{\partial x_3} = \frac{\partial u_i}{\partial x_i}. \tag{22}$$

The last expression is called the *divergence* of the vector u_i, and will sometimes be denoted as div (u_i).

A (cubical) *compression* is a negative dilatation.

2.2.4. The equation of conservation. We now seek to express in a formula the fact that the mass of any given portion of matter is (in ordinary physical theory) conserved. Consider the matter inside an indefinitely small parallelepiped S which has the point x_i at one corner and has side-lengths δx_i; let $\delta\tau = \delta x_1 \delta x_2 \delta x_3$. Suppose first that S is fixed in space. The rate of increase of mass within S is then $(\partial\rho/\partial t)\,\delta\tau$, where ρ is the density at x_i at time t. The net rate of inflow of mass across the surface of S is found (by an argument similar to that used in deriving the term $\partial p_{ij}/\partial x_j$ in (9)) to be $-\partial/\partial x_i\{(\rho v_i)\,\delta\tau\}$, where v_i is the velocity of the particle at x_i at time t. The conservation principle is expressed by equating these two terms. This gives the *conservation equation*

$$\frac{\partial\rho}{\partial t}+\frac{\partial(\rho v_i)}{\partial x_i}=0. \tag{23}$$

It is convenient for some purposes to express (23) in the form

$$\frac{d\rho}{dt}+\rho\frac{\partial v_i}{\partial x_i}=0, \tag{24}$$

where the operation
$$\frac{d}{dt}=\frac{\partial}{\partial t}+v_i\frac{\partial}{\partial x_i} \tag{25}$$

denotes 'differentiation following the motion'; the symbol $\partial/\partial t$ is concerned with time changes at an assigned point, while d/dt (often denoted D/Dt) is concerned with time changes in the behaviour of an assigned particle or group of particles.

Secondly, suppose that S is not fixed in space, but moves with the particles initially enclosed in it. The conservation principle may then be expressed in the alternative form

$$\frac{d}{dt}(\rho\,\delta\tau)=0. \tag{26}$$

We may note that it is possible to set up a 'rate of strain' theory analogous to the strain theory set up in the preceding subsections. If in particular we consider the analogue of the dilatation θ, we find that we may write

$$\frac{\partial v_i}{\partial x_i}=\frac{1}{\delta\tau}\frac{d}{dt}(\delta\tau),$$

which shows the equivalence of (24) and (26).

We may note also that the equations (23), (24) and (26) are relevant in a wider context to other conservation cases, e.g. conservation of energy (§ 3.3.6).

The name 'equation of continuity' is commonly used for the equation of conservation in any of its forms.

We note incidentally that the velocity v_i is connected with the displacement u_i by the relation $v_i = du_i/dt$. From this and (25) it may be shown that

$$\frac{\partial v_i}{\partial x_j} = \frac{d}{dt}\left(\frac{\partial u_i}{\partial x_j}\right), \tag{27}$$

neglecting the second-order terms $\{(\partial v_k/\partial x_j)(\partial u_i/\partial x_k)\}$. The formula (27) will be useful in later parts of this chapter; we leave its proof as an exercise to the reader.

2.3. Perfect elasticity. The occurrence of stress in deformable matter is found to be accompanied by the occurrence of strain. The case in which (for a given substance under specified thermo-dynamical conditions) the components of strain at any point are determined by the components of stress at the point is that of perfect elasticity. Thus in perfect elasticity the components of strain are (on the infinitesimal strain theory) homogeneous linear functions of the components of stress, and vice versa. This constitutes a generalisation of *Hooke's Law*, and in many circumstances agrees closely with what happens in practice.

We shall assume that the standard equilibrium configuration is stable; this is so in ordinary problems.

2.3.1. Stress-strain relations for a perfectly elastic isotropic material. Let p_{ij} and e_{ij} be the stress and strain tensors at time t at the point x_i in such a material. By *isotropic*, we mean that the elastic behaviour is entirely independent of any particular direction. Then, on account of the linearity of the stress-strain relations and the symmetry associated with isotropy, we may write

$$p_{11} = Ae_{11} + B(e_{22} + e_{33}) + Ce_{23} + D(e_{31} + e_{12}), \tag{28}$$

$$p_{23} = Ee_{11} + F(e_{22} + e_{33}) + Ge_{23} + H(e_{31} + e_{12}), \tag{29}$$

where the coefficients A, B, C, D, E, F, G, H depend only on the particular material and on the thermodynamical conditions, together with two pairs of similar equations involving the same eight coefficients. These coefficients are independent of the directions of the particular axes taken.

Take, in particular, axes (1-, 2-, 3-) coinciding with the principal axes of strain at the point, P say. Then (28) and (29) become

$$p_{11} = Ae_{11} + B(e_{22} + e_{33}), \tag{28a}$$

$$p_{23} = Ee_{11} + F(e_{22} + e_{33}). \tag{29a}$$

Now take a second set of axes (1'-, 2'-, 3'-) obtained by rotating the first reference frame through $\frac{1}{2}\pi$ about the 1-axis; thus the 1'- and 1-axes coincide, the 2'- and 3-axes coincide, and the 3'-axis is opposite to the 2-axis. Since the new axes also coincide with the principal axes of strain at P, we have by (29)

$$p_{2'3'} = Ee_{1'1'} + F(e_{2'2'} + e_{3'3'}),$$

and hence
$$-p_{32} = Ee_{11} + F(e_{33} + e_{22}).$$

Hence, by (29a) and (3), $p_{23} = 0$. We can similarly show that when the axes are principal axes of strain, $p_{31} = 0$ and $p_{12} = 0$.

We have thus shown that for a perfectly elastic isotropic substance, the principal axes of stress at P coincide with the principal axes of strain at P.

Now consider the tensor

$$p_{ij} - B\theta\delta_{ij} - (A - B)\,e_{ij}.$$

Its components are all zero when referred to principal axes of strain (and hence also of stress) at P; this is obvious for $i \neq j$, and follows by (28a) for the cases $i = j$. Hence, by the tensor transformation rule (1), the components of this tensor are zero whatever the directions of the axes.

Thus for a perfectly elastic isotropic substance, the stress-strain relations are of the form

$$p_{ij} = B\theta\delta_{ij} + (A - B)\,e_{ij}.$$

Moreover, it follows that the eight coefficients above are expressible in terms of just two *elastic parameters*. (We have in effect shown that $C = D = E = F = H = 0$, and that $A - B = G$.) The two parameters are commonly taken as λ and μ (the Lamé elastic parameters), where $\lambda = B$, and $\mu = \frac{1}{2}(A - B)$. Thus in place of (28) and (29), we have

$$p_{11} = \lambda\theta + 2\mu e_{11}, \tag{30}$$

and
$$p_{23} = 2\mu e_{23}. \tag{31}$$

and the full stress-strain relations are

$$p_{ij} = \lambda\theta\delta_{ij} + 2\mu e_{ij}. \tag{32}$$

The use of λ, μ (or corresponding pairs of elastic parameters such as k, μ and E, σ—see §§ 2.3.3., 2.3.4) in the sequel will be understood to imply without special mention that the elastic behaviour under consideration is isotropic.

It is an easy exercise to deduce from (32) that if, in particular, the stress system is such that all the components of stress except p_{23} and p_{32} vanish, then all the components of strain vanish except e_{23} and e_{32}. Thus such a stress system is associated with a simple shear, and is called a *shearing stress*. A shearing stress is also given by the stress system in which $p_{22} = -p_{33}$ and all the other components of p_{ij} are zero. (This may be seen on rotating the 2- and 3-axes through $\frac{1}{4}\pi$ about the 1-axis, and applying the necessary transformation formulae obtained from (1).) We then have

$$e_{22} = -e_{33} = p_{22}/2\mu$$

and all the other e_{ij} zero. The dilatation θ is of course zero.

2.3.2. Equations of motion in terms of displacement. By equations (9) and (32), we have

$$\rho f_i = \frac{\partial}{\partial x_j}(\lambda\theta\delta_{ij} + 2\mu e_{ij}) + \rho X_i.$$

Hence, by (4) and (13),

$$\rho f_i = \frac{\partial}{\partial x_i}(\lambda\theta) + \frac{\partial}{\partial x_j}\left\{\mu\left(\frac{\partial u_j}{\partial x_i} + \frac{\partial u_i}{\partial x_j}\right)\right\} + \rho X_i.$$

If the material is uniform, so that λ and μ are constants, we have

$$\rho f_i = \lambda\frac{\partial\theta}{\partial x_i} + \mu\frac{\partial}{\partial x_i}\frac{\partial u_j}{\partial x_j} + \mu\nabla^2 u_i + \rho X_i,$$

where ∇^2 is *Laplace's operator*, $\partial^2/\partial x_i^2$. Hence, by (22),

$$\rho\frac{d^2 u_i}{dt^2} = (\lambda + \mu)\frac{\partial\theta}{\partial x_i} + \mu\nabla^2 u_i + \rho X_i. \tag{33}$$

If the displacement u_i and the velocity v_i are always small (this is the case in ordinary problems in elasticity, but not in hydrodynamics), we may by (25) replace d/dt by $\partial/\partial t$ on the left-hand side of (33), for we are already neglecting second powers of components of $\partial u_i/\partial x_j$. In this case, we may thus write

$$\rho\frac{\partial^2 u_i}{\partial t^2} = (\lambda + \mu)\frac{\partial\theta}{\partial x_i} + \mu\nabla^2 u_i + \rho X_i. \tag{34}$$

Since $\theta = \partial u_i/\partial x_i$, the equation (34) is homogeneous linear in the

u_i and X_i. Hence (34) will still hold true if the u_i are measured from any equilibrium configuration as standard, and the X_i are components of additional body force per unit mass; correspondingly, the p_{ij} will be the components of additional stress. This interpretation is of course subject to the condition that the total strain continues to be compatible with the requirements of the infinitesimal strain theory and perfect elasticity. Similar remarks apply to all the linear equations in the present theory, and we shall now usually interpret equations in u_i, p_{ij} and X_i in this way. (An exception to this arises when we consider the strain-energy function (§§ 2.3.5, 2.3.6), which is quadratic in the e_{ij}.)

2.3.3. Some types of perfectly elastic substances. We now consider substances to which the equations (32) apply. By (31), it is seen that the ratio of a shear component of stress to the corresponding shear is independent of the particular axes taken; this ratio, μ, is called the *rigidity*. Perfectly elastic isotropic substances are classified into three types according to the magnitude of μ. If λ and μ are everywhere infinite, so that by (32) the e_{ij} are zero for finite p_{ij}, the substance is an (ideal) *rigid body*; if μ is finite and not zero, the substance is a *perfect solid*; if μ is zero, the substance is a *perfect fluid*.

It is a matter of observation that a fluid at rest obeys closely the conditions stated at the beginning of § 2.3. On putting $\mu = 0$ in (32), we have that if $i \neq j$, $p_{ij} = 0$, whatever the directions of the axes. It follows from the equation (6) of the stress quadric that at any point of a fluid at rest all axes are principal axes, and hence that the stress quadric is a sphere. In this case, the stress across any small plane area is normal to the area. There is now only one independent component of the stress tensor; this component, reversed in sign, is the ordinary fluid pressure of hydrostatics. The term *hydrostatic pressure* is used in general cases with any type of substance when the stress take this form; a hydrostatic pressure p corresponds to a stress $-p\delta_{ij}$.

Now suppose that during a time increment dt, the material in the vicinity of a particle P of a perfectly elastic isotropic body is subjected to an additional stress in the form of a hydrostatic pressure dp. The ratio of this pressure to the compression produced is called the *bulk modulus* or *incompressibility* k at P. We can express k simply in terms of λ and μ. For, by (32), we may write

$$-dp\delta_{ij} = \lambda d\theta \delta_{ij} + 2\mu de_{ij};$$

contracting (i.e. replacing j by i and doing the thus indicated summation), we have by (21)

$$-3dp = 3\lambda d\theta + 2\mu d\theta,$$

i.e.
$$k = -\frac{dp}{d\theta} = \lambda + \tfrac{2}{3}\mu. \tag{35}$$

We note incidentally that by (35) and (26)

$$k = \rho\frac{dp}{d\rho}. \tag{36}$$

It is convenient for some purposes to write the equations (32) in terms of k and μ instead of λ and μ; thus

$$p_{ij} = (k - \tfrac{2}{3}\mu)\,\theta\delta_{ij} + 2\mu e_{ij}. \tag{37}$$

For the particular case $\mu = 0$, (37) degenerates to the *perfect fluid relation*
$$p_{ij} = k\theta\delta_{ij}, \tag{38}$$

i.e. $p = -k\theta$, where $-p = p_{11} = p_{22} = p_{33}$. In particular, the fluid is called *gas* or *liquid* according as k is moderate or very great. An ideal liquid is incompressible and has k infinitely great.

2.3.4. Young's modulus and Poisson's ratio. Suppose now that P is inside a small cylinder (of a perfectly elastic isotropic material) whose plane ends are perpendicular to the generators, that the stress at each end is entirely normal (the magnitude being the same at each end), and that there is no traction across the lateral surface. Then *Young's modulus E* at P is defined as the ratio of the stress at an end to the longitudinal extension of the cylinder; and *Poisson's ratio* σ as the ratio of the lateral contraction to the longitudinal extension.

E and σ are elastic parameters which, like λ and μ, may vary from point to point of the material. They are readily expressible in terms of λ and μ. To show this, take the 1-axis parallel to the cylinder's generators. Then since p_{22}, p_{33} are both zero, we

Fig. 5

have on adding the three equations like (30) and using (21)

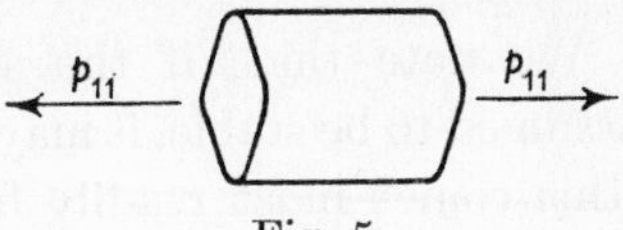

$$p_{11} = (3\lambda + 2\mu)\,\theta.$$

Using (30) again, we see that p_{11}, e_{11} are connected by the relation

$$p_{11} = \frac{\lambda p_{11}}{3\lambda + 2\mu} + 2\mu e_{11}.$$

Hence
$$E = \frac{p_{11}}{e_{11}} = \frac{\mu(3\lambda + 2\mu)}{\lambda + \mu}. \tag{39}$$

Again from the equations like (30), we have

$$e_{22} = e_{33} = -\lambda\theta/2\mu$$
$$= -\lambda(e_{11} + 2e_{22})/2\mu.$$

Hence
$$\sigma = -\frac{e_{22}}{e_{11}} = \frac{\lambda}{2(\lambda + \mu)}. \tag{40}$$

By simple algebra, we can from (39), (40) and (35) express λ, μ, k in terms of E, σ. We obtain

$$\lambda = E\sigma/(1 + \sigma)(1 - 2\sigma), \tag{41}$$

$$\mu = E/2(1 + \sigma), \tag{42}$$

$$k = E/3(1 - 2\sigma). \tag{43}$$

We note also that
$$\lambda/\mu = 2\sigma/(1 - 2\sigma). \tag{44}$$

The relations (32) express the p_{ij} in terms of the e_{ij}. The parameters E, σ are useful when we wish to express the e_{ij} in terms of the p_{ij}. Thus, contracting (32) and then using (35), we have

$$p_{kk} = (3\lambda + 2\mu)\theta = 3k\theta.$$

Hence, by (32),
$$2\mu e_{ij} = p_{ij} - \lambda\theta\delta_{ij}$$
$$= p_{ij} - \frac{\lambda}{3k}p_{kk}\delta_{ij}.$$

Finally, by (41), (42) and (43),

$$e_{ij} = \frac{1 + \sigma}{E}p_{ij} - \frac{\sigma}{E}p_{kk}\delta_{ij}. \tag{45}$$

We note that, if the standard equilibrium configuration is assumed to be stable, it may be deduced that each of μ and k is $\geqslant 0$ (this comes most readily from (56), p. 26). By (35) and (39) it follows that $E \geqslant 0$, and from (42) and (43) that $-1 \leqslant \sigma \leqslant \frac{1}{2}$.

2.3.5. Energy in a perfectly elastic body. We consider again the matter, M say, within a small parallelepiped (see Fig. 2) which has the particle P at one corner, and shall in §§ 2.3.5, 2.3.6 take the standard configuration as that in which $p_{ij} = 0$. At time t, let x_i be the coordinates of P's position, δx_i the side-lengths of the parallelepiped, and $\delta\tau = \delta x_1 \delta x_2 \delta x_3$ its volume; let u_i, v_i and f_i be the displacement, velocity and acceleration of P. During the ensuing small time dt, let du_i be the additional displacement of P, $dw\,\delta\tau$ the work done on M, $dT\,\delta\tau$ the increase in kinetic energy, and $dQ\,\delta\tau$ the mechanical equivalent of the heat emitted from M. Then, by the first law of thermodynamics,

$$dw = dU + dT + dQ, \tag{46}$$

where $dU\,\delta\tau$ is the increase in the internal energy of M.

The work done on M by the body force, X_i per unit mass, is $\rho\,\delta\tau\,X_i\,du_i$. The work done by the 3-components of the tractions across the pair of faces normal to the 2-axis is

$$-p_{23}\delta x_1 \delta x_3 du_3 + \left(p_{23}du_3 + \frac{\partial(p_{23}du_3)}{\partial x_2}\delta x_2\right)\delta x_1 \delta x_3,$$

i.e.

$$\frac{\partial(p_{23}du_3)}{\partial x_2}\delta\tau;$$

and similarly for the work done by other components of traction.

Hence
$$dw = \rho X_i du_i + \frac{\partial(p_{ij}du_i)}{\partial x_j}. \tag{47}$$

Also
$$dT\,\delta\tau = d(\tfrac{1}{2}\rho\,\delta\tau v_i^2);$$

hence, by (26),
$$dT = \rho d(\tfrac{1}{2}v_i^2)$$

$$= \rho v_i \frac{dv_i}{dt} dt$$

$$= \rho f_i du_i. \tag{48}$$

By (47), (49) and (9),
$$dw - dT = p_{ij}\frac{\partial(du_i)}{\partial x_j}. \tag{49}$$

Now by (27),
$$\frac{\partial}{\partial x_j}(du_i) = d\left(\frac{\partial u_i}{\partial x_j}\right) \quad \text{(to sufficient accuracy)}$$

$$= de_{ij} - d\xi_{ij}, \tag{50}$$

by (12) and (13). By (46), (49) and (50), we thus have

$$p_{ij}de_{ij} = dU + dQ, \tag{51}$$

the omitted term $-p_{ij}d\xi_{ij}$ being seen to be zero since p_{ij} is a symmetrical tensor, and ξ_{ij} antisymmetrical (see the fourth paragraph of § 2.2).

When the thermodynamical conditions of the change are isothermal with the absolute temperature ϑ assigned, the state of M is sufficiently described by the values of the e_{ij}. By the second law of thermodynamics, dQ/ϑ, and hence also dQ (ϑ being here constant), is then a perfect differential in the e_{ij}. By the first law of thermodynamics, dU is also a perfect differential in the e_{ij}. It then follows from (51) that we may write

$$p_{ij}de_{ij} = dW, \tag{52}$$

where W is a function of the e_{ij}, called the (isothermal) *strain-energy function*. By (52),

$$p_{ij} = \frac{\partial W}{\partial e_{ij}}. \tag{53}$$

Since for perfect elasticity the p_{ij} are (on the infinitesimal strain theory) homogeneous linear functions of the e_{ij}, it follows from (53) that (apart from an additive arbitrary constant, which we shall take as zero) W is a homogeneous quadratic function of the e_{ij}. By Euler's theorem and (53), we thus have

$$2W = e_{ij}\frac{\partial W}{\partial e_{ij}} = e_{ij}p_{ij}. \tag{54}$$

If, in particular, the elastic behaviour is isotropic, we have by (54), (32) and (21)

$$2W = e_{ij}(\lambda\theta\delta_{ij} + 2\mu e_{ij})$$
$$= \lambda\theta^2 + 2\mu e_{ij}^2, \tag{55}$$

λ, μ being isothermal parameters (by e_{ij}^2, we understand $e_{ij}e_{ij}$, the summation convention holding as usual). In terms of k and μ, the isotropic strain-energy function is, by (35), given by

$$2W = k\theta^2 + 2\mu(e_{ij}^2 - \tfrac{1}{3}\theta^2). \tag{56}$$

A strain-energy function also exists when the conditions are adiabatic, for in this case $dQ = 0$, and so $p_{ij}de_{ij}$ is again a perfect differential. The strain-energy function in this case agrees with the forms (52), (53) and (54); but in (55) and (56) it is necessary to interpret λ, μ, k as adiabatic parameters.

It may be shown (see Jeffreys, *Cartesian Tensors* (C.U.P., 1952) , chapter 8) that the adiabatic and isothermal parameters (indicated here by the suffixes a, i, respectively) are connected by the relations

$$\lambda_a = \lambda_i + \frac{k_i^2 \gamma^2 \vartheta}{\rho c}, \quad \mu_a = \mu_i, \quad k_a = k_i \left(1 + \frac{k_i \gamma^2 \vartheta}{\rho c}\right), \qquad (57)$$

where γ denotes the coefficient of cubical expansion and c the specific heat at constant strain, other symbols being as previously.

In the cases above discussed, the total energy (including elastic strain energy) is conserved. In other cases, $dU + dQ$ will exceed dW, where W is defined by a formula of the type (55). By (51) the energy dissipated per unit volume in time dt is then $p_{ij} de_{ij} - dW$.

2.3.6. Theorems on elastic equilibrium. It will be convenient in this section to make use of *Green's lemma* in the form

$$\iiint \frac{\partial v_i}{\partial x_i} d\tau = \iint \nu_i v_i dS, \qquad (58)$$

where v_i is any vector, the triple integral is taken throughout the volume of a body, the double integral is taken over the boundary surface, and ν_i are the direction-cosines of the outward normal at a point of this surface. Triple and double integrals and ν_i will have this significance throughout this section. It will be presumed that the thermodynamical conditions are prescribed and are such that a strain-energy function exists.

We now prove Kirchhoff's theorem that if either (a) the surface displacements or (b) the surface tractions of a perfectly elastic body in equilibrium are assigned, then there is at most one solution for the state of strain (and hence also of stress) throughout the body.

The proof is as follows. By (9) and (53), we have, since $f_i = 0$,

$$\frac{\partial}{\partial x_j} \frac{\partial W}{\partial e_{ij}} + \rho X_i = 0. \qquad (59)$$

Suppose that u_i', u_i'' are two different sets of displacements each compatible with the assigned conditions, and now introduce $u_i = u_i' - u_i''$. If W, e_{ij}, etc., are now taken to be associated with the u_i as just defined, we deduce from (59) that

$$\frac{\partial}{\partial x_j} \frac{\partial W}{\partial e_{ij}} = 0.$$

Hence
$$0 = \iiint u_i \frac{\partial}{\partial x_j} \frac{\partial W}{\partial e_{ij}} d\tau$$

$$= \iiint \left\{ \frac{\partial}{\partial x_j} \left(u_i \frac{\partial W}{\partial e_{ij}} \right) - \frac{\partial u_i}{\partial x_j} \frac{\partial W}{\partial e_{ij}} \right\} d\tau$$

$$= \iint u_i \nu_j \frac{\partial W}{\partial e_{ij}} dS - \iiint e_{ij} \frac{\partial W}{\partial e_{ij}} d\tau,$$

the last line following by use of Green's lemma (58) and the fact that (by (12) and (13)) e_{ij} differs from $\partial u_i / \partial x_j$ by an antisymmetrical tensor (ξ_{ij}). Now when the data (a) are assigned, u_i is zero at all points of the boundary; and when (b) are assigned, $\nu_j (\partial W / \partial e_{ij})$ is, by (53) and (5), zero at all points of the boundary. Hence in both cases

$$0 = \iiint e_{ij} \frac{\partial W}{\partial e_{ij}} d\tau$$

$$= \iiint 2W d\tau \qquad (60)$$

by (54). Since W cannot be negative at any point (the standard configuration is being taken as one of stable equilibrium), it follows from (60) that W is everywhere zero, and hence that the e_{ij} as defined in this paragraph are all zero at all points of the body. From this the theorem follows.

This theorem may be extended to cover the case of a perfectly elastic vibrating body. For example, when there are no variable body forces and the surface is free from traction, the state of stress and strain is uniquely determined throughout the body at all times if the initial displacements and velocities are assigned at all points (see Love, *Mathematical Theory of Elasticity* (C.U.P., 1920), § 124).

A further theorem is that when the surface displacements of a perfectly elastic body and also the body forces (the field of which is conservative) are assigned, the total potential energy in the corresponding equilibrium configuration C is less than that in any other configuration C_1 compatible with the assigned conditions.

To prove this theorem, let u_i now be the displacement at any point of the body in the configuration C, and $u_i + u_i'$ that in C_1; let e_{ij}' correspond to u_i'. Let W be the strain-energy function corresponding to e_{ij}, W' to e'_{ij}, and W_1 to $e_{ij} + e'_{ij}$. Since W is a homogeneous quadratic function of the e_{ij}, it follows that

$$W_1 = W + e'_{ij} \frac{\partial W}{\partial e_{ij}} + W'.$$

(This step may be shown by writing W in the form $a_{rs} b_r b_s$, where b_r (or b_s) stands for any one of the nine components of e_{ij}; each of the suffixes r, s here runs from 1 to 9; then $W' = a_{rs} b'_r b'_s$, and

$$W_1 = a_{rs}(b_r + b'_r)(b_s + b'_s);$$

it is then necessary to use the result, easily proved, that

$$\partial W / \partial b_r = (a_{rs} + a_{sr}) b_{s}.)$$

Hence, by (53), $W_1 - W = W' + e'_{ij} p_{ij}$

$$= W' + p_{ij} \frac{\partial u'_i}{\partial x_j}, \tag{61}$$

since e'_{ij} differs from $\partial u'_i / \partial x_j$ by an antisymmetrical tensor. Also,

$$p_{ij} \frac{\partial u'_i}{\partial x_j} = \frac{\partial}{\partial x_j}(p_{ij} u'_i) - u'_i \frac{\partial p_{ij}}{\partial x_j}$$

$$= \frac{\partial}{\partial x_j}(p_{ij} u'_i) + X_i u'_i \rho, \tag{62}$$

by (9), since $f_i = 0$. Using (61) and (62), and then (58), we have

$$\iiint (W_1 - W)\, d\tau - \iiint X_i u'_i \rho\, d\tau = \iiint W'\, d\tau + \iiint \frac{\partial}{\partial x_j}(p_{ij} u'_i)\, d\tau$$

$$= \iiint W'\, d\tau + \iint \nu_j p_{ij} u'_i\, dS. \tag{63}$$

The surface integral vanishes by virtue of the assigned boundary conditions. Hence, since W' is everywhere positive, the left-hand side of (63) is positive; but this left-hand side consists of the excess in the configuration C_1 over that in C of the sum of the strain energy and the energy associated with the field of X_i. Hence the theorem follows.

2.3.7. On solving problems in elasticity. In elementary equilibrium problems, we are frequently given the boundary conditions and the body forces on a piece of uniform perfectly elastic isotropic matter, and we know from Kirchhoff's theorem that (on the infinitesimal strain theory) there is then at most one solution for the distribution of stress and strain. If therefore we succeed in finding, in terms of x_i, λ and μ (by trial or otherwise), any set of expressions for the e_{ij} which satisfy (32) and the relations (9) with $f_i = 0$, or alternatively which satisfy (34) with $\partial^2 u_i/\partial t^2 = 0$, and which also satisfy the boundary conditions, then this set of expressions must give the solution. On account of the large number of dependent variables (e_{ij} has six distinct components in general), this method can be expected to succeed only in very simple problems.

In practice the procedure has been followed to some extent of starting with any set of expressions of the e_{ij} (compatible with the relations (13)) which are found to satisfy the equilibrium equations, and then seeking the boundary conditions which these expressions fit. In this way, experience is gained of the problems in perfect elasticity that are likely to be exactly soluble.

The use of the strain-energy function and the minimum-energy theorem leads to alternative and fruitful methods of solving problems. The number of problems in elasticity that have been solved exactly is small, and energy methods form the basis of many useful approximations.

In seismology, the main problems are dynamical, being concerned with the effects of the passage of disturbances through the Earth, and the equations (9) and (34) with non-vanishing accelerations are relevant. These problems are of course the main concern in this book, and it will be seen that the equations (34) have a central place in the theory developed in later chapters.

In the two following sections, we shall give some indication of methods of allowing for departures from the comparatively simple conditions of isotropy and perfect elasticity that we have so far been mainly considering. In § 2.6 we shall comment briefly on the effects of the second-order terms that we have so far neglected.

2.4. Non-isotropic materials. If a material (still taken to be perfectly elastic) is *aelotropic* (or *anisotropic*), i.e. deviates from the directionally regular elastic behaviour of an isotropic material, it is necessary to replace the discussion in §2.3.1 by one starting from more general stress-strain relations of the form

$$p_{kl} = A_{ijkl} e_{ij}, \tag{64}$$

where the A_{ijkl} constitute a set of 81 coefficients. Of these coefficients not more than 36 could be independent, since each of the tensors p_{ij}, e_{ij}, being symmetrical, has only six independent components; thus $A_{ijkl} = A_{jikl} = A_{ijlk}$.

The existence of a strain-energy function in isothermal (or adiabatic) conditions, satisfying the relations (52) and (53), was established in §2.3.5 independently of the isotropic formula (32). It follows from (53) that in these conditions $\partial p_{kl}/\partial e_{ij} = \partial p_{ij}/\partial e_{kl}$, and hence that further relations, of the form $A_{ijkl} = A_{klij}$, hold between the coefficients in (64). From this it follows that in these conditions not more than 21 of the A_{ijkl} can be independent.

Crystals are substances which show some degree of symmetry in their elastic behaviour, but on account of special systematic structure are not completely isotropic. The number of parameters needed to specify the elastic behaviour (under isothermal or adiabatic conditions) of a perfectly elastic crystal of any given type is therefore less than or equal to 21, but greater than the total of two which we found to be sufficient for an isotropic substance.

Rocks of the Earth contain crystals, but it is to be expected that in a piece of rock large enough to contain many crystals, the crystals will be oriented in all directions at random, so that differences in elastic behaviour in different directions will be expected to neutralise one another to a large extent. For this reason, in seismology conditions are as a rule assumed to be isotropic; Stoneley and others have investigated the significance of anisotropy in seismological problems.

2.5. Departures from perfect elasticity due to time effects.

When a perfectly elastic (isotropic) body is in equilibrium under an assigned stress distribution (the thermodynamic conditions being also assigned), the strain distribution is uniquely determined by the equations (37). We shall in the following subsections consider cases in which (37) need modification; in particular, cases where the time t enters into the stress-strain relations.

As a preliminary it will be convenient to introduce the tensors P_{ij} and E_{ij}, defined by

$$P_{ij} = p_{ij} - \tfrac{1}{3}p_{kk}\delta_{ij}, \tag{65}$$

$$E_{ij} = e_{ij} - \tfrac{1}{3}e_{kk}\delta_{ij}. \tag{66}$$

P_{ij} and E_{ij} are called the *deviatoric* (or *distortional*) *stress tensor* and *deviatoric strain tensor*, respectively. We note that when $i \neq j$, $P_{ij} = p_{ij}$ and $E_{ij} = e_{ij}$.

From (37) we immediately deduce that

$$\tfrac{1}{3}p_{kk} = k\theta. \tag{67}$$

Using (65), (67), (37) and then (66), we obtain

$$P_{ij} = 2\mu E_{ij}, \tag{68}$$

for all i, j. The relations (67) and (68) together are precisely equivalent to (37); only five of the equations (68) are independent since, by (65) and (66), P_{ii} and E_{ii} are clearly both zero. For perfect elasticity, the relation (67) describes adequately the behaviour under a completely symmetrical stress, while (68) describes the effects of any departures from symmetry.

It is easy to deduce from (66) that

$$E_{ij}^2 = e_{ij}^2 - \tfrac{1}{3}\theta^2, \tag{69}$$

and hence by (56) that

$$2W = k\theta^2 + 2\mu E_{ij}^2. \tag{70}$$

The main imperfections of elasticity that are observed in practice arise only under stresses that are not fully symmetrical. Hence in setting up formulae to describe these imperfections, we shall keep (67) unchanged throughout, but shall modify (68) in various ways. All the elastic parameters to be used will be taken to be independent of t.

2.5.1. Fluid viscosity. The simplest mathematical model showing a deviation from perfectly elastic behaviour is that of an ideal viscous fluid. In this case (67) continues to hold, but in place of (68) we write

$$P_{ij} = 2\nu \frac{d}{dt} E_{ij}, \tag{71}$$

where ν is a new parameter denoting the *viscosity* of the fluid. We notice that the deviatoric stress is here connected with the rate of deviatoric strain in the same way as with the actual deviatoric strain in the case of a perfectly elastic solid.

For the particular case of laminar flow parallel to the 1-axis in planes perpendicular to the 2-axis (Fig. 6), we derive from (71), using (27),

$$p_{21} = \nu \frac{\partial v_1}{\partial x_2} \tag{72}$$

(where v_i denotes velocity), which agrees with a commonly used definition of fluid viscosity.

We notice that if in particular ν is zero, (71) reduces to $P_{ij} = 0$, which by (65) and (67) gives the perfect fluid relation (38).

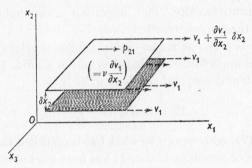

Fig. 6

The presence of terms involving d/dt in the stress-strain relations is associated with dissipation of energy see (§ 3.1.2). By the last paragraph of § 2.3.5, the rate of dissipation of energy per unit volume is given by

$$\Phi = p_{ij} \frac{de_{ij}}{dt} - \frac{dW}{dt},$$

where W in the present case ($\mu = 0$) is, by (70), equal to $\frac{1}{2}k\theta^2$. Thus, by (65), (66),

$$\Phi = (P_{ij} + \tfrac{1}{3}p_{kk}\delta_{ij})\frac{d}{dt}(E_{ij} + \tfrac{1}{3}\theta\delta_{ij}) - \frac{d}{dt}(\tfrac{1}{2}k\theta^2)$$

$$= P_{ij}\frac{d}{dt}E_{ij} + \tfrac{1}{3}p_{kk}\frac{1}{3}\frac{d\theta}{dt}3 - k\theta\frac{d\theta}{dt},$$

3

since $\delta_{ij}E_{ij} = E_{ii} = 0$, and $\delta_{ij}P_{ij} = P_{ii} = 0$. By (67) and (71) we then have

$$\Phi = P_{ij}\frac{d}{dt}E_{ij}$$

$$= 2\nu\left(\frac{d}{dt}E_{ij}\right)^2. \tag{73}$$

The reader may as an exercise be interested to deduce from (9), (71), (27) and the definitions of P_{ij}, E_{ij}, the Navier–Stokes equations of viscous fluid motion, namely,

$$\rho\frac{dv_i}{dt} = \rho X_i - \frac{\partial p}{\partial x_i} + \tfrac{1}{3}\nu\frac{\partial\theta'}{\partial x_i} + \nu\nabla^2 v_i,$$

where $p = -\tfrac{1}{3}p_{kk}$, and $\theta' = \partial v_j/\partial x_j$.

2.5.2. Firmoviscosity.

The suggestion arises that by suitably combining the perfect elasticity relations (68) with the viscous fluid relations (71), one might obtain a formula relevant to a possible type of imperfectly elastic behaviour of a solid. The simplest way of combining (68) and (71) is to write

$$P_{ij} = 2\mu E_{ij} + 2\nu\frac{dE_{ij}}{dt}. \tag{74}$$

The law (74) corresponds to what has been called the Kelvin or Voigt model or *firmoviscous* law. It has been used in some calculations to represent certain wave-scattering effects in seismology, and to indicate the order of attenuation in seismic wave transmission.

The presence of the term in ν implies exponential delay in reaching the full strain under an applied deviatoric stress, and also in recovery of an initial configuration after removal of a stress. It also implies dissipation of energy in accordance with the viscous fluid formula (73).

Next, consider the effect of an applied periodic deviatoric stress of period T, say $P_{ij} = A_{ij}\cos(2\pi t/T)$ (see § 3.1.1). If T is small compared with ν/μ, we find that E_{ij}, as given by (74), is of the order of $(T/\nu)A_{ij}$, which is small compared with A_{ij}/μ; hence under rapidly changing stresses, (74) implies an effective rigidity much greater than μ. On the other hand, if the stress periods are long compared with ν/μ, the term in ν in (74) is unimportant.

The last paragraph brings to notice the important point—relevant to all cases of imperfections of elasticity in a solid—that the rigidity may no longer be described by the single parameter μ, as is the case with perfect elasticity; with (74), the rigidity depends in general also on ν and on the form of the applied stress.

In order to give a qualitatively satisfactory account of imperfections of elasticity it is in general necessary to take into account more parameters than the three (k, μ, ν) involved in (67) and (74). We further note that it is not in general permissible to refer to the viscosity of a solid as a property that can be described by the value of a single parameter.

2.5.3. Elastic afterworking. The relations (74) go a little distance towards representing the observed phenomenon of elastic afterworking, wherein there is slow movement or *creep*, often of long duration, following application or removal of a deviatoric stress. But with most solids that exhibit elastic afterworking, this is not the whole story; following a sudden change in the deviatoric stress, the creep is preceded by some immediate change of strain not allowed for in (74). We can meet this complication qualitatively by adding to (74) a term in dP_{ij}/dt analogous to the previously added term $2\nu dE_{ij}/dt$, obtaining the form

$$P_{ij} + \tau \frac{dP_{ij}}{dt} = 2\mu E_{ij} + 2\nu \frac{dE_{ij}}{dt}, \tag{75}$$

where τ is a further parameter. The perfect elasticity relation (67) is taken still to hold, in keeping with the observed behaviour of many solids showing elastic afterworking.

To show that (75) meets the qualitative requirements of elastic afterworking, suppose that at time $t = 0$ the solid is unstrained and that a constant deviatoric stress is then applied. By (75), we have (the parameters are being taken to be independent of t—§ 2.5)

$$\int_0^t P_{ij}dt + \tau P_{ij} = 2\mu \int_0^t E_{ij}dt + 2\nu E_{ij}, \tag{76}$$

showing that there is an immediate deviatoric strain equal to $(\tau/2\nu)P_{ij}$. Subsequently, P_{ij} being taken constant, we deduce from (75)

$$E_{ij} = \frac{\tau P_{ij}}{2\nu} \left\{ \left(1 - \frac{\tau'}{\tau}\right) e^{-t/\tau'} + \frac{\tau'}{\tau} \right\}, \tag{77}$$

where we have written τ' for ν/μ. By (77), E_{ij} cannot exceed the value $P_{ij}/2\mu$, no matter how long the stress is applied. Now suppose the stress is removed. We see by (76) that there is an immediate reduction of amount $(\tau/2\nu)P_{ij}$ in the deviatoric strain, and this is followed by an exponential creep to zero strain; the larger the parameter τ' is, the slower is the rate of recovery. Fig. 7 shows the main features of the variation of E_{ij} with the time, when a constant deviatoric stress is applied and subsequently removed.

We note that it is necessary that $\tau' > \tau$ for elastic afterworking; for we require the E_{ij} as given in (77) to be increasing functions of t, and therefore $d/dt\{[1-(\tau'/\tau)]\,e^{-t/\tau'}\}$ to be positive.

Under very slowly changing stresses, the terms in τ and ν in (75) are unimportant and the behaviour approximates to that of a perfectly elastic solid of rigidity μ. Under very rapidly changing stresses the terms in τ and ν predominate, and the behaviour approximates to that of a perfectly elastic solid of rigidity ν/τ.

Under changing stresses of intermediate periods there is appreciable damping and dissipation of energy.

We note again that the rigidity does not depend on μ alone; it depends on the character of the applied stress and may depend on the para-

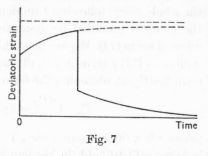

Fig. 7

meters ν, τ. It follows that in (77) there is no objection to replacing ν/τ by the symbol μ (a different μ of course from that in (75) and (76), but still having the dimensions of rigidity); this notation (in which the parameters are k, τ, τ' and the new μ) has been used by Jeffreys.

A point of mathematical interest is that (75) may be formally constructed from the perfect elasticity relations (68) or (37) by replacing μ by the operator $(\nu/\tau)\,(p+1/\tau')\,(p+1/\tau)^{-1}$, where $p \equiv d/dt$. This suggests the possible use of the operational calculus in estimating the effects of elastic afterworking in a problem that has been formally solved for the case of perfect elasticity.

2.5.4. Elasticoviscosity. If we take an extreme form of (75) in which the parameter μ is zero (this is equivalent to taking $\tau' = \infty$), we have the relations

$$2\nu \frac{dE_{ij}}{dt} = P_{ij} + \tau \frac{dP_{ij}}{dt}. \tag{78}$$

A substance whose elastic behaviour is described by (67) and (78) is said to be *elasticoviscous*; (78) corresponds to what is sometimes called the Maxwell model.

If at time $t = 0$ a constant deviatoric stress P_{ij} is applied to an elasticoviscous substance previously unstrained, we see (using (76) with $\mu = 0$) that a deviatoric strain equal to $(\tau/2\nu)\,P_{ij}$ is immediately produced. Subsequently the deviatoric strain increases at the

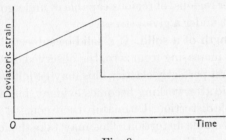

Fig. 8

steady rate of $P_{ij}/2\nu$, as with a viscous fluid, and can become indefinitely great. If at time $t = t_1$ the stress is removed, there is an immediate reduction of amount $(\tau/2\nu)\,P_{ij}$ in the deviatoric strain, but now a permanent deviatoric strain of amount $(2\nu)^{-1}\int_0^{t_1} P_{ij}\,dt$ remains. This is illustrated in Fig. 8.

Under deviatoric stresses that change very slowly with the time, the first term on the right-hand side of (78) predominates, so that in this case elasticoviscous behaviour approximates to that of a fluid of viscosity ν. If, on the other hand, the stresses are changing very rapidly, the second term predominates, and the behaviour approximates to that of a perfectly elastic solid of rigidity ν/τ.

These results are all in qualitative agreement with the observed behaviour of some plastic materials. A substance such as pitch or plastic sulphur can be indefinitely strained under sustained deviatoric stress (i.e. suffers *plastic flow*), and only partially recovers an initial configuration on removal of the stress (i.e. has acquired a *permanent set*).

It is of some interest to note that Jeffreys has shown that the qualitative effects of elastic afterworking, as described by (75), can be realised in certain models consisting of perfectly elastic material enclosing pockets of elasticoviscous material satisfying the relations (78); the values of the parameters in the corresponding elastic afterworking equations are found to vary considerably with the distribution of the elasticoviscous material. Jeffreys has suggested, therefore, that the nature of the imperfectly elastic behaviour of a solid may be largely a question of the distribution, within stronger regions, of regions capable of undergoing molecular rearrangement under a given stress.

2.5.5. Strength of a solid. If a solid be subjected to deviatoric stress steadily increasing from zero, the observed elastic behaviour is usually at first perfectly elastic. This may be followed by a stage in which elastic afterworking becomes evident, but as yet there is no irrecoverable distortion. Ultimately there comes a stage in which there is irrecoverable distortion. This may take the form of plastic flow or of fracture. Fracture may occur immediately on application of a stress if sufficiently high, but usually there is a finite range of deviatoric stress between the smallest to produce plastic flow and the smallest to produce immediate fracture.

The question arises as to whether the stage of irrecoverable distortion is determined by any simple function of the stress components. A natural function to consider in this connection is the scalar P_{ij}^2. From (65) we obtain on multiplying out

$$P_{ij}^2 = \tfrac{1}{3}\{(p_{22}-p_{33})^2 + (p_{33}-p_{11})^2 + (p_{11}-p_{22})^2\} \\ + 2(p_{23}^2 + p_{31}^2 + p_{12}^2), \quad (79)$$

and this expression is in fact proportional to a function whose value is on one theory (that of Mises) assumed to determine the stage of onset of plastic flow. There is some experimental support for this assumption in the case of metals, and the value of $(3P_{ij}^2)^{\frac{1}{2}}$ at which the flow starts has been used as an index of the *strength* of the solid.

Actually the stage of irrecoverable distortion may of course depend significantly on the values of other functions in addition to

P_{ij}^2, for example, the scalar p_{kk}. On one theory this stage is assumed to be determined by the value of the *stress-difference*, defined as the difference between the greatest and least principal stresses. In geophysics, it happens that the difference between results on this theory and those on the Mises theory is unimportant; for we can deduce from (79) that $(P_{ij}^2)^{\frac{1}{2}}$ must lie between 0·71 and 0·82 times the stress-difference, a range of variation of only 15%.

The term 'strength' has been used also in connection with the stress needed to produce immediate fracture. With a view to avoiding confusion, Griggs introduced the term *fundamental strength*, defined as the greatest stress-difference under which neither plastic flow nor fracture takes place. The fundamental strength of a substance such as pitch is thus zero.

It is important to notice that the terms 'strength' and 'rigidity' are not synonymous. Thus whereas an elasticoviscous substance has zero strength, we have seen that in certain circumstances it behaves as a perfectly elastic solid with significant rigidity.

2.5.6. Solids and fluids. In § 2.3.3, we classified perfectly elastic substances into perfect solids and perfect fluids according to the value of the parameter μ. This mode of classification is too simple for actual substances. It is questionable whether μ would be precisely zero for any actual substance; in addition, we have seen that a single parameter μ may be insufficient to describe rigidity; also a substance may show rigidity when μ is zero. In so far as we may wish to classify any given substance (in a given thermo-dynamical state) as solid or fluid (rather than be content with a classification in terms of values of μ, ν, etc.), it is therefore necessary to lay down some further convention.

Some writers have taken absence of strength as the criterion that a substance is a fluid, others absence of rigidity; as we have seen these criteria are not equivalent. Since some substances lacking strength (e.g. pitch at ordinary temperatures) can in certain circumstances behave as perfectly elastic solids, it appears that absence of rigidity is the better criterion. The question then arises as to the detectability of rigidity in practice. It appears from the preceding subsections that rigidity is most likely to be detected under rapidly changing stress. We shall see in chapter 4 that there is a connection between the rigidity of a substance and the transmission of rotational waves through it. Following Jeffreys, we shall therefore call a substance a *solid* if there can be detectable transmission of rotational waves through it; otherwise, a *fluid*. An elasticoviscous substance is thus a solid on this classification.

Before closing the present section, we point out that the question of imperfections has many further complications that we have not considered here. While equations such as (75) and (78) are in qualitative agreement with certain observed types of imperfectly elastic behaviour, the theory we have set down must be regarded as only a first step towards a full discussion. At the present time, much experimental work is proceeding with a view to determining fuller quantitative details. For many purposes in seismology, however, a knowledge of the broad qualitative effects of imperfections is all that is needed, and in this case the mathematical models we have set down are sufficient.

2.6. Finite-strain theory. The theory we have so far developed rests on the assumption (see § 2.2) that strains are sufficiently small to permit neglect of higher-order terms; but it is evident from practical observations that in some cases where the stress is high this assumption cannot hold. It is found, for instance, that if a long, thin, straight, cylindrical rod (the 'Euler column') be subjected to increasing compressive forces at its ends, a state of elastic instability in due course develops, as a result of which the configuration suddenly changes to one in which the rod is appreciably curved. This behaviour is in discord with the uniqueness theorem of Kirchhoff (§ 2.3.6), and since it is found to take place in the effective absence of imperfections of elasticity, implies that second-order terms are important in some problems. Theory which takes these terms into consideration is called finite-strain theory.

When higher-order terms are taken into account, the expression for the strain tensor is more complicated. Thus, whereas in the first-order theory we obtained the equation

$$d(PQ)^2 = 2e_{ij}y_iy_j,\tag{79}$$

where the e_{ij} are given by (13), the second-order theory would by (18) give

$$d(PQ)^2 = \left(\frac{\partial u_j}{\partial x_i} + \frac{\partial u_i}{\partial x_j}\right) y_i y_j - \frac{\partial u_i}{\partial x_j} \frac{\partial u_i}{\partial x_k} y_j y_k,$$

i.e.

$$d(PQ)^2 = 2\epsilon_{ij} y_i y_j, \tag{80}$$

where

$$\epsilon_{ij} = \frac{1}{2}\left(\frac{\partial u_j}{\partial x_i} + \frac{\partial u_i}{\partial x_j} - \frac{\partial u_k}{\partial x_i} \frac{\partial u_k}{\partial x_j}\right). \tag{81}$$

Thus any component of the more accurate strain tensor ϵ_{ij} differs from the corresponding component of e_{ij} by the sum of three second-order terms.

For the case of finite hydrostatic stress (i.e. complete symmetry), (22) and (81) yield $\epsilon_{ii} = \theta - \theta^2/6 = 3\epsilon$, say. (82)

From §2.2.3 and (82), the density ρ is found to be related to ϵ by

$$\rho = \rho_0(1 - 2\epsilon)^{\frac{3}{2}}, \tag{83}$$

where the zero suffix relates to the unstrained state.

On the second-order theory, further questions arise such as the influence of rotation on the stress-strain relations, the possible variation of k, μ as the stress increases, and possible departures from isotropy if an initial stress is high and unsymmetrical. It is evident, therefore, that the mathematics of finite-strain theory is much more complicated than that of the infinitesimal theory, and in general it is necessary to introduce simplifying assumptions relevant to particular contexts.

In important pioneering work, Birch has applied finite-strain theory developed by Murnaghan to problems of the Earth's interior, assuming the presence of an initial finite hydrostatic stress $-p\delta_{ij}$ (see §4.7). On certain experimentally based assumptions, he has used equations based on (82) and (83) to derive equations of state for internal regions of the Earth. Examples of his equations for chemically homogeneous regions are

$$p = -3k_0\epsilon(1-2\epsilon)^{\frac{5}{2}}(1 + 2\xi\epsilon), \tag{84}$$

$$k = k_0(1-2\epsilon)^{\frac{5}{2}}\{1 - 7\epsilon + 2\xi\epsilon(2 - 9\epsilon)\}, \tag{85}$$

$$\frac{dk}{dp} = \frac{12 - 49\epsilon}{3(1 - 7\epsilon)}, \tag{86}$$

where ξ is a function of temperature; in (86), terms in ξ have been neglected.

Further reference to finite strain is made in §4.7.

CHAPTER 3

VIBRATIONS AND WAVES

Before we can follow out the implications of the elasticity equations of motion such as $(2, (34))$, it will be necessary to develop the theory of vibrations and waves to some extent. It will be convenient here to set up also certain results that will be relevant to the chapter on the theory of the seismograph.

3.1. Vibrations of systems with one degree of freedom

3.1.1. Simple harmonic motion. The simplest vibrating system is one whose configuration is expressible in terms of a single co-ordinate x which is changing according to the law

$$\ddot{x} + \omega^2 x = 0, \tag{1}$$

where ω is a real constant, and dots denote differentiations with respect to the time t. This is the case of (undamped) simple harmonic motion. The general solution of (1) is expressible as

$$\left. \begin{array}{l} x = A\cos\omega t + B\sin\omega t, \\ x = C\cos(\omega t + \epsilon), \end{array} \right\} \tag{2}$$

or as

where A, B and C, ϵ are constants of integration, determinate if the initial values of x and $\dot{x}$ are known. The motion is (time) periodic, the *period* being $2\pi/\omega$; the *frequency* is $\omega/2\pi$; the *amplitude* is the coefficient (C in this case) of the periodic factor in the second form of (2); and the *phase constant* is ϵ.

3.1.2. Damped vibrations. In any vibrating system, friction is always present in practice to a greater or less degree; this involves the presence in the equations of motion of terms depending on velocities, and causes *damping* of the motion. We shall consider only cases where the friction forces are proportional to first powers of velocities. The main features of such cases are illustrated in a study of the equation $\ddot{x} + 2\lambda\omega\dot{x} + \omega^2 x = 0,$ (3)

which (see chapter 9) corresponds to the free motion of an ideal seismograph, the coefficient λ being an index of the extent of damping.

The solution of linear differential equations like (3), and also of the more complicated equations (including systems of differential equations and partial differential equations) that we shall meet later, is often facilitated by the use of imaginary exponentials; and we shall carry through the solution of (3) in some detail in order to illustrate this process. Writing ι for $\sqrt{-1}$, we add to (3) ι times the equation obtained on replacing x by y in (3), obtaining

$$\ddot{z} + 2\lambda\omega\dot{z} + \omega^2 z = 0, \tag{4}$$

where $z = x + \iota y$. As a trial solution of (4), we put

$$z = K \exp(\iota\gamma t), \tag{5}$$

where K and γ are independent of t. We note that for operations on any function of the form of the right-hand side of (5), we have

$$\frac{\partial}{\partial t} = \iota\gamma, \quad \frac{\partial^2}{\partial t^2} = -\gamma^2. \tag{6}$$

The trial solution (5) is thus seen to satisfy (4) if γ is such that

$$(\iota\gamma)^2 + 2\lambda\omega\iota\gamma + \omega^2 = 0,$$

i.e. if $$\iota\gamma = -(\lambda \pm \sqrt{[\lambda^2 - 1]})\,\omega. \tag{7}$$

The coefficient K in (5) is left undetermined, and the two values of γ in (7) lead to two independent solutions of (4), each of the type (5), the coefficients K_1, K_2 say (corresponding to K) being independent and (if initial conditions or their equivalent are not specified) arbitrary. Since (4) is linear in z, we may superpose these two solutions to obtain the general solution of (4), K_1 and K_2 being the two integration constants. We note that K_1, K_2 may be complex numbers.

The general solution of (3) is then deduced from the fact that x is the real part of z. It is clear from (7) that this solution will take different forms according as the damping coefficient λ is less than or greater than unity. We derive when $\lambda < 1$

$$x = \{A \cos(\sqrt{[1-\lambda^2]}\,\omega t) + B \sin(\sqrt{[1-\lambda^2]}\,\omega t)\} \exp(-\lambda\omega t),$$
$$\text{or} \quad x = C \exp(-\lambda\omega t) \cos(\sqrt{[1-\lambda^2]}\,\omega t + \epsilon); \tag{8a}$$

and when $\lambda > 1$

$$x = A \exp\{-(\lambda + \sqrt{[\lambda^2 - 1]})\,\omega t\} + B \exp\{-(\lambda - \sqrt{[\lambda^2 - 1]})\,\omega t\}, \tag{8c}$$

where A, B and C, ϵ are real constants of integration. When $\lambda = 1$, (7) yields only one distinct value of γ, but the general solution (containing two independent integration constants) may be deduced from either $(8a)$ or $(8c)$. Thus if, for instance, we expand in power series the cosine and sine terms in the first of $(8a)$ and replace $B\omega \sqrt{(1 - \lambda^2)}$ by B, we then obtain for the case $\lambda = 1$

$$x = (A + Bt) \exp(-\omega t). \tag{8b}$$

The solution $(8a)$ corresponds to vibratory motion of period $2\pi/\omega \sqrt{(1 - \lambda^2)}$ and amplitude $C \exp(-\lambda \omega t)$; it is seen that this amplitude diminishes steadily towards zero as time goes on. Neither of the solutions $(8b)$ and $(8c)$ gives vibratory motion; in both cases there can be at most one zero of x within a finite time, after which x creeps asymptotically to zero. Thus the motion is *periodic* if $\lambda < 1$, *aperiodic* if $\lambda \geqslant 1$. It may be noted that if λ is only a little less than unity, the amplitude factor has already appreciably diminished by the time one half-period has elapsed, so that the practical result in this case is not greatly different from aperiodicity. In connection with the theory of the seismograph, it will be a useful exercise to the reader to compare the graphs of x against t for the cases $\lambda = 1$ and $\lambda = 1/\sqrt{2}$; it will be found that the difference in the values of x for these two cases will, if initially small, be always small, compared with the maximum value of x.

3.1.3. Forced vibrations. If a dynamical system like that just considered is further subject to variable external forces, additional terms will need to be included in equations such as (1) and (3). We shall here investigate the equation

$$\ddot{x} + 2\lambda\omega\dot{x} + \omega^2 x = b \cos pt, \tag{9}$$

where b and p are further given constants. The additional term $b \cos pt$ corresponds to the presence of a superimposed periodic force of period $2\pi/p$. Towards solving (9), we introduce y which satisfies the conjugate equation

$$\ddot{y} + 2\lambda\omega\dot{y} + \omega^2 y = b \sin pt,$$

so that, if again $z = x + \iota y$, we have

$$\ddot{z} + 2\lambda\omega\dot{z} + \omega^2 z = b \exp(\iota pt). \tag{10}$$

Putting $z = K \exp(\iota pt)$ as a trial solution of (10) gives

$$(-p^2 + 2\iota\lambda\omega p + \omega^2) K = b.$$

Thus a particular solution of (18) is

$$z = b \exp(\iota pt)/(\omega^2 - p^2 + 2i\lambda\omega p).$$

We can rewrite this in the form

$$z = b \exp\{\iota(pt - \delta)\}/\{(\omega^2 - p^2)^2 + 4\lambda^2\omega^2 p^2\}^{\frac{1}{2}},$$

where $\delta = \tan^{-1}\{2\lambda\omega p/(\omega^2 - p^2)\}.$ (11)

We then deduce that a particular solution of (9) is

$$x = b \cos(pt - \delta)/\{(\omega^2 - p^2)^2 + 4\lambda^2\omega^2 p^2\}^{\frac{1}{2}}, \tag{12}$$

where the *phase lag* δ is given by (11). The general solution of (9) is given by equating x to the sum of the *complementary function*, i.e. the right-hand side of (8*a*), (8*b*) or (8*c*) (whichever is relevant) obtained in the process of solving (3), and the *particular integral*, i.e. the right-hand side of (12).

It is evident that the complementary function (which has a real exponential factor in all cases) becomes increasingly less important as time goes on. The period of the ultimately dominant term (i.e. the particular integral), namely, $2\pi/p$, is that of the superimposed force. The phase lag δ depends on λ, ω and p. An important feature of the solution is that when the damping is slight (i.e. λ small), and also p and ω are nearly equal, x as given by (12) can become very great; this is the case of *resonance*.

3.1.4. In practice, when solving linear equations like (3) and (9) with the help of a complex dependent variable, we do not as a rule bother to change the symbol (as from x to z above) during this process, but we understand that the real part is to be extracted from the solution finally obtained. This practice will be followed in the sequel.

3.2. Vibrations of systems with more than one degree of freedom. We shall confine consideration to *holonomic* systems (i.e. systems for which all the differential constraint relations can be integrated). Suppose that the specification of the configuration of such a system requires knowledge of the value of n coordinates. These coordinates, which we denote as q_r $(r = 1, 2, ..., n)$, may be distances measured from fixed or moving points or lines, or may be angles or other functions of position. They are called *generalised coordinates*, and the system is said to have *n degrees of freedom.*

In investigating the vibrations of such a system, we shall not in the remainder of this chapter include terms due to friction in the equations. Allowance for friction involves additional algebra, and it suffices to state that the general effects of friction are quite similar to the damping effects found for the particular case of § 3.1.2. When the friction is not too great, its presence does not alter the vibratory character of the motion, but entails the presence in the amplitudes of real exponential factors diminishing as t increases, as in (8a). The presence of such factors is of course associated with dissipation of energy. In general dynamics, elegant use is made of a *dissipation function* in this connection (cf. also § 2.5.1, equation (2, (73))).

3.2.1. Vibrations of systems with finite freedom. We shall first take n finite and examine the small vibrations of the system about a stable equilibrium configuration. We take the q_r to be all zero in this configuration. The kinetic energy T is expressible in the form

$$2T = \sum_r \sum_s a_{rs} \dot{q}_r \dot{q}_s, \tag{13}$$

where the coefficients a_{rs} will in general be functions of the q_r, but may, if we neglect in (13) terms of higher order than the second, be taken as constants for motion in the vicinity of the equilibrium configuration. In the absence of dissipative forces there exists a potential energy V. Since $\partial V/\partial q_r = 0$ for equilibrium, we may, expanding V in a Taylor series and neglecting terms of higher order than the second, write

$$2V = \sum_r \sum_s b_{rs} q_r q_s, \tag{14}$$

where the coefficients b_{rs} are constants. Without loss of generality, we may take $a_{rs} = a_{sr}$ and $b_{rs} = b_{sr}$. By Lagrange's equations

$$\frac{d}{dt}\left(\frac{\partial T}{\partial \dot{q}_r}\right) - \frac{\partial T}{\partial q_r} = -\frac{\partial V}{\partial q_r} \quad (r = 1, 2, ..., n), \tag{15}$$

we then obtain, correct to the first order in the q_r, the n equations of motion

$$\sum_s a_{rs} \ddot{q}_s + \sum_s b_{rs} q_s = 0 \quad (r = 1, 2, ..., n). \tag{16}$$

The equilibrium configuration being stable, we can show by taking a trial solution of the form

$$q_r = K_r \exp(\iota \gamma t) \quad (r = 1, 2, ..., n) \tag{17}$$

(analogously to (5)), that the general solution of the set of equations (16) is expressible in the real form

$$\left. \begin{aligned} q_r &= \sum_s A_{rs} \cos \gamma_s t + \sum_s B_{rs} \sin \gamma_s t \\ \text{or} \quad q_r &= \sum_s C_{rs} \cos(\gamma_s t + \epsilon_s) \end{aligned} \right\} \quad (r = 1, 2, ..., n). \tag{18}$$

In the second of (18), the γ_s, and also the ratios of the C_{rs} for any assigned s, are found to be expressible in terms of the constants a_{rs} and b_{rs} in (16); but for each s one particular member of the corresponding C_{rs} may be taken independently of the a_{rs} and b_{rs}. The $2n$ constants of integration may be taken as the particular n members of C_{rs} that are taken independently of the a_{rs} and b_{rs}, together with the n phase constants ϵ_s.

The solution (18) may be regarded as a linear combination of n *normal modes*, each mode corresponding to a particular value of the suffix s, and being possessed of the following properties: (i) the frequency is the same for every coordinate q_r and depends only on the coefficients a_{rs} and b_{rs}; (ii) the phase constant is the same for every q_r but is otherwise arbitrary; (iii) the ratio of the amplitudes of the various q_r is determined by the a_{rs} and b_{rs}. The system if suitably excited can vibrate in any one of the n normal modes; this is merely a matter of arranging the initial conditions so that all but the relevant two integration constants are zero. The frequencies in the n normal modes are sometimes called the *eigen-frequencies* of the system. Points at which the displacement is permanently zero in a particular normal mode are called *nodes* of that mode.

A further important property of normal modes is that in any particular mode, the mean values, over a period, of the kinetic and potential energies are equal. To show this, let us write a particular solution (extracted from (18)) corresponding to any particular normal mode in the form

$$q_r = C_r \cos(\gamma t + \epsilon) \quad (r = 1, 2, ..., n). \tag{19}$$

On substituting from (19) into (13) and (14), respectively, we find that the corresponding mean kinetic and potential energies over a period are

$$\tfrac{1}{4}\gamma^2 \sum_r \sum_s a_{rs} C_r C_s, \quad \tfrac{1}{4} \sum_r \sum_s b_{rs} C_r C_s. \tag{20}$$

By substituting from (19) into the equations of motion (16), we then find that the two expressions in (20) are equal.

3.2.2. Rayleigh's principle. If instead of (19) we substituted into (13) and (14) the expressions

$$q_r = c_r \cos(\mu t + \epsilon) \quad (r = 1, 2, \ldots, n), \tag{21}$$

where the c_r and $2\pi/\mu$ are not necessarily the actual amplitudes and period in a normal mode, and then equated the two expressions analogous to (20), we should obtain the equation

$$\mu^2 \sum_r \sum_s a_{rs} c_r c_s = \sum_r \sum_s b_{rs} c_r c_s. \tag{22}$$

Rayleigh showed that if the c_r in (21) should happen to be taken approximately equal to the actual amplitudes C_r in a normal mode, then the value of $2\pi/\mu$ as obtained from (22) would differ from the actual period $2\pi/\gamma$ of the mode by a small fraction which would be of the order of the squares of the quantities $(C_r - c_r)/C_r$.

It follows that if we have sufficient knowledge in a particular problem to enable us to estimate approximate values of the amplitude ratios of a particular normal mode of vibration, we can then by (22) infer the period of this mode within a fractional error of the order of the squares of the errors in the trial amplitude ratios. In practice, this principle has frequently been made the basis of a rapid determination of the frequency of vibration in the lowest mode.

3.2.3. An illustrative problem. In order to illustrate the theory of § 3.2.1, we shall consider vibrations of a light straight flexible elastic string of length l, fixed at both ends and having n particles, each of mass m, attached at equal intervals $h = l/(n+1)$; the tension S will be taken to be uniform along the string. We shall discuss (in outline) the free vibrations of this system, neglecting gravity and friction, following the initial presence of small lateral coplanar displacements and velocities of the particles.

We take as generalised coordinates the n (lateral) displacements

y_r of the particles. It is then easy to derive the equations of small motion of the system in the form

$$m\ddot{y}_r + S\left(\frac{y_r - y_{r-1}}{h} - \frac{y_{r+1} - y_r}{h}\right) = 0 \quad (r = 1, 2, ..., n), \qquad (23)$$

where $y_0 = y_{n+1} = 0$. On substituting into (23) a trial solution of the form $y_r = K_r \exp(\iota\gamma t)$, corresponding to (17), we derive (after some algebra) the general solution of (23) in the form

$$y_r(t) = \sum_{s=1}^{n}\left(A_s \sin\frac{s\pi x_r}{l}\cos\gamma_s t + B_s \sin\frac{s\pi x_r}{l}\sin\gamma_s t\right) \quad (r = 1, 2, ..., n),$$

$$\qquad (24)$$

where $\qquad \gamma_s = \left\{\frac{2S}{mh}\left(1 - \cos\frac{s\pi}{n+1}\right)\right\}^{\frac{1}{2}} \quad (s = 1, 2, ..., n); \qquad (25)$

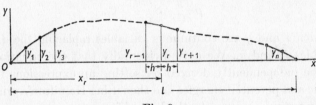

Fig. 9

in these equations, x_r is the distance of the rth particle from the end O of the string (Fig. 9), and the A_s and B_s are $2n$ integration constants. There is one normal mode corresponding to each particular value of s, the associated eigen-frequency being $\gamma_s/2\pi$. The phase in the sth mode is determined solely by the particular value of A_s/B_s; this verifies that the phase is the same for each coordinate y_r in a particular mode. We verify also that the ratio of the amplitudes of the y_r in the sth mode is independent of the integration constants.

Particular values of the $2n$ integration constants A_s, B_s may be determined if the initial displacements and velocities are known, for we immediately derive from (24) the $2n$ equations

$$\left.\begin{array}{l} y_r(0) = \sum_s A_s \sin\dfrac{s\pi x_r}{l} \\[2mm] \left(\dfrac{dy_r}{dt}\right)_{t=0} = \sum_s B_s \gamma_s \sin\dfrac{s\pi x_r}{l} \end{array}\right\} \quad (r = 1, 2, ..., n), \qquad (26)$$

which are precisely sufficient for this purpose.

3.2.4. Vibrations of continuous systems.

The theory described above may be extended to the case of a vibrating continuous system, the number of degrees of freedom being now infinite. We shall make use of the problem of § 3.2.3 to illustrate this case (again only in outline), letting the number n of the particles increase indefinitely in such a way that the total mass of the particles remains finite; we then have the problem of the transverse vibrations of a continuous massive string of length l and uniform line-density, ρ say, fixed at its end-points.

Application of the necessary limit operation to the finite set of ordinary differential equations (23) gives in place of (23) the single partial differential equation

$$\rho \frac{\partial^2 y}{\partial t^2} - S \frac{\partial^2 y}{\partial x^2} = 0, \tag{27}$$

in which x and y are continuous variables replacing the discrete variables x_r and y_r. We note incidentally that the equation (27) may be independently derived by setting up expressions for the kinetic and potential energies and then using Hamilton's principle, or may again be independently derived from elementary principles.

Application of the limit operation to the solution (24) gives

$$y(x,t) = \sum_{s=1}^{\infty} \left(A_s \sin \frac{s\pi x}{l} \cos \gamma_s t + B_s \sin \frac{s\pi x}{l} \sin \gamma_s t \right), \tag{28}$$

where, from (25),

$$\frac{\gamma_s}{2\pi} = \frac{s}{2l} \sqrt{\frac{S}{\rho}}. \tag{29}$$

We shall later (§ 3.3) show how to derive this solution directly from (27). The solution (28) is seen to be equivalent to the effect of superposing an infinite number of normal modes, each possessing properties as in the case of finite freedom. The eigen-frequencies are given by (29).

As in the case of finite freedom, the values of all the A_s, B_s can be determined if the initial velocities and displacements of all points of the string are known. By (28),

$$\left. \begin{array}{l} y(x,0) = \displaystyle\sum_{s=1}^{\infty} A_s \sin \frac{s\pi x}{l}, \\[2ex] \dfrac{\partial y}{\partial t}(x,0) = \displaystyle\sum_{s=1}^{\infty} B_s \gamma_s \sin \frac{s\pi x}{l}. \end{array} \right\} \tag{30}$$

Using the method of Fourier, we obtain from the first of (30)

$$\int_0^l y(x, 0) \sin\frac{r\pi x}{l}\, dx = \sum_{s=1}^{\infty} A_s \int_0^l \sin\frac{s\pi x}{l} \sin\frac{r\pi x}{l}\, dx.$$

Since $\int_0^\pi \sin s\xi \sin r\xi\, d\xi$ is equal to zero if $r \neq s$, and equal to $\tfrac{1}{2}\pi$ if $r = s$, we then obtain

$$\int_0^l y(x, 0) \sin\frac{r\pi x}{l}\, dx = A_r \int_0^l \sin\frac{r\pi x}{l} \sin\frac{r\pi x}{l}\, dx$$

$$= \tfrac{1}{2} A_r l.$$

Hence
$$A_s = \frac{2}{l} \int_0^l y(x, 0) \sin\frac{s\pi x}{l}\, dx. \tag{31}$$

Similarly, using the second of (30) and (29), we may show that

$$B_s = \frac{2}{s\pi} \sqrt{\left(\frac{\rho}{S}\right)} \int_0^l \frac{\partial y}{\partial t}(x, 0) \sin\frac{s\pi x}{l}\, dx. \tag{32}$$

3.2.5. Seismological considerations. The normal mode theory that we have discussed in the preceding subsections forms the basis of one line of investigation of earthquake phenomena; for, following the occurrence of an earthquake, the Earth may be considered as a vibrating continuous system.

A second line of investigation makes immediate use of the special feature that the initial disturbance in an earthquake is confined to a comparatively small part of the whole region traversed by the ensuing disturbances. In these circumstances, properties of equations analogous to (27) may be developed by a method somewhat different from that so far discussed; this development, which is called wave theory, will be considered in §§ 3.3–3.5.

The vibration theory based on normal mode considerations and the wave theory are of course quite complementary; either method will lead to the same results, but in particular problems the one method may lead to results more readily than the other. In elementary problems the wave-theory method is usually the simpler in application.

The complementary character of the two methods will be illustrated in a simple example to be discussed in the third paragraph of §3.3 and in §3.3.1. As another example, it may be noted that

Rayleigh pointed out that the Rayleigh surface waves (to be discussed in chapter 5, using the wave-theory method) must be included in Lamb's theory of the vibrations of an elastic sphere (based on the normal mode method); actually Bromwich later deduced from Lamb's theory the equation (5, (16)) for the velocity of Rayleigh waves. Some further direct applications of the normal mode theory may be read in Love, *Some Problems of Geodynamics* (C.U.P., 1911).

It may be noted further that the normal mode theory is often the direct source of elegant results in seismological theory. An instance of this is the use that has been made by Jeffreys of Rayleigh's principle (§ 3.2.2) in the theory of seismic surface waves (see chapter 5). The use of the principle makes possible the estimation of approximate answers to problems that would be very difficult to solve by ordinary methods. (See also chapter 14.)

Another instance is the use that has been made of a certain reciprocal theorem in the theory of vibrations. Suppose that the application of an impulse at one point P in a dynamical system causes a vibration in which the velocity at some second point Q has the component v in a particular normal mode. The theorem then states that if the same impulse be instead applied at Q, it will produce at P the same component v in the normal mode in question. As a corollary, it follows that if an impulse is applied at a node of any normal mode, then this particular normal mode will be missing from the ensuing vibrations; if the point of application be near such a node, the amplitude of the normal mode in question will be abnormally small.

Now, as we shall see in chapter 5, the amplitudes of seismic surface waves (which may be regarded as equivalent to a superposed set of normal modes of vibration) decrease exponentially with increase of depth below the Earth's outer surface. It then follows by the last paragraph, that if some particular earthquake originates at a much greater depth below this surface than the normal earthquake, then the surface waves ensuing should be less marked than in the normal case—a result that is in striking agreement with observations. (In fact at an earlier stage of seismological history, the virtual absence of observations of surface waves from some earthquakes was shown by Jeffreys and Stoneley to be crucial evidence of the occurrence of 'deep-focus' earthquakes—see § 15.5.1.)

3.3. Plane waves. We now proceed to an independent discussion of the equation

$$\frac{\partial^2 y}{\partial t^2} = c^2 \frac{\partial^2 y}{\partial x^2}, \tag{33}$$

where c is an assigned constant, t denotes the time, x is a rectangular cartesian coordinate in some region, and y is a function of x and t which represents a disturbance in the values of some physical quantity; in the applications we shall make, y will denote a component of displacement.

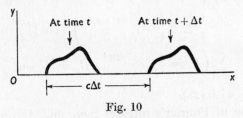

Fig. 10

We can readily show (by changing to new independent variables equal to $x - ct$, $x + ct$, respectively) that the general solution of (33) is

$$y(x, t) = f(x - ct) + F(x + ct), \tag{34}$$

where the forms of f and F are restricted only by initial and boundary conditions. If t is increased by any value, Δt say, and simultaneously x by $c \Delta t$, the value of $f(x - ct)$ is clearly not altered; hence the first term on the right-hand side of (34) represents (see Fig. 10) a disturbance advancing unchanged in form in the positive x-direction with speed $c \Delta t / \Delta t$, i.e. c. At any given instant, y depends only on x, and so is the same at all points of any plane normal to the x-axis; thus $f(x - ct)$ represents an advancing *plane wave*. The term $F(x + ct)$ clearly represents a plane wave proceeding in the negative direction.

The equation (27) obtained for the problem on the vibrating continuous string is a particular case of (33), the speed c being $(S/\rho)^{\frac{1}{2}}$. The solution (28) must therefore be deducible from the form (34). The process of deduction is as follows. The particular boundary condition $y(0, t) = 0$ when applied to (34) gives $0 = f(-ct) + F(ct)$

for all t; hence $f(\xi) = -F(-\xi)$, and so $y(x, t) = F(x+ct) - F(-x+ct)$. The other particular boundary condition $y(l, t) = 0$ then gives $0 = F(l+ct) - F(-l+ct)$ for all t; hence $F(\xi+2l) = F(\xi)$, which shows that F is a periodic function of period $2l$. It follows from Fourier theory that $F(\xi)$ is then expressible in the form

$$F(\xi) = \frac{1}{2} \sum_{s=1}^{\infty} A_s \sin \frac{s\pi\xi}{l} - \frac{1}{2} \sum_{s=0}^{\infty} B_s \cos \frac{s\pi\xi}{l},$$

where the A_s, B_s are constants (the fractions $\frac{1}{2}$ and the minus sign have been included with a view to making the A_s, B_s correspond exactly to the A_s, B_s in (28)). Hence

$$
\begin{aligned}
y(x, t) &= \frac{1}{2} \sum_{s=1}^{\infty} A_s \left\{ \sin \left(\frac{s\pi x}{l} + \frac{s\pi ct}{l} \right) + \sin \left(\frac{s\pi x}{l} - \frac{s\pi ct}{l} \right) \right\} \\
&\quad - \frac{1}{2} \sum_{s=0}^{\infty} B_s \left\{ \cos \left(\frac{s\pi x}{l} + \frac{s\pi ct}{l} \right) - \cos \left(\frac{s\pi x}{l} - \frac{s\pi ct}{l} \right) \right\} \\
&= \sum_{s=1}^{\infty} \left(A_s \sin \frac{s\pi x}{l} \cos \frac{s\pi ct}{l} + B_s \sin \frac{s\pi x}{l} \sin \frac{s\pi ct}{l} \right),
\end{aligned}
$$

which agrees with (28).

3.3.1. Use of Fourier's integral theorem. According to this theorem, a function $f(x)$ (subject to very few restrictions, which we shall ignore here) may be expressed in the form

$$f(x) = \frac{1}{\pi} \int_0^{\infty} d\kappa \int_{-\infty}^{\infty} f(\eta) \cos \{\kappa(x-\eta)\} \, d\eta \qquad (35)$$

(see Whittaker and Watson, *Modern Analysis*, § 9.7 (C.U.P., 1927)). This enables us to write the solution (34) of the equation (33) in the very useful form

$$y(x, t) = \frac{1}{\pi} \int_0^{\infty} d\kappa \int_{-\infty}^{\infty} d\eta [f(\eta) \cos \{\kappa(x-ct-\eta)\} + F(\eta) \cos \{\kappa(x+ct-\eta)\}]. \quad (36)$$

We notice that the form (36) indicates the connection between the equation (33) and the normal modes discussed in § 3.2.1, and it will be instructive to indicate how the solution (28) for the vibrating continuous string may be constructed using (36). The first boundary condition $y(0, t) = 0$ is satisfied if the expression

$$\{f(\eta) + F(\eta)\} \cos \kappa\eta \, \cos \kappa ct - \{f(\eta) - F(\eta)\} \sin \kappa\eta \, \sin \kappa ct$$

is zero for all t; this will be the case (i) if $\cos \kappa \eta = 0$ and $f(\eta) = F(\eta)$, or (ii) if $\sin \kappa \eta = 0$ and $f(\eta) = -F(\eta)$. The second boundary condition, $y(l, t) = 0$, is then satisfied (i) if $2F(\eta) \sin \kappa l \sin \kappa \eta \cos \kappa ct$, or (ii) if $2F(\eta) \sin \kappa l \cos \kappa \eta \sin \kappa ct$ is zero for all t; i.e. if

$$\sin \kappa l = 0. \tag{37}$$

The equation (37) restricts values of κ to the discrete set $\kappa_s = s\pi/l$, where s is an integer, and implies that κ is not a continuous variable; from (i) $\cos \kappa \eta = 0$ or from (ii) $\sin \kappa \eta = 0$, it is implied that η also is discontinuous. Thus due to the boundary conditions in this problem, it is indicated that the form (36) must degenerate from an integral to an infinite series; it is in fact easy (superposing results given separately by (i) and (ii)) now to construct the form (28) previously obtained. We note that the *characteristic equation* (37) yields a discrete set of values of κ and hence also of the eigen-frequencies. This type of result, which is due to the special boundary conditions of the problem, is sometimes described as a discrete *spectrum* of frequencies; in the particular problem taken the frequencies are given by equation (29).

In seismology, we shall be more particularly concerned with the case when the form (36) does not degenerate to a series. In this case, κ being a continuous variable, there exists a continuous set of values of the eigen-frequencies, i.e. a *continuous spectrum*.

3.3.2. Simple harmonic plane wave. The form (36) may be regarded as the result of superposing many elementary waves of the form

$$y = A \cos \{\kappa(x - ct) + \epsilon\}, \tag{38}$$

in which A, κ, ϵ may vary from element to element (together with waves of similar form travelling in the opposite direction). The equation (38), which represents a *simple harmonic* (or *sinusoidal*) *advancing plane wave*, is thus fundamental in wave theory; we easily verify of course that (38) is a particular solution of (33). If we write (38) in the form

$$y = A \cos \left\{ 2\pi \left(\frac{x}{\lambda} - \frac{t}{\tau} \right) + \epsilon \right\}, \tag{39}$$

we see that at any given point the value of y oscillates with (time) *period* τ; while at any given instant, y is a periodic function of x, the periodic distance being λ, the *wave-length*. We obviously have the relations

$$\lambda = 2\pi/\kappa, \quad \tau = 2\pi/\kappa c, \quad \lambda/\tau = c, \quad \nu = 1/\tau, \tag{40}$$

ν being the *frequency*. For mathematical convenience, we shall frequently use instead of (38) the relation

$$y = A \exp\{\iota(\kappa(x - ct) + \epsilon)\}, \tag{41}$$

where we understand that the real part is to be taken when the physical interpretation is being made. We shall also frequently write γ for κc; then $2\pi/\gamma$ is the period.

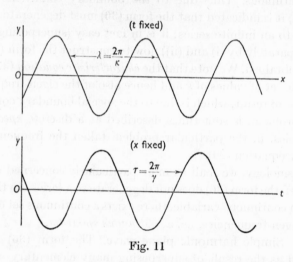

Fig. 11

3.3.3. Vector waves. Polarisation.

Many physical problems are concerned with the transmission through some medium of a disturbance that is vectorial in character. In such a case we may meet a set of three equations each of the form (33), namely,

$$\frac{\partial^2 u_i}{\partial t^2} = c^2 \frac{\partial^2 u_i}{\partial x_1^2} \quad (i = 1, 2, 3), \tag{42}$$

where the u_i are the components of the disturbance (which we here take to be a displacement), and x_1 is a particular one of the three rectangular coordinates x_i. Suppose further that

$$\frac{\partial u_i}{\partial x_2} = \frac{\partial u_i}{\partial x_3} = 0 \quad (i = 1, 2, 3). \tag{43}$$

The general solution of the equations (42) and (43) is of the form

$$u_i = f_i(x_1 - ct) + F_i(x_1 + ct) \quad (i = 1, 2, 3), \tag{44}$$

and corresponds to the superposition of two vector plane waves travelling in the positive and negative directions of the 1-axis, respectively, with speed c. On account of the relations (43) the waves are plane waves.

It commonly happens that there is a further limitation on the freedom of variation of the components u_i of the transmitted disturbance; when this is so the disturbance is said to be *polarised*. If, for instance, the u_i constitute a *solenoidal vector* (i.e. div (u_i) vanishes at all times and places), it follows from (44) and (2, (22)) that $\partial u_1 / \partial x_1$ is zero at all times and places; thus only the components u_2, u_3 are associated with the wave transmission, i.e. the disturbance is in this case restricted to being always at right angles to the 1-axis.

Consider the particular case of polarisation given by

$$u_i = A_i \cos \{\kappa(x_1 - ct) + \epsilon_i\} \quad (i = 1, 2, 3),$$

with $A_1 = 0$. We derive from this

$$\frac{u_2^2}{A_2^2} + \frac{u_3^2}{A_3^2} - \frac{2u_2 u_3}{A_2 A_3} \cos(\epsilon_3 - \epsilon_2) = \sin^2(\epsilon_3 - \epsilon_2),$$

which shows that in this case the particles of the medium will in general describe ellipses in planes normal to the direction of propagation. In this case the disturbance is *elliptically polarised*; the particles will describe ellipses in senses corresponding to the right-hand or left-hand screw law according as the phase difference $\epsilon_3 - \epsilon_2$ of the two components u_2 and u_3 lies between 0 and π or between 0 and $-\pi$; the former case is illustrated in Fig. 12. If it should happen that $|\epsilon_3 - \epsilon_2| = \frac{1}{2}\pi$ and $A_2 = A_3$, the ellipses are circles and the disturbance is *circularly polarised*. If

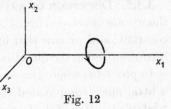

Fig. 12

the ellipses degenerate to straight lines (which will all be parallel to a particular plane through the 1-axis), the disturbance is *plane polarised*; this will be the case for instance when one of A_2 or A_3 is zero, or when $\epsilon_2 = \epsilon_3$.

3.3.4. Standing waves. If we superpose a pair of simple harmonic plane waves of the same amplitude A, wave-length $2\pi/\kappa$ and speed c, travelling in opposite directions, we find that the resultant disturbance is given by

$$y = 2A \cos(\kappa x + \epsilon) \cos(\kappa ct + \epsilon'), \qquad (45)$$

where ϵ, ϵ' depend on the phase constants of the constituent waves. The equation (45) corresponds to what is called a *standing wave*, since there is no resultant progressive wave motion. It will be noticed that in (45), x and t occur in separate factors, and that the disturbance is permanently zero at points where $\kappa x + \epsilon = (r + \frac{1}{2})\pi$, r being any integer, and is a maximum where $\kappa x + \epsilon = r\pi$; the former points are *nodes* and the latter *antinodes*.

The disturbance represented by (45) corresponds to the superposition of a pair of simple harmonic waves. In more general cases, a standing wave may take the form

$$y = X(x)\,T(t), \qquad (46)$$

where X and T are any functions of x alone and t alone, respectively. It is easy to show that general plane wave motion may be regarded as the result of superposing standing waves of the form (46). In fact, a further method of solving the plane wave differential equation (33) is to start by substituting the trial form (46) into (33). It is to be noted that in general the result of superposing a set of standing waves is not itself a standing wave, since the sum of a number of terms like that in (46) is not in general expressible as a product of two factors containing x alone and t alone, respectively.

3.3.5. Dispersion of waves. The preceding discussion of wave theory was developed from the equation (33) in which c is an assigned constant; and we saw that in these circumstances the disturbance is transmitted in the direction of the x-axis without change of form.

In problems where the equations of motion of a disturbance are a little more complicated than (33), it sometimes happens that a trial substitution of the form (41) leads to a solution of the form (36), with the qualification that c instead of depending entirely on assigned constants varies with κ from element to element of the integrand. A simple illustration of this happening is provided by modifying the vibrating string problem of § 3.2.4 so that each element of the string is now subject to an additional applied force proportional to the displacement. The equation of motion replacing (27) is found to be

$$\rho \frac{\partial^2 y}{\partial t^2} = S \frac{\partial^2 y}{\partial x^2} - hy, \qquad (47)$$

where h is a new assigned constant. The trial substitution (41) clearly satisfies the new equation (47) if

$$\rho c^2 \kappa^2 = S\kappa^2 + h, \qquad (48)$$

and we can readily build up a solution of the form (36); but on account of (48), we see that c is now a function of κ and not determined by assigned constants. Another illustration will be found in § 5.3 on Love waves.

Such dependence of c on κ (and thus by (40) on the wave-length and period) implies that the shape of the disturbance will in general continually change as time goes on, since each simple harmonic constituent represented in (36) will now travel with a wave velocity special to itself. If the initial disturbance is confined to a finite range of values of x and the medium is unlimited, it follows that as time goes on there will be a continual spreading out of the disturbance into trains of waves. This phenomenon is called *dispersion*.

3.3.5.1. We shall now investigate the nature of the dispersion which takes place in problems for which the form (36), with c a function of κ, is relevant; and shall take the case where the initial disturbance $y(x, 0)$ is confined to the region $|x| \leqslant a$. For convenience of exposition, we shall further take the initial disturbance to be symmetrical about the point $x = 0$, and the initial velocity, $\partial y/\partial t(x, 0)$, to be everywhere zero.

The assumed symmetry of $y(x, 0)$ enables us to replace (36) by the form

$$y(x, t) = \frac{1}{\pi} \int_0^\infty d\kappa \int_{-\infty}^\infty d\eta \cos(\kappa\eta) [f(\eta) \cos\{\kappa(x - ct)\} + F(\eta) \cos\{\kappa(x + ct)\}].$$

The initial conditions give further (putting $t = 0$ in (36), and using (35)) that $f(\eta) + F(\eta) = y(\eta, 0)$, and (since $\partial y/\partial t$ is initially zero) that

$f(\eta) = F(\eta)$. Hence for $x > a$ (it will be sufficient to consider just the advancing waves), we have

$$y(x, t) = \frac{1}{2\pi} \int_0^\infty d\kappa \int_{-\infty}^\infty y(\eta, 0) \cos(\kappa\eta) \cos\{\kappa(x - ct)\} d\eta,$$

which we may rewrite in the form

$$y(x, t) = \frac{1}{\pi} \int_0^\infty \phi(\kappa) \cos\{\kappa(x - ct)\} d\kappa, \qquad (49)$$

where

$$\phi(\kappa) = \int_0^a y(\eta, 0) \cos(\kappa\eta) d\eta. \qquad (50)$$

We note that since

$$\phi'(\kappa) = - \int_0^a \eta y(\eta, 0) \sin(\kappa\eta) d\eta,$$

if follows that, except for values of κ for which $\phi(\kappa)$ is abnormally small (it is evident from (50) that there may be a number of such values, depending on the form of $y(x, 0)$), $\phi'(\kappa)$ is of the order of $a\phi(\kappa)$ or less.

We shall now obtain an approximation to $y(x, t)$ for large t. We shall write $C(\kappa)$ for $d\gamma/d\kappa$, where $\gamma = \kappa c$. Let κ_r be a value of κ such that $\phi(\kappa_r)$ is not abnormally small; we shall use the suffix r to denote values which functions of κ take when $\kappa = \kappa_r$. We take t to be of such size that

$$t \left(\frac{dC}{d\kappa}\right)_r^3 \left(\frac{d^2C}{d\kappa^2}\right)_r^{-2} = \beta(t) \epsilon^{-3}, \qquad (51)$$

where $\beta \geqslant 1$, and ϵ is sufficiently small to validate the approximations which follow. We consider first the contribution—which we denote as $y_r(x, t)$—to $y(x, t)$ from the particular 'cluster' of elements in (49) for which $|\kappa - \kappa_r| \leqslant \epsilon a^{-1}$. Thus

$$y_r(x, t) = \frac{1}{\pi} \int_{-\epsilon/a}^{\epsilon/a} \phi(\kappa) \cos(\kappa x - \gamma t) d\mu, \qquad (52)$$

where $\mu = \kappa - \kappa_r$. In (52), we may replace $\phi(\kappa)$ by $(1 + \delta)\phi(\kappa_r)$, where δ is of the order of ϵ or less; this follows since $\phi'(\kappa_r)$ is at most of the order of $a\phi(\kappa_r)$. If, further,

$$\frac{1}{a} \left(\frac{d^2C}{d\kappa^2}\right)_r \Big/ \left(\frac{dC}{d\kappa}\right)_r = O(1), \qquad (53)$$

we may write

$$y_r(x, t) \approx \frac{\phi(\kappa_r)}{\pi} \int_{-\epsilon/a}^{\epsilon/a} \cos\left\{(\kappa_r x - \gamma_r t) + \mu(x - C_r t) - \tfrac{1}{2}\mu^2\left(\frac{dC}{d\kappa}\right)_r t\right\} d\mu. \tag{54}$$

We can easily evaluate y_r at time t near the point, P_r say, at which $x = C_r t$. For this evaluation we may ignore the term $\mu(x - C_r t)$ in (54), which then becomes

$$y_r(x, t) \approx \frac{\phi(\kappa_r)}{\pi} \int_{-\infty}^{\infty} \cos\left\{(\kappa_r x - \gamma_r t) - \tfrac{1}{2}\mu^2\left(\frac{dC}{d\kappa}\right)_r t\right\} d\mu, \tag{55}$$

the replacement of the limits of integration $\pm \epsilon/a$ by $\pm \infty$ being justified, since by (51) and (53)

$$\left(\frac{\epsilon}{a}\right)^2 \left(\frac{dC}{d\kappa}\right)_r t = O(\beta\epsilon^{-1}). \tag{56}$$

Using the formulae

$$\int_{-\infty}^{\infty} \cos \xi^2 d\xi = \int_{-\infty}^{\infty} \sin \xi^2 d\xi = \sqrt{(\tfrac{1}{2}\pi)},$$

we then obtain from (55) the desired asymptotic approximation

$$y_r(x, t) \approx \frac{\phi(\kappa_r)}{\sqrt{[\tfrac{1}{2}\pi \,|(dC/d\kappa)_r|\, t]}} \cos(\kappa_r x - \gamma_r t \mp \tfrac{1}{4}\pi), \tag{57}$$

the upper or lower sign being taken according as $(dC/d\kappa)_r$ is positive or negative. Thus at time t, y_r has near the point P_r the form of simple harmonic waves of wave-length $2\pi/\kappa_r$, and (by (56)) amplitude of order $\beta^{-\frac{1}{2}}\epsilon^{\frac{3}{2}}\phi(\kappa_r)/a$.

As the magnitude of the distance from P_r increases, the term $\mu(x - C_r t)$ in (54) starts to become important, and has the effect of lessening the amplitude just found. If for the given value of t we write

$$|x - C_r t| = \alpha(x)\beta\epsilon^{-2}a, \tag{58}$$

then if α is appreciable we may by (56) and (58) neglect the term in μ^2 in (54), and then integrating obtain

$$y_r(x, t) \approx 2\pi^{-1}\phi(\kappa_r)(x - C_r t)^{-1} \sin\{\epsilon(x - C_r t)/\alpha\} \cos(\kappa_r x - \gamma_r t). \tag{59}$$

The form (59) corresponds to trains of waves of wave-length $2\pi/\kappa_r$, which on account of the sine factor occur in belts of length $a\pi/\epsilon$. The maximum amplitudes in the belts decrease steadily as $|x - C_r t|$

increases, and by (58) the order of these maxima (this also holds if α is near unity) is seen to be $\alpha^{-1}\beta^{-\frac{1}{2}}\epsilon^{\frac{1}{2}}$ times the order of the amplitude at P_r. It is evident therefore that at time t, y_r makes its predominant contribution to y in the vicinity of the point $x = C_r t$.

The distance at time t between P_r and the corresponding point for the next cluster is approximately $(dC/d\kappa)_r (2\epsilon/a) t$, which by (56) is of the order of $\beta\epsilon^{-2}a$. Thus the effect at P_r of this next cluster will in general be roughly $\beta^{-\frac{1}{2}}\epsilon^{\frac{1}{2}}$ times that of the cluster centred at κ_r. It is found further that at time t (sufficiently large) the accumulated effect at P_r of all other clusters is in general small compared with that of the cluster centred at κ_r. Thus, in general, the right-hand side of (57) is a good approximation to y at time t at the position P_r. The proof of this complete result is difficult by elementary methods. A very elegant account of dispersion using the 'method of steepest descents' may be read in Jeffreys, *Operational Methods in Mathematical Physics* (C.U.P., 1931).

3.3.5.2. Summing up the foregoing discussion, we have—see Fig. 13—that the predominant effect at time t (sufficiently large) and place x arises in general from the cluster with wave-lengths near $2\pi/\kappa_r$, and is approximately of the form (57), where κ_r is such that

$$(d\gamma/d\kappa)_r = C_r = x/t.$$

It follows that as time goes on, the original disturbance is continually sorting itself out into groups of simple harmonic waves, each group being associated with a particular wave-length, and travelling forward with its *group velocity* $C(\kappa)$ where

$$C(\kappa) = d\gamma/d\kappa = d(\kappa c)/d\kappa. \tag{60}$$

The extent of dispersion that has taken place at time t may be estimated from a detailed consideration of equations such as (51).

We note incidentally from (60) that when there is dispersion the group velocity C is in general different from the wave velocity c.

We note also that the predominant effect (57) is associated with that value of κ which makes the integrand in (49) stationary.

3.3.5.3. For the modified vibrating string problem referred to earlier in § 3.3.5, we find from (48) and (60) that the group velocity is

$$C = S/c\rho = S\kappa/\gamma\rho. \tag{61}$$

3.3.5.4. Exceptions to the above results can occur significantly in practice. We have pointed out in § 3.3.5.1 that (depending on the form of the initial disturbance) there may be a number of values of κ for which $\phi(\kappa)$ is abnormally small; for these values, corresponding groups as given by the right-hand side of (57) will not ordinarily be observable.

We note further that the formula (57) fails for any group for which the assumption (53) does not hold. Such failure occurs for values of κ for which $dC/d\kappa$ is abnormally small, i.e. in the vicinity of stationary values of C. Jeffreys has shown that such stationary values can occur in a wide class of problems, for instance, when c is an even function of κ finite for all values of κ. (It may be pointed out

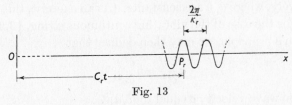

Fig. 13

that in these circumstances, some range of values of C may lie outside the entire range of values of c.) Suppose C is stationary, say a minimum, when $\kappa = \kappa_s$. Then the approximate expression for $y_s(x, t)$ analogous to (54) must include an additional term in μ^3 in the integrand. Also in place of (56) we need to take t of such size that

$$\left(\frac{\epsilon}{a}\right)^3 \left(\frac{d^2 C}{d\kappa^2}\right)_s t = O(\gamma \epsilon^{-1}), \tag{62}$$

where $\gamma(t) \geqslant 1$. With the use of an Airy integral, Jeffreys has investigated the form of the contribution y_s due to the cluster centred round the wave-length $2\pi/\kappa_s$. The maximum of y_s, which is of the order of $\gamma^{-\frac{1}{6}}\epsilon^{\frac{4}{3}}\phi(\kappa_s)/a$, occurs near a point, M_s say, distant about $\gamma^{\frac{1}{3}}\epsilon^{-\frac{1}{3}}a$ in front of the point P_s at which $x = C_s t$. Behind M_s, the amplitude continually diminishes, falling away fairly rapidly behind P_s. In front of M_s are belts of waves, the maxima in which diminish slowly but steadily with increasing x. Since by (62) γ increases as t increases, it follows that the distance $P_s M_s$ steadily increases as time goes on. Also since the maximum amplitude in this case is proportional to $\gamma^{-\frac{1}{6}}$, i.e. (by (62)) to $t^{-\frac{1}{6}}$, whereas the maximum amplitude in (57) is proportional to $\beta^{-\frac{1}{2}}$, i.e. (by (56)) to $t^{-\frac{1}{2}}$, it follows that as time goes on, the maximum amplitude for the s-cluster becomes increasingly large compared with the maximum amplitude for an ordinary cluster. Thus a cluster corresponding to a stationary value of C will develop relatively large amplitudes.

3.3.6. Energy in plane wave motion. At any instant, the kinetic and potential energies of the vibrating system (or medium) between the planes $x = x'$ and $x = x''$, due to the displacements associated with a wave of the simple type described at the start of § 3.3, are expressible in the forms

$$\tfrac{1}{2}a \int_{x'}^{x''} \left(\frac{\partial y}{\partial t}\right)^2 dx, \quad \tfrac{1}{2}b \int_{x'}^{x''} \left(\frac{\partial y}{\partial x}\right)^2 dx, \tag{63}$$

respectively, where a, b are constants. (As an exercise, this may be verified for the case of the vibrating continuous string, § 3.2.4.) By Hamilton's principle, we may then deduce that

$$a \frac{\partial^2 y}{\partial t^2} = b \frac{\partial^2 y}{\partial x^2}, \tag{64}$$

giving the wave velocity c equal to $(b/a)^{\frac{1}{2}}$.

If we substitute $f(x - ct)$ for y in the expressions (63), we find that the results are equal. It follows that in an advancing (or receding) plane wave, the energy at any instant is half kinetic and half potential. An interesting alternative derivation by Rayleigh of this conclusion may be read in Lamb, *Hydrodynamics* (C.U.P., 1930), § 174. We may note the correspondence between this conclusion and the result on mean energies stated in the last paragraph of § 3.2.1.

If in (63) we replace y by ky, where k is any constant, we see that the energies are multiplied by k^2. Thus for sets of waves of similar shape which differ only in the magnitudes of the amplitudes, the energies are proportional to the squares of corresponding amplitudes.

In some problems, it is convenient to make use of the *energy density*, w say, i.e. the energy per unit volume in the medium. In the absence of energy dissipation, we can then write down a conservation equation analogous to (2, (23)), namely,

$$\frac{\partial w}{\partial t} + \frac{\partial}{\partial x_i}(wv_i) = 0, \tag{65}$$

where v_i is the velocity of energy transmission.

The one-dimensional form of (65) is

$$\frac{\partial w}{\partial t} + \frac{\partial}{\partial x}(wv) = 0, \qquad (65a)$$

where w is now the energy per unit length in the direction of propagation of the wave.

As an instance of the use of this equation, we can verify that when the wave disturbance is transmitted unchanged in form, energy is conveyed through the medium with the wave velocity c. To demonstrate this, we have by (63) for the case in question

$$w = \tfrac{1}{2}a\left(\frac{\partial y}{\partial t}\right)^2 + \tfrac{1}{2}b\left(\frac{\partial y}{\partial x}\right)^2. \qquad (66)$$

Hence
$$\frac{\partial w}{\partial t} = a\frac{\partial y}{\partial t}\frac{\partial^2 y}{\partial t^2} + b\frac{\partial y}{\partial x}\frac{\partial^2 y}{\partial x\,\partial t}$$

$$= b\frac{\partial y}{\partial t}\frac{\partial^2 y}{\partial x^2} + b\frac{\partial y}{\partial x}\frac{\partial^2 y}{\partial x\,\partial t} \quad \text{(by (64))}$$

$$= -\frac{\partial}{\partial x}\left(-b\frac{\partial y}{\partial t}\frac{\partial y}{\partial x}\right).$$

Thus by (65 a) the speed of energy flow is $-\{b(\partial y/\partial t)(\partial y/\partial x)\}/w$; on putting $y = f(x - ct)$ in this expression, we find that this speed is equal to c.

When there is dispersion, the expression (66) for the energy density needs modification. For instance, in the case of the modified string problem considered in § 3.3.5, we have in place of (66)

$$w = \tfrac{1}{2}\rho\left(\frac{\partial y}{\partial t}\right)^2 + \tfrac{1}{2}S\left(\frac{\partial y}{\partial x}\right)^2 + \tfrac{1}{2}hy^2. \qquad (67)$$

By (47), (65 a) and (67), it is then easy to shown that the local speed of transmission of energy at time t is $\{-S(\partial y/\partial t)(\partial y/\partial x)\}/w$, which is similar to the corresponding result in the last paragraph. But by (57), y is now essentially proportional to $t^{-\frac{1}{2}}\cos\{\kappa(x-ct) \mp \tfrac{1}{4}\pi\}$, where κ and c are appropriate to the particular values of x, t. If we then determine $\partial y/\partial t$ and $\partial y/\partial x$, ignoring terms of order $t^{-\frac{3}{2}}$ (t being assumed large), we find on taking mean values over a wavelength that the speed of transmission of energy in the vicinity of a given time and place is equal to the appropriate group velocity, a

5   BS

result which may be shown to hold in general for cases of dispersion of the type we have been considering.

3.3.7. Propagation of plane waves in a general direction. We have previously considered the propagation of plane waves in the direction of one of the axes of reference. If instead the direction of propagation has direction-cosines l_i ($i = 1, 2, 3$), we obtain from (34), (38) and (41) by transforming axes the relevant corresponding equations

$$y = f(l_i x_i - ct) + F(l_i x_i + ct), \tag{68}$$

$$y = A \cos\{\kappa(l_i x_i - ct) + \epsilon\}, \tag{69}$$

$$y = A \exp\{\iota(\kappa(l_i x_i - ct) + \epsilon)\}, \tag{70}$$

the summation convention being understood.

3.4. The wave equation. There are numerous equations associated with wave propagation. One of these, *the* (classical) wave equation, is of fundamental importance, namely,

$$\frac{\partial^2 y}{\partial t^2} = c^2 \nabla^2 y, \tag{71}$$

where c is constant and $\nabla^2 \equiv \partial^2/\partial x_i^2$. Equation (33) is the one-dimensional form of (71).

It will be seen on substitution that each of (68), (69), (70) is a particular solution of (71) for all directions l_i. Thus a linear combination of plane waves of any form travelling in any direction with the same speed c and not changing in form constitutes a solution of (71).

3.4.1. Case of spherical symmetry. It is easy to derive the most general solution of (71) subject to the restriction that y is symmetrical about some centre O. If r denotes the distance from O, we can deduce from (71) that in this case

$$\frac{\partial^2(ry)}{\partial t^2} = c^2 \frac{\partial^2(ry)}{\partial r^2}, \tag{72}$$

of which the general solution is seen by comparison with (33) and (34) to be of the form

$$y = r^{-1}\{f(r - ct) + F(r + ct)\}. \tag{73}$$

The result (73) differs from the one-dimensional result (34) only in that r replaces x and that there is an additional amplitude factor

r^{-1}. The solution (73) thus corresponds to the transmission of a *spherical wave*, the value of y at any fixed instant being the same at all points on the surface of any sphere of centre O. In many simple physical applications, the term in F is not relevant; we are then left with the solution $y = r^{-1}f(r - ct)$, which corresponds to a wave advancing spherically outward with speed c, the amplitude being inversely proportional to the distance from P. We note also that in this case there is at any instant a spherical *wave front*.

3.4.2. General solution. A form of the general solution of the wave equation (71) has been obtained by Kirchhoff (a proof may be read, for example, in Jeans, *Electricity and Magnetism* (C.U.P., 1927), § 580). The solution gives an expression for $y_P(t)$, the value of y at time t at any point P, in terms of the circumstances existing at certain previous instants at points of any arbitrary closed surface S surrounding P. For convenience we use square brackets here to denote that a function is to be evaluated at a point Q of S at the instant $t - r/c$, where r is the distance PQ. The result is then that

$$y_P(t) = \frac{1}{4\pi} \iint \left\{ \frac{1}{cr} \frac{\partial r}{\partial \nu} \left[\frac{\partial y}{\partial t} \right] - [y] \frac{\partial}{\partial \nu} \left(\frac{1}{r} \right) + \frac{1}{r} \left[\frac{\partial y}{\partial \nu} \right] \right\} dS, \qquad (74)$$

where the integration is taken over the surface S, and $\delta\nu$ is an element of the outward normal at a point of S.

For any point Q of S, it is seen that the instant at which the square-bracket functions are to be evaluated precedes the instant t by PQ/c, which is the time a disturbance would take to travel in a straight line from Q to P with speed c. In the right-hand side of (74), y occurs only inside square brackets, and it follows that $y_P(t)$ is fully determined as the resultant of appropriate effects travelling with speed c from all points of S towards P. This result is in accord with the indication of the solution (68) in implying propagation with speed c in all directions.

It is now seen further that any disturbed small region may be regarded as a *secondary source* transmitting a secondary disturbance in all directions. This corresponds to Huygens's principle in optics, and the subsequent superposition of effects at any point P to the interference-reinforcement principles of Fresnel and Young. The results of course apply quite generally, and not merely to optics.

3.5. Two-dimensional wave motion. The two-dimensional form of the wave equation (71) is

$$\frac{\partial^2 y}{\partial t^2} = c^2 \left(\frac{\partial^2 y}{\partial x_1^2} + \frac{\partial^2 y}{\partial x_2^2} \right). \tag{75}$$

We shall consider here the solution of (75) for the special case in which y is symmetrical about a centre O. Changing to polar co-ordinates (r, θ), we obtain from (75) for the case of symmetry

$$\frac{\partial^2 y}{\partial t^2} = c^2 \left(\frac{\partial^2 y}{\partial r^2} + \frac{1}{r} \frac{\partial y}{\partial r} \right). \tag{76}$$

The solution of this equation is not as easily obtained as in the corresponding three-dimensional case (§ 3.4.1), and involves Bessel functions. In accordance with a method indicated in § 3.3.4, we take as a trial solution of (76) $y = R(r)\,T(t)$, analogous to (46), where R and T are functions of r alone and t alone, respectively. Substituting into (76) gives

$$\frac{1}{c^2 T} \frac{d^2 T}{dt^2} = \frac{1}{R} \frac{d^2 R}{dr^2} + \frac{1}{rR} \frac{dR}{dr}. \tag{77}$$

In (77), the left-hand side is independent of r, and the right-hand side of t; hence both sides are constant, equal to $-\kappa^2$ say. Hence (77) implies that

$$T = C \cos(\kappa c t + \epsilon), \tag{78}$$

where C, ϵ are constants, and that

$$r^2 \frac{d^2 R}{dr^2} + r \frac{dR}{dr} + \kappa^2 r^2 R = 0. \tag{79}$$

The equation (79) is equivalent to Bessel's equation of zero order for R in terms of κr, and its solution is found by the method of series to be

$$R = A J_0(\kappa r) + B Y_0(\kappa r), \tag{80}$$

where A, B are constants,

$$J_0(x) = 1 - \frac{x^2}{2^2} + \frac{x^4}{2^2 4^2} - \frac{x^6}{2^2 4^2 6^2} + \dots, \tag{81}$$

and

$$Y_0(x) = J_0(x) \log x + \frac{x^2}{2^2} - \frac{x^4}{2^2 4^2} \left(1 + \tfrac{1}{2}\right) + \frac{x^6}{2^2 4^2 6^2} \left(1 + \tfrac{1}{2} + \tfrac{1}{3}\right) - \dots; \tag{82}$$

$J_0(x)$ and $Y_0(x)$ are Bessel's functions of zero order of the first and second kinds, respectively. By (78) and (80), a solution of (76) is therefore

$$y = \{AJ_0(\kappa r) + BY_0(\kappa r)\}\cos(\kappa ct + \epsilon); \tag{83}$$

and a more general solution can be obtained by superposing solutions of the form (83) with different values of κ.

It may be shown (see Whittaker and Watson, *Modern Analysis* (C.U.P., 1927), §§ 17.5, 17.6) that for large values of x

$$J_0(x) \approx \left(\frac{2}{\pi x}\right)^{\frac{1}{2}}\cos\left(x - \tfrac{1}{4}\pi\right) \tag{84}$$

and

$$Y_0(x) \approx \left(\frac{2}{\pi x}\right)^{\frac{1}{2}}\sin\left(x - \tfrac{1}{4}\pi\right), \tag{85}$$

the neglected terms being of the order of $x^{-\frac{3}{2}}$. It follows from (83), (84) and (85) that at large distances from an initially confined disturbance, the amplitude is in the present case essentially inversely proportional to the square root of the distance from the centre. This property is important in the theory of the transmission of seismic surface waves.

3.6. Ray theory and diffraction. We return now to the propagation of waves in three dimensions, and introduce the concept of rays.

3.6.1. Rays in a homogeneous medium. Consider the transmission of waves through a homogeneous medium, following an initial disturbance that is completely symmetrical about a centre O and is confined to within a small sphere surrounding O. If c is the speed of wave transmission in the medium, it follows from (73) that after the lapse of time t, the disturbance will be confined to the vicinity of the surface of a sphere of centre O and radius ct. Now consider what happens as time goes on within a cone of small solid angle, or *pencil*, whose vertex is at O. Looking at the matter from the point of view of the general solution given in § 3.4.2, we see that all the secondary disturbances referred to in § 3.4.2 must be interfering with one another to such an extent that a relevant part of the whole disturbance is in effect being transmitted with speed c in the direction of the cone's axis. It follows that in the conditions stated, the circumstances are essentially equivalent to rectilinear propagation of parts of the disturbance along *rays* as in geometrical optics, each ray proceeding normally outwards from the wave front at any instant.

3.6.2. Rays in a heterogeneous medium.

When, as in the case of the Earth, the properties of the medium vary from point to point, the wave velocity will be a function of position and not a constant. In this case, the wave front at time t after the occurrence of an initially confined disturbance will not in general be a sphere, even if the initial disturbance is symmetrical about a centre. But use may still be made of the concept of rays, the paths of which cut wave fronts at right angles; the rays will now, of course, be not rectilinear.

Consider the passage of waves through a part of the region whose linear dimensions are small compared with the local radius of curvature of the wave front, and hence usually small compared with the distance from the place of occurrence of the initial disturbance. We may then with good accuracy consider the waves as plane waves. (This set of circumstances is relevant to many wave problems, and in particular to problems in seismology; the one-dimensional analysis of §§ 3.2, 3.3 is therefore of much direct utility in certain three-dimensional problems.)

If in the vicinity of such a region there is a surface of discontinuity (the radius of curvature of which is sufficiently large), on opposite sides of which the wave velocity has different but constant values, the plane wave theory may be used to determine the essential character of the reflected and refracted waves. This process is carried out in chapter 6 for the case of elastic waves, and it is found (§ 6.1) that laws hold which are analogous to the laws of reflection and refraction in geometrical optics.

The case in which the properties of the medium are varying continuously may be deduced by considering this case as the limit of the case in which there is a large number of discontinuity surfaces at small distances apart, the portion of the medium between any pair of adjacent discontinuity surfaces being homogeneous and only slightly different from that between the next pair. It is evident that in this case rays can exist as before but that they will be curved.

In all these cases, it may be shown that the rays obey *Fermat's principle*, according to which among possible paths joining any two assigned points in the medium, the actual ray is such that the travel-time along it is stationary.

The question of the connection of energy transmission with the ray paths will be discussed in chapter 8 for the case of elastic waves. It will be shown (§ 8.5.1) that in a medium of continuously varying properties, the energy is in general transmitted along the rays with negligible loss on the way.

3.6.3. Diffraction. If a region under consideration contains a discontinuity surface whose curvature is large compared with the curvature of the incident wave front, the reflected or refracted wave front will be sharply curved, and the ray theory (which is based on the existence of cones of small solid angles) will cease to be fully applicable. When this is the case, the waves are said to be *diffracted*. The particular diffraction effects which are caused by the presence of small obstacles or small-scale irregularities of structure in a medium are sometimes referred to as *scattering* of a wave.

The existence of an edge to a wave front will also cause diffraction. It is found, for instance, that if a screen be placed in front of an advancing beam of plane light waves, there is some light transmitted to that part of the region on the far side of the screen that would remain quite dark on the pure ray theory; this is related to the discontinuity associated with the edge of the wave front.

A similar happening can occur with elastic waves. Jeffreys, for instance, illustrates this by considering dilatational elastic waves propagated in the direction of the axis along the interior of a circular cylinder inside a solid. As the waves travelled along they would set up variable stresses on the surface of the cylinder, and these would act on the matter on the outside of the cylinder and so set up diffraction effects in the fringing region.

Diffraction is also important close to the centre of an initially confined disturbance, where the conditions assumed for the ray theory fail to hold. Thus, for instance, it is not permissible to apply the ray theory to the region close to the origin of an earthquake.

It is important, however, to note that even when diffraction effects are significant, the time of arrival at any point in the medium of the first part of any transmitted disturbance is always given by Fermat's principle, suitably applied. This is a consequence of the general solution described in § 3.4.2.

When diffraction effects are significant, the mathematical analysis needed is of a character special to the particular problem, and does not lend itself to a general treatment.

The ray theory is of much avail in many (but not all) problems in seismology; much use of it will be made in later chapters.

CHAPTER 4

BODILY ELASTIC WAVES

We now investigate some features of the transmission of a disturbance through a material substance. To begin with, we shall assume the substance to be homogeneous, isotropic and perfectly elastic, and shall use the infinitesimal strain theory. We take the undisturbed configuration as standard, and to begin with shall ignore the effects of possible fluctuations in the local external forces during the passage of the disturbance. Later we shall consider how far the simple theory based on these assumptions may need to be amended to meet the case of the transmission of seismic waves through the Earth.

4.1. *P* and *S* waves. In the circumstances just described, the relevant equations of motion of the disturbance are (2, (34)) with $X_i = 0$, i.e.

$$\rho \frac{\partial^2 u_i}{\partial t^2} = (\lambda + \mu) \frac{\partial \theta}{\partial x_i} + \mu \nabla^2 u_i. \tag{1}$$

If we differentiate both sides of (1) with respect to x_i (this involves, in accordance with the summation convention, adding the results of separate differentiations for $i = 1, 2, 3$), we obtain using (2, (22))

$$\rho \frac{\partial^2 \theta}{\partial t^2} = (\lambda + 2\mu) \nabla^2 \theta = (k + \tfrac{4}{3}\mu) \nabla^2 \theta, \tag{2}$$

since $\lambda = k - \tfrac{2}{3}\mu$ by (2, (35)). If we apply the operation curl to both sides of (1), we obtain

$$\rho \frac{\partial^2}{\partial t^2} \operatorname{curl}(u_i) = (\lambda + \mu) \operatorname{curl}\left(\frac{\partial \theta}{\partial x_i}\right) + \mu \nabla^2 \operatorname{curl}(u_i).$$

But a typical component of curl $(\partial\theta/\partial x_i)$ is of the form

$$\left(\frac{\partial}{\partial x_i} \frac{\partial \theta}{\partial x_j} - \frac{\partial}{\partial x_j} \frac{\partial \theta}{\partial x_i}\right),$$

which is zero. Hence

$$\rho \frac{\partial^2}{\partial t^2} \operatorname{curl}(u_i) = \mu \nabla^2 \operatorname{curl}(u_i). \tag{3}$$

The equations (2) and (3) are both forms of the wave equation

(3, (71)), and may therefore be immediately interpreted. By (2), a *dilatational* (or *irrotational*) disturbance θ may be transmitted through the substance with speed α, where

$$\alpha = \sqrt{\frac{\lambda + 2\mu}{\rho}} = \sqrt{\frac{k + \frac{4}{3}\mu}{\rho}}. \tag{4}$$

By (3), a *rotational* (or *equivoluminal*) disturbance may be transmitted with speed β, where

$$\beta = \sqrt{\frac{\mu}{\rho}}. \tag{5}$$

We notice that $\beta < \alpha$. In seismology, the two types of waves are called respectively the *primary*, P, or 'push' waves, and the *secondary*, S, or 'shake' waves. In the case we have taken, both speeds depend only on the elastic parameters and the density of the substance, and there is no dispersion. In the circumstances of the transmission of seismic waves, the elastic parameters λ, μ, k will be taken as the adiabatic ones.

If, in particular, μ is zero, then by (5) β is zero. Thus rotational waves are not transmitted through a substance of zero rigidity, a result already referred to in § 2.5.6 in connection with the discrimination between the fluid and solid states.

We may note incidentally that if k/ρ is infinite and μ/ρ finite, only rotational waves are transmitted with finite speed. This result is the basis of the old 'incompressible solid ether' theory of light and electromagnetism.

4.1.1. Case of plane waves.

In the vicinity of points sufficiently distant from the source of an initially confined disturbance, the waves may be regarded as plane. This is relevant to many seismological problems, for the distance of a station recording the local displacements caused by an earthquake is usually great compared with the dimensions of the initially disturbed region. In this case, the displacements associated with the P and S waves are in effect *longitudinal* and *transverse*, respectively. The transverse character of the S waves is incidentally indicated by the theory of § 3.3.3, since div curl (u_i) is readily seen to be zero.

The theory of plane waves may be set up independently of (2) and (3) by making a trial substitution (cf. (3, (70)) of the form

$$u_i = A_i \exp\{\iota\kappa(l_j x_j - ct)\}, \tag{6}$$

where $l_j^2 = 1$, in the equations (1). On eliminating the three A_i from the resulting equations, it is found that the form (6) is a possible solution of (1) if and only if the square of the speed c obeys a cubic equation whose roots are α^2, β^2, β^2, where α, β are given by (4), (5). The speeds α, β are found as before to be associated with longitudinal and transverse waves, respectively, and it follows that the types of waves described in the last paragraph are the only possible types of bodily plane waves.

It emerges also that the two types P and S are independent of each other, and further that the latter may be plane polarised. In seismology, when an S wave is polarised so that all particles of the substance move horizontally during its passage, it is denoted SH; when the particles all move in vertical planes containing the direction of propagation, the wave is denoted SV.

4.1.2. Poisson's relation. For many solids, and in particular for most rocks of the Earth, it is found that the values of the two elastic parameters λ and μ are not greatly different. Poisson's relation is an approximation which neglects any difference in the values of λ and μ; it may be expressed by any one of the following equations:

$$\lambda = \mu, \quad k = \tfrac{5}{3}\mu, \quad \sigma = \tfrac{1}{4}, \quad \alpha = \sqrt{3}\,\beta, \quad \alpha^2 = 3\mu/\rho. \tag{7}$$

In some of the problems to be considered, it is convenient to assume that Poisson's relation holds. This simplification reduces the algebra substantially, and enables fairly accurate answers to be found for problems whose solution would otherwise demand a prohibitive amount of labour.

4.2. Inclusion of initial conditions. We discuss now the type of disturbance to be expected at distant points following the occurrence of an initial disturbance inside a certain confined region. We here consider two particular cases of initial disturbances which, though specially simple, will serve as a suitable basis for investigating movements in the Earth following an earthquake.

Suppose that a dilatational wave is generated by the sudden occurrence within a sphere of radius a and centre O (inside the given medium) of a pressure symmetrical with respect to O. More precisely, let r denote the distance from O, t the time, and $H(t)$ Heaviside's unit function ($H(t) = 0$ if $t < 0$; $= 1$ if $t > 0$). Then we suppose there is zero displacement at all points for $t < 0$, and that the sphere $r = a$ is acted on from inside by a symmetrical pressure $AH(t)$, where A is constant. It follows from the theory of chapter 3 that at any point r outside the sphere, the displacement remains zero until the instant t_1, where $t_1 = (r-a)/\alpha$. For $t > t_1$, Jeffreys has shown (assuming Poisson's relation (7) to hold) that there is a radial displacement u_r given by

$$u_r = \frac{Aa^3}{4\mu r^2}\left[1 + \left\{\left(\frac{r}{a} - \frac{1}{2}\right)\sqrt{2}\sin\left(\frac{2\sqrt{2}\,\alpha t'}{3a}\right)\right.\right.$$
$$\left.\left. - \cos\left(\frac{2\sqrt{2}\,\alpha t'}{3a}\right)\right\}\exp\left(-\frac{2\alpha t'}{3a}\right)\right], \qquad (8)$$

where $t' = t - t_1$. If the point is at an appreciable distance from the centre and t' is not too great, (8) gives

$$u_r \approx \frac{\sqrt{2}\,Aa^2}{4\mu r}\sin\left(\frac{2\sqrt{2}\,\alpha t'}{3a}\right)\exp\left(-\frac{2\alpha t'}{3a}\right). \qquad (9)$$

When $t' = 0$, the value of the exponential factor in (9) is unity. When the sine term is passing through zero for the first time after $t' = 0$, t' is equal to about $3\cdot 4a/\alpha$, and the value of the exponential factor has been reduced to about one-tenth. After this time, the right-hand side of (8) is always small compared with its first maximum. Thus the displacement at any point of the medium for which r/α is appreciable is essentially a single swing from the zero position, followed by a rapid approach to nearly zero.

Suppose next that a rotational wave is generated by the action of a tangential impulse over the sphere $r = a$, the impulse being symmetrical about a diameter. More precisely, let r, θ, ϕ be spherical polar coordinates referred to O as origin, and let the stress across the sphere $r = a$ be $-AH(t)\sin\theta$ in the direction of ϕ increasing. There will then be no displacement at a point r outside the sphere until the instant t_2, where $t_2 = (r-a)/\beta$. For $t > t_2$, Jeffreys has obtained the necessary expression analogous to (8) for the relevant displacement component u_ϕ. When r/a is appreciable and $t - t_2$, $= t''$ say, is not too great, the approximate form analogous to (9) is

$$u_\phi \approx \frac{2Aa^2}{\sqrt{3}\,\mu r}\sin\left(\frac{\sqrt{3}\,\beta t''}{2a}\right)\exp\left(-\frac{3\beta t''}{2a}\right). \qquad (10)$$

This result is similar in form to (9), but the numerical values of the coefficients are a little different from those in (9). The value of t'' when the sine term in (10) is passing through zero for the first time after $t'' = 0$ is now $3 \cdot 6a/\beta$. The exponential factor in (10) diminishes even more rapidly than that in (9).

On account of the independence of the transmission of P and S waves, we may superpose the effects discussed in the two preceding paragraphs, and we then have conditions corresponding to a simple hypothetical earthquake sending out both P and S waves through a homogeneous medium. In these circumstances, the graph of the

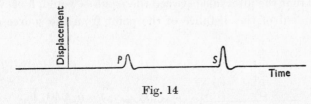

Fig. 14

displacement of a distant particle following the occurrence of such an earthquake would (subject of course to the various earlier assumptions made) be of the form shown in Fig. 14. Essential features of this graph are the virtual absence of trains of waves and the existence of a quiescent interval between the arrivals of the P and S disturbances.

4.3. The form of the earth movement following an earthquake. It transpires that, following an actual earthquake, the displacement of any point of the Earth's surface is markedly different from that pictured in Fig. 14. Fig. 15 shows the earlier portion of the graph of a component of the relative earth movement recorded on a seismograph following a typical actual earthquake, the arrows indicating the arrival-times of the first P and S movements. We notice that there is a train of waves following both the first P movement and the first S movement, and that there is no interval of quiescence.

We now discuss the possibility of these oscillatory movements being due to one or more of the following causes: (i) the existence of initial conditions more complicated than those taken in §4.2; (ii) fluctuations in the local gravity value during the passage of a disturbance (we ignored the term ρX_i in forming (1)); (iii) imperfections of elasticity; (iv) departures from homogeneity within the Earth.

In regard to (i), it is evident that the initial conditions taken in § 4.2 are of course simpler than those in a usual earthquake. The initial dislocation of material causing the earthquake would normally be spread over a finite interval of time, and if there were several distinct movements of comparable size during this interval, it would follow from superposition considerations that there would be several distinct P and S pulses at a distant point. It would follow further that the intervals between these pulses would, however, be independent of the distance of the point from the source of the

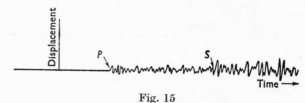

Fig. 15

disturbances, and this gives a means of deciding whether (i) is a cause of the generally observed oscillatory movements. There is in fact considerable evidence that a proportion of earthquakes do in fact show the features in question. The existence of such multiple earthquakes was first put beyond doubt by Stoneley as a result of a statistical study of observatory readings of the Mongolian earthquake of 1931 August 10. Stoneley showed that there were two shocks of comparable intensity separated by an interval of about 33 sec, and possibly two other shocks in between.

Nevertheless, it is equally well established that most earthquakes are not significantly multiple, the part of the initial disturbance which sends out the main energy being confined to a short interval of time. Conditions approximate to the occurrence of an instantaneous initial impulse (as assumed in § 4.2), followed by a swift displacement and return to near the undisturbed position, all taking place within a few seconds at most. The cause of the main oscillatory movements observed at the surface is therefore not to be found in complicated initial conditions.

We shall in §§ 4.4, 4.5 show that neither (ii) nor (iii) can be a cause of dispersion of the disturbance as it travels outwards.

It emerges, therefore, that the essential cause of the observed oscillatory movements must be sought in (iv)—heterogeneity of the Earth.

We note first that in the theory of §§ 4.1, 4.2 we ignored the implications of the presence of the Earth's outer boundary. The question immediately arises as to the possibility of the transmission of surface waves along this outer boundary, as distinct types from the bodily waves we have been considering. This question will be considered in detail in chapter 5; it transpires that such surface waves do exist and are important; also they may suffer dispersion. But their speed is always less than the relevant speeds of the P and S bodily waves, and hence they will not affect the earlier earth movements at any given place. Thus the surface waves following an earthquake cannot be a cause of the particular oscillatory movements we are discussing.

We note next that these oscillatory movements are observed at points fairly close to the source of an earthquake (as well as at distant points). This indicates that the Earth must be markedly heterogeneous in the region immediately below the outside surface. We shall see in chapter 12 that the Earth has a composite 'crust' of 30–40 km thickness, inside which there are quite considerable changes of property. The existence of such a composite structure is likely to account for the observed dispersion of bodily waves, but knowledge of the precise way in which the dispersion occurs must await more detailed knowledge of the crustal structure than is yet available. One among a number of hypotheses that have been put forward is that the dispersion may be due to strong repeated reflections of bodily waves between the Earth's outer surface and interfaces, assumed horizontal, between the layers; this is not fully satisfactory, since there is evidence that these interfaces are not sufficiently sharp. Jeffreys, who considered this hypothesis in some detail, pointed out that for the more steeply incident waves the reflections at the interfaces would be insignificant (see § 8.5.1), while less steeply incident P waves at the outer surface would mostly be strongly and steeply reflected into S waves (see § 6.4), leaving the observed strong dispersion of the bodily P waves still unexplained. Jeffreys further put forward the hypothesis that the observed distribution of amplitudes in near earthquakes is substantially influenced by diffuse refraction at irregular interfaces in the Earth's crust.

We now proceed to discuss the possible effects of gravity fluctuations and of imperfections of elasticity on the transmission of bodily waves. Finally, in the last two sections of this chapter, we shall refer to the influence of temperature conditions on the theory, and to the possible significance of finite-strain theory.

4.4. The effect of gravity fluctuations.

In (1), we excluded the term ρX_i of (2, (34)). But this term will not be zero if there are changes in the gravity value at any point x_i as an elastic wave passes by. We shall use the suffix 0 to denote values of certain scalars in the undisturbed configuration. Then on the Newtonian theory of attraction, X_i is expressible in the form $-\partial/\partial x_i (V - V_0)$, where V is the gravitational potential at x_i. Hence in place of (1), we have

$$\rho \frac{\partial^2 u_i}{\partial t^2} = (\lambda + \mu) \frac{\partial \theta}{\partial x_i} + \mu \nabla^2 u_i - \rho \frac{\partial}{\partial x_i} (V - V_0). \tag{11}$$

Now V, V_0 satisfy Poisson's equation, i.e.

$$\nabla^2 V = 4\pi G \rho, \quad \nabla^2 V_0 = 4\pi G \rho_0, \tag{12}$$

where G is the constant of gravitation. From (2, (26)), we deduce that

$$\rho - \rho_0 = -\rho \theta, \tag{13}$$

approximately. By (12) and (13),

$$\nabla^2 (V - V_0) = -4\pi G \rho \theta. \tag{14}$$

Differentiating (11) with respect to x_i and using (14), we have in place of (2), correct to the first order in the displacements,

$$\rho \frac{\partial^2 \theta}{\partial t^2} = (\lambda + 2\mu) \nabla^2 \theta + 4\pi G \rho^2 \theta;$$

i.e.

$$\frac{\partial^2 \theta}{\partial t^2} = \alpha^2 \nabla^2 \theta + \omega^2 \theta, \tag{15}$$

where

$$\omega^2 = 4\pi G \rho. \tag{16}$$

The equation (15) was solved by Jeffreys (for the case $\lambda = \mu$), using the first set of initial conditions in § 4.2. As before, there is (using the notation of § 4.2) no disturbance at the point r until the instant t_1. For $t > t_1$, the expression (8) for the displacement needs to be modified chiefly in the following ways: (i) the term unity inside the square brackets in (8) needs to be replaced by $1 + \frac{1}{2}\omega^2 tt'$; (ii) the exponential term inside the square brackets needs to be multiplied by $1 + \epsilon$, where ϵ is of the order of $\omega^2 at/\alpha$.

In discussing this result, Jeffreys took representative values for a typical earthquake problem as $\rho = 5\,\mathrm{g/cm^3}$, $a/\alpha = 1\,\mathrm{sec}$; also, $G = 6\cdot7 \times 10^{-8}$ c.g.s. units. It then follows that

$$\tfrac{1}{2}\omega^2 tt' \approx 2 \times 10^{-6} t'(t_1 + t'),$$

which is small compared with unity until t' is of the order of several hundred seconds. But at a time as great as this (t' denotes the time that has elapsed after the onset of the first pulse at a particular place), the displacement associated with direct P waves would in the actual earthquake conditions be unobservable. Thus in practice the modification (i) is normally insignificant. The modification (ii) is also insignificant, since on the above data $\omega^2 at/\alpha = 4 \times 10^{-6} t$.

If we apply the operation curl to (11) we obtain the equation (3) unaltered, showing that the allowance for the gravity term has no effect in the propagation of S waves. This is, of course, an immediate consequence of the fact that a purely rotational disturbance causes no disturbance in density.

We conclude, therefore, that neglect of gravity effects is unimportant in all ordinary problems on seismological bodily waves. In particular, these effects cannot account for the observed dispersion of these waves.

4.5. The effects of imperfections of elasticity. In obtaining the equations (1), or (2, (34)), we used the perfect elasticity stress-strain relations (2, (32)). We now consider the significance of deviations from (2, (32)) of the type set down in § 2.5 and its subsections.

4.5.1. Elastic afterworking. Equations for the elastic afterworking model (§ 2.5.3) given by (2, (67)) and (2, (75)) are derived by keeping k unchanged and replacing μ in the perfect elasticity equations by an operator of the form

$$\mu(p+1/\tau')\,(p+1/\tau)^{-1}, \tag{17}$$

where p denotes d/dt. Jeffreys applied this modification to the case of plane distortional waves moving parallel to the x-axis; the initial displacement is taken to be confined to the vicinity of the origin $(x = 0)$ and to be equal to $AH(t)$, where A is constant. The displacement at the position x is found to be zero until the instant $t - x/\beta$, where β is given by (5), taking μ in (5) as the parameter μ in (17). When $t - x/\beta$ is positive but not too great, the displacement is found to be given approximately by

$$u = A\left\{1 + \frac{x}{8\beta}\left(\frac{1}{\tau} - \frac{1}{\tau'}\right)\left(\frac{1}{\tau} + \frac{3}{\tau'}\right)\left(t - \frac{x}{\beta}\right)\right\}\exp\left\{-\frac{x}{2\beta}\left(\frac{1}{\tau} - \frac{1}{\tau'}\right)\right\}; \tag{18}$$

while when t is large compared with x/β, it is found that $u \to A$.

Since $\tau' > \tau$ (see § 2.5.3), the exponential factor in (18) is less than unity; thus elastic afterworking would cause the amplitude at the distance x to be diminished by an amount depending on $(\tau^{-1} - \tau'^{-1})$. The onset of a pulse is, however, sharp, as in the perfect elasticity case; and there is no dispersion introduced. Similar results hold for both P and S waves in the three-dimensional case.

When observations of bodily seismic waves are made, it is found that the damping is very small. Work of Gutenberg indicated that the damping effect may be represented by the presence of a factor of the form e^{-kD}, where D is the distance travelled by a wave and k is of the order of $10^{-4}\,\mathrm{km}^{-1}$. By (18) this would indicate a value for $(\tau^{-1} - \tau'^{-1})$ of the order of $10^{-3}\,\mathrm{sec}^{-1}$ (taking $\beta = 5\,\mathrm{km/sec}$). This damping is, however, probably not entirely attributable to elastic afterworking; scattering and reflection when the waves cross regions where the properties of the Earth's materials are changing rapidly are probably also contributing causes.

The fact that, with the use of the elastic afterworking equations (2, (75)), the expression $(\tau^{-1} - \tau'^{-1})$ turns out to be so small justifies our use of the equations of perfect elasticity in ordinary seismological problems.

4.5.2. The Jeffreys–Lomnitz law.

In 1956, Lomnitz proposed

a simple modification of the form (2, (77)) which Jeffreys in 1959 generalised to the equivalent of

$$E_{ij} = (\tau/2\nu)\, P_{ij}\{1 + q[(1 + at)^{\alpha} - 1]\}, \tag{19}$$

where q, a and α are further positive constants. Jeffreys brought evidence to bear to show that (19), with $\alpha = 0 \cdot 25$, gives an effective model not only in seismological problems where imperfections of elasticity need to be considered but also in wider geophysical problems where periods of geological interest are involved.

4.5.3. Elasticoviscosity. We saw in §2.5.4 that the elastico-viscosity equations (2, (67)) and (2, (78)) are formally derived from the elastic afterworking equations by taking τ' infinitely great. The general conclusions of §4.5.1 therefore still hold if the medium is of elasticoviscous type. In particular, there is no displacement at a given point until the instant of onset as given on the perfect elasticity theory; there is then a sharp onset (again with slightly reduced amplitude); and there is no dispersion.

4.6. Thermodynamical conditions. The thermodynamical conditions during the transmission of seismic waves will be approximately adiabatic, and so, as pointed out in §4.1, we take the elastic parameters λ, μ, k to be the adiabatic ones. It is desirable, however, to compare the speeds of travel of P and S waves under adiabatic and isothermal conditions.

As in §2.3.5, we let γ denote the coefficient of cubical expansion of the medium, c the specific heat at constant strain, and ϑ the absolute temperature. Then, to sufficient accuracy, it follows from (2, (57)) and (4) that the speed of P waves would in isothermal conditions be given by

$$\left\{k\left(1 - \frac{k\gamma^2\vartheta}{\rho c}\right) + \tfrac{4}{3}\mu\right\}^{\frac{1}{2}} \rho^{-\frac{1}{2}}, \tag{20}$$

where k is the adiabatic incompressibility. For an ordinary solid, the difference in the speeds given by (4) and (19) is only about 1%, but it might approach 10% in the Earth's deep interior where ϑ and k/ρ have greater values than at the surface.

Since the rigidity μ is the same in adiabatic and isothermal conditions (see (2, (57))), the speed of S waves is precisely the same in both cases.

4.7. Finite-strain theory. The high stresses reached in the Earth's interior involve finite strains. But there is the simplifying feature that the strengths of materials in the Earth set limits of the order of 10^9 dynes/cm^2 to the stress-differences that can be sustained; any cause tending to raise the stress-difference beyond the limit results in fracture (and hence an earthquake) or plastic flow. On the other hand, the mean, $-p$ say, of the principal stresses, p_1, p_2, p_3, say, is already (see § 13.5) 10^{10} dynes/cm^2 at a depth of 35 km, and steadily increases to values exceeding 10^{12} dynes/cm^2 in the deeper interior. Thus throughout most of the Earth, $p_1 \approx p_2 \approx p_3$, and the stress is effectively of the form $-p\delta_{ij}$ and representable in terms of a hydrostatic pressure p.

The stresses accompanying seismic wave transmission may therefore to good accuracy be treated as additional infinitesimal stresses superposed on a finite hydrostatic stress. In these circumstances, it is permissible to ignore effects of anisotropy which would enter significantly if the initial stress were not hydrostatic. The initial stress also causes ρ, k and μ to vary in otherwise homogeneous regions of the Earth, but the effect on wave transmission is negligible when ρ, k and μ change only by small proportions inside one wave-length. Hence theory based on $(4, (4))$ and $(4, (5))$ remains closely serviceable in general.

Finite-strain theory based on $(2, (81-6))$ is of importance in applying the results of seismological investigations to questions of the Earth's internal composition. In particular, results on the variation of ρ, k and μ with p have led to useful progress by Birch. Parameters additional to those on the first-order theory have to be introduced, and data from high-pressure experiments have to be brought to bear. (See also § 13.9 and subsections.)

CHAPTER 5

SURFACE ELASTIC WAVES

We now proceed to examine the possibility of waves being transmitted over the boundary surface of an elastic substance. Except where explicitly stated (as in § 5.8), we shall take the substance to be perfectly elastic and isotropic, shall ignore effects of fluctuations in the external forces, and shall use the infinitesimal strain theory. We have in chapter 4 examined in some detail the effects of possible departures from these ideal conditions for the case of bodily seismic waves, and found that these effects are very small. We expect, therefore, that the theory of surface waves that we are about to set up will likewise apply with good accuracy to actual seismic surface waves.

In accordance with the above remarks, our starting-point in the present chapter will be the equations (4, (1)). We shall devote special attention to Rayleigh and Love waves, which are important in seismology. These two types of waves are transmitted along the free surface of a solid in appropriate circumstances; but it will be convenient for us first to examine a somewhat more general problem.

5.1. Surface waves along the plane boundary between two homogeneous perfectly elastic media. Let M and M' be two homogeneous perfectly elastic media in welded contact, separated by a plane horizontal boundary and extending to indefinitely great distances from the boundary, M' being above M (the boundary is taken horizontal to enable us later to use the symbols SH and SV — see § 4.1.1). We shall use the usual symbols (such as ρ, α, β, etc.) to denote properties of the medium M, and dashed symbols for M'. As reference system we take a set of orthogonal cartesian axes $Ox_1 x_2 x_3$, the origin O being any point of the boundary, and Ox_3 pointing normally into M' (see Fig. 16).

Consider the possibility of a wave travelling in the direction Ox_1 in such a manner that (a) the disturbance is largely confined to the neighbourhood of the boundary, and (b) at any instant all particles in any line parallel to Ox_2 have equal displacements. On account of (a), the wave is a *surface wave*; and on account of (b), the case we have taken is analogous to the plane waves described in chapter 3.

It follows from (b) that all partial derivatives with respect to the coordinate x_2 are zero. Function, ϕ and ψ say, of the coordinates x_i and the time t, then exist such that the components u_1 and u_3 of the displacement at any point may be expressed in the form

$$u_1 = \frac{\partial\phi}{\partial x_1} + \frac{\partial\psi}{\partial x_3}, \quad u_3 = \frac{\partial\phi}{\partial x_3} - \frac{\partial\psi}{\partial x_1}. \tag{1}$$

From (1) we deduce

$$\nabla^2\phi = \theta \tag{2}$$

and

$$\nabla^2\psi = \frac{\partial u_1}{\partial x_3} - \frac{\partial u_3}{\partial x_1}. \tag{3}$$

The equations (2) and (3) illustrate the reason for the introduction of the functions ϕ and ψ, which is that we are thereby enabled to separate out the purely dilatational and the purely rotational disturbances associated with the components u_1, u_3. The component u_2 is of course associated with

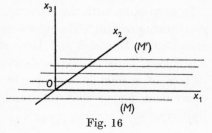

Fig. 16

purely distortional movement. Thus ϕ is associated with P waves, ψ with SV waves, and u_2 with SH waves.

Our assumptions (stated at the beginning of this chapter) are such that the u_i within the medium M satisfy (4, (1)). This will be the case if ϕ, ψ and u_2 satisfy the relations

$$\left. \begin{aligned} \frac{\partial^2\phi}{\partial t^2} &= \alpha^2\nabla^2\phi, \\ \frac{\partial^2\psi}{\partial t^2} &= \beta^2\nabla^2\psi, \end{aligned} \right\} \tag{4a}$$

$$\frac{\partial^2 u_2}{\partial t^2} = \beta^2\nabla^2 u_2 \tag{4b}$$

in M; and similar relations in M', with α, β replaced by α', β'. This step follows from a consideration of (2), (3) and the various equations of §4.1.

Towards solving the equations (4), we put

$$\phi = f(x_3) \exp\{\iota\kappa(x_1 - ct)\}, \left.\right\} \\ \psi = g(x_3) \exp\{\iota\kappa(x_1 - ct)\}, \right\} \tag{5a}$$

$$u_2 = h(x_3) \exp\{\iota\kappa(x_1 - ct)\} \tag{5b}$$

in M; and similar relations in M', the symbols f, g, h being replaced by f', g', h'. This will lead us to a particular solution corresponding to a group of simple harmonic waves of wave-length $2\pi/\kappa$ travelling forward with speed c.

It is convenient to introduce r, s, r', s', where

$$r = \left(\frac{c^2}{\alpha^2} - 1\right)^{\frac{1}{2}}, \quad s = \left(\frac{c^2}{\beta^2} - 1\right)^{\frac{1}{2}}, \quad r' = \left(\frac{c^2}{\alpha'^2} - 1\right)^{\frac{1}{2}}, \quad s' = \left(\frac{c^2}{\beta'^2} - 1\right)^{\frac{1}{2}}, \tag{6}$$

the positive value of the square root being taken in each case.

Substituting from (5) into (4), we have in a typical case for the medium M'

$$\frac{d^2h'}{dx_3^2} + h'\kappa^2\left(\frac{c^2}{\beta'^2} - 1\right) = 0,$$

of which the solution is

$$h'(x_3) = C' \exp(-\iota\kappa s'x_3) + F' \exp(\iota\kappa s'x_3), \tag{7}$$

where C', F' are constants of integration. For the effect to be essentially a surface one, $h'(x_3)$ must diminish indefinitely with increasing distance from the boundary. This will be the case if $h'(x_3)$ contains an exponential factor in which the exponent is real and negative. Hence s', and similarly s, r and r', are taken to be imaginary. Furthermore, constants corresponding to C' must vanish in M', and likewise those corresponding to F' in M.

The form of the solution in M is therefore

$$\phi = A \exp\{\iota\kappa(-rx_3 + x_1 - ct)\}, \left.\right\} \\ \psi = B \exp\{\iota\kappa(-sx_3 + x_1 - ct)\}, \right\} \tag{8a}$$

$$u_2 = C \exp\{\iota\kappa(-sx_3 + x_1 - ct)\}; \tag{8b}$$

and in M'
$$\phi = D' \exp\{\iota\kappa(r'x_3 + x_1 - ct)\},$$
$$\psi = E' \exp\{\iota\kappa(s'x_3 + x_1 - ct)\}, \tag{9a}$$

$$u_2 = F' \exp\{\iota\kappa(s'x_3 + x_1 - ct)\}, \tag{9b}$$

where A, B, C, D', E', F' are constants, and r, s, r', s' are all positive imaginaries.

We have now to apply the boundary conditions, which are that (i) the displacement at, and (ii) the stress across the boundary surface between M and M' shall be continuous at all times and places.

Using (1) we see that the conditions (i) give

$$A - Bs = D' + E's',$$
$$-Ar - B = D'r' - E', \tag{10a}$$

$$C = F'. \tag{10b}$$

The components of stress involved in (ii) are p_{31}, p_{32}, p_{33}. By $(2, (32))$ and (1), these components are for M

$$p_{33} = \lambda\theta + 2\mu\frac{\partial u_3}{\partial x_3}$$
$$= \lambda\nabla^2\phi + 2\mu\left(\frac{\partial^2\phi}{\partial x_3^2} - \frac{\partial^2\psi}{\partial x_3\partial x_1}\right), \tag{11}$$

$$p_{31} = \mu\left(\frac{\partial u_3}{\partial x_1} + \frac{\partial u_1}{\partial x_3}\right)$$
$$= \mu\left(2\frac{\partial^2\phi}{\partial x_3\partial x_1} - \frac{\partial^2\psi}{\partial x_1^2} + \frac{\partial^2\psi}{\partial x_3^2}\right), \tag{12}$$

$$p_{32} = \mu\frac{\partial u_2}{\partial x_3}, \tag{13}$$

and similarly for M'. On substituting from (8) and (9) into (11), (12) and (13), and using $(4, (4))$ and $(4, (5))$, we find that the conditions (ii) give

$$[\{\alpha^2(1+r^2) - 2\beta^2\}A + 2\beta^2sB]\rho$$
$$= [\{\alpha'^2(1+r'^2) - 2\beta'^2\}D' - 2\beta'^2s'E']\rho',$$
$$[-2rA - (1-s^2)B]\beta^2\rho \tag{14a}$$
$$= [2r'D' - (1-s'^2)E']\beta'^2\rho',$$
$$-sC\beta^2\rho = s'F'\beta'^2\rho'. \tag{14b}$$

Since s and s' are both positive imaginaries, $(10b)$ and $(14b)$ immediately give that C and F' are both zero. Thus there is no propagation of the component u_2 of displacement, i.e. in the problem here discussed there are no SH waves.

The detailed solution for the components u_1 and u_3 depends on the equations $(10a)$ and $(14a)$, and involves heavy algebra in the general case. In the following sections certain important special cases will be considered. Further discussion of the general problem and also of some other particular cases may be found in papers of Stoneley.

5.2. Rayleigh waves. The particular case of the foregoing problem in which the plane boundary is a free surface (so that M' say is replaced by a vacuum) was first examined by Rayleigh, and the corresponding waves are called *Rayleigh waves*.

As before, there are no SH surface waves.

For the other components of displacement, the absence of stress over the free surface enables us to replace the right-hand sides of $(14a)$ by zero, giving

$$\{\alpha^2(1+r^2) - 2\beta^2\} A + 2\beta^2 sB = 0$$

and
$$2rA + (1-s^2)B = 0. \tag{15}$$

Eliminating A and B, we obtain

$$\{\alpha^2(1+r^2) - 2\beta^2\}(1-s^2) = 4\beta^2 rs,$$

i.e. by (6),
$$\left(2 - \frac{c^2}{\beta^2}\right)^2 = 4\left(1 - \frac{c^2}{\alpha^2}\right)^{\frac{1}{2}}\left(1 - \frac{c^2}{\beta^2}\right)^{\frac{1}{2}}.$$

On rationalising this equation and removing the factor c^2/β^2, we then have
$$\frac{c^6}{\beta^6} - 8\frac{c^4}{\beta^4} + c^2\left(\frac{24}{\beta^2} - \frac{16}{\alpha^2}\right) - 16\left(1 - \frac{\beta^2}{\alpha^2}\right) = 0, \tag{16}$$

from which c may be determined.

If we substitute into the left-hand side of (16) the values $c = \beta$ and $c = 0$, we obtain unity and $-16(1 - \beta^2/\alpha^2)$, respectively; this last expression is negative, since β is always less than α. Hence (16) has a real root of c lying between 0 and β; it is immediately verified from (6) that such a root makes r and s both imaginary, thus satisfying the restriction on r and s stated in § 5.1 (this check needs to be carried out because of the rationalisation involved in deriving (16)). Thus, given suitable generating conditions, Rayleigh waves must necessarily persist along a free boundary in the circumstances stated. The waves are polarised so that the particles of the medium move in vertical planes parallel to the direction of the wave motion.

In (8) and (9), κ may have any real positive value, and solutions for particular values of κ may be superposed (cf. §§ 3.3.1, 3.3.2) to give more general solutions. But since in the present problem the velocity c is by (16) determined independently of κ, it follows that there will be no dispersion of a general wave form in the present boundary conditions.

When Poisson's relation (§ 4.1.2) holds, (16) yields three real values of c^2/β^2, namely, 4, $(2 + 2/\sqrt{3})$ and $(2 - 2/\sqrt{3})$. The first two of these values are both greater than 3 and thus make both r and s real, so that there could be no corresponding surface wave solutions. The third value leads to the results

$$c = 0{\cdot}92\beta, \quad r = 0{\cdot}85\iota, \quad s = 0{\cdot}39\iota. \tag{17}$$

The first of the equations (17) shows that the speed of Rayleigh waves in the circumstances taken is $0{\cdot}92$ of the speed of S bodily waves in the medium. The relevant expressions for u_1 and u_3 corresponding to simple harmonic waves of wave-length $2\pi/\kappa$ are found from (17) using (1), (8 a) and (15), and taking real parts. The results are

$$\left. \begin{array}{l} u_1 = a\{\exp(0{\cdot}85\kappa x_3) - 0{\cdot}58\exp(0{\cdot}39\kappa x_3)\}\sin\{\kappa(x_1 - ct)\}, \\ u_3 = a\{-0{\cdot}85\exp(0{\cdot}85\kappa x_3) + 1{\cdot}47\exp(0{\cdot}39\kappa x_3)\}\cos\{\kappa(x_1 - ct)\}, \end{array} \right\} \tag{18}$$

where a is a constant formally related to A and κ. Putting x_3 equal to zero, we see that during the passage of the disturbance, a surface particle describes an ellipse given by

$$u_1 = 0{\cdot}42a\sin\eta, \quad u_3 = 0{\cdot}62a\cos\eta, \tag{19}$$

where η is a parameter which decreases as the time increases. The ellipse is therefore described in a 'retrograde' fashion (see Fig. 37) and the maximum displacement parallel to the direction of transmission is about two-thirds of that in the vertical direction.

5.3. Love waves. Surface waves of the SH type are observed to occur on the Earth's surface. In addition, observations of the components u_1 and u_3 of the earth movement during the passage of seismic surface waves do not accord with (19). It follows that the actual conditions in the Earth must differ in some essential respect from those set down in the preceding problem.

Suppose now that a homogeneous layer M' is bounded above by a plane (horizontal) free surface, and below by a parallel boundary at a finite distance H' away, the latter boundary separating M' from another homogeneous substance M, below M' and extending to an indefinitely great distance, the contact being, as before, welded. Love showed that in these circumstances, waves of the SH type can occur in the free surface. It is sufficient for this purpose merely to consider the component u_2 of the displacement; reference to the other components of the displacement in these circumstances will be made in § 5.4.

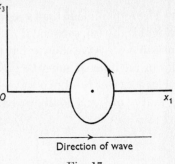

Fig. 17

We take an origin in the plane boundary between M and M', and directions of axes as in § 5.1 (see Fig. 18). The essential difference between the analysis of § 5.1 and that now required arises from the fact that the displacement in M' may no longer diminish with distance from the boundary between M and M'. Thus for the medium M' we preserve the full solution obtained using (7), and replace (9b) by

$$u_2 = C' \exp\{\iota\kappa(-s'x_3+x_1-ct)\} + F' \exp\{\iota\kappa(s'x_3+x_1-ct)\}, \quad (20)$$

where s' is now not necessarily imaginary. For M we, of course, still have (8b) with s imaginary.

The boundary conditions are (i) and (ii) of § 5.1, together with the requirement (iii) that there shall be no stress across the free surface $x_3 = H'$. These three conditions give, using (8b), (13) and (20),

$$C = C' + F', \quad (21a)$$

$$\mu s C = \mu' s'(C' - F'), \quad (21b)$$

$$C' \exp(-\iota\kappa s'H') = F' \exp(\iota\kappa s'H'). \quad (21c)$$

Eliminating C, C' and F' from (21 a, b, c), we obtain

$$\mu s + \mu' s' \tan(\kappa s' H') = 0. \qquad (22)$$

SH surface (Love) waves can therefore exist if (22) can be satisfied. Substitution for s and s' from (6) into (22) gives the relevant equation for the velocity c of Love waves, namely,

$$\mu \left(1 - \frac{c^2}{\beta^2}\right)^{\frac{1}{2}} - \mu' \left(\frac{c^2}{\beta'^2} - 1\right)^{\frac{1}{2}} \tan \left\{\kappa H'\left(\frac{c^2}{\beta'^2} - 1\right)^{\frac{1}{2}}\right\} = 0. \qquad (23)$$

The requirement that s should be imaginary and hence, by (22), s' real is, by (6), satisfied if $\beta' < c < \beta$. Hence for Love waves to be possible, we have shown that the velocity of S bodily waves in the lower medium M must be greater than that in M', and the wave velocities c of the Love waves must lie between the two velocities β and β' of the S bodily waves.

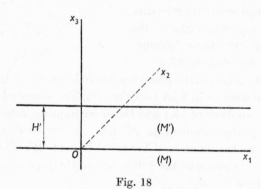

Fig. 18

The equation (23) shows that c is dependent on the particular value of κ, and not a fixed constant, so that in the present boundary conditions there will be dispersion of a general wave form. We see from (23) that if κ is small, $c \to \beta$; i.e. the velocities of the longer Love waves approach the velocity of S bodily waves in M. Also if κ is large, $c \to \beta'$, i.e. the velocities of the very short waves approach the velocity of S bodily waves in the upper medium M'.

5.3.1. Nodal planes. Now change the origin of axes to a point in the free surface (i.e. the upper boundary of M') and reverse the direction of the 3-axis. We find on using (20) and (21c) that the displacement in M' corresponding to a given κ is given by the real part of

$$2C' \cos(\kappa s' x_3) \exp\{\iota\kappa(-s'H' + x_1 - ct)\}. \tag{24}$$

The presence of the real cosine factor containing x_3 shows that the displacement is zero for all values of x_1, x_2 and t, if $\kappa s' x_3$ takes any of the particular values $\frac{1}{2}\pi$, $\frac{3}{2}\pi$, $\frac{5}{2}\pi$, ... The corresponding planes (which are parallel to the free surface) are *nodal planes* (cf. § 3.2.1). For values of κ for which $\kappa s'H' < \frac{1}{2}\pi$, there will be no nodal planes; for values of κ for which $\frac{1}{2}\pi < \kappa s'H' < \frac{3}{2}\pi$, one nodal plane; and so on. It follows that the cases of no, one, two, etc., nodal planes will be associated with ranges of values of κ which correspond to different branches of the tangent function in (22) or (23).

In practice in seismology, the case of no nodal planes is of the most (but by no means exclusive) importance; for a large part of the total energy is generally associated with the longer wave-lengths, i.e. with the smaller values of κ. For the case of no nodal planes we require that $2\pi s'H'/\lambda$ should be less than $\frac{1}{2}\pi$, where λ is the wave-length, i.e. $\lambda > 4s'H'$.

5.3.2. Dispersion curves. Let C be the group velocity associated with any particular values of κ; then, by (3, (60)),

$$\frac{C}{\beta'} = \frac{1}{\beta'} \frac{d(\kappa c)}{d\kappa}$$

$$= \frac{c}{\beta'} + \kappa H' \frac{d(c/\beta')}{d(\kappa H')}. \tag{25}$$

If we take assigned values of μ/μ' and ρ/ρ', we can, using (23) and (4, (5)), draw up a corresponding table connecting values of c/β' and $\kappa H'$ for the case of any particular number of nodal planes. Using this table and (25), we can then find values of C/β' in terms of c/β' and also in terms of $\kappa H'$. The curves connecting these values in any particular problem are called dispersion curves; their forms depend on the values taken for μ/μ' and ρ/ρ'.

In seismology, various periods ($2\pi/\kappa c$) may be measured from an earthquake record and the corresponding group velocities determined from a knowledge of the time and location of the earthquake's origin. If the waves are Love waves, the dispersion curves constructed as described then enable us to estimate H', if β, μ/μ' and

ρ/ρ' be presumed known. This method has been usefully employed in the study of the Earth's crustal structure, and will be referred to again in chapter 12. Early examples of dispersion curves and their use are to be found in papers of Jeffreys, Stoneley, Sezawa, Guten-berg, Byerly and J. T. Wilson.

Jeffreys showed, using (23) and (3, (60)), that with materials similar to those in the Earth's crust there exists a minimum group velocity of Love waves, which is less than β'; §3.3.5.4 is then relevant.

5.4. Rayleigh waves in the presence of a surface layer. The persistence of SH surface waves following an actual earthquake is evidence of heterogeneity within the Earth, and makes it desirable to study the other two components of displacement (u_1, u_3) under the conditions of §5.3. The method of investigation follows the trend of argument in §5.3, but the algebra is more severe.

The essential features of the solution are as follows. In the medium M, ϕ and ψ are given by (8a) as before, with r and s imaginary. But for the medium M', it is necessary to add to the right-hand sides of the equations (9a) expressions of the forms

$$A' \exp\{\iota\kappa(-r'x_3 + x_1 - ct)\} \quad \text{and} \quad B' \exp\{\iota\kappa(-s'x_3 + x_1 - ct)\},$$

respectively; r' and s' are real for the same reason that s' is real in §5.3.

The application of the boundary conditions stated in §5.3 now leads to six equations containing the constants A, B, A', B', D', E', and the derivation of the required equation in c requires the elimination of these six constants from the six equations. The six equations in question (in a somewhat different notation) may be found in a paper by Jeffreys (*Mon. Not. R. Astr. Soc. Geophys. Suppl.* 1935, p. 253) for the particular case in which Poisson's relation (4, (7)) holds. It transpires that, unlike the simple case of Rayleigh waves described in §5.2, c now depends on κ, and hence there is dispersion in the present circumstances. Jeffreys, in the paper cited, applied Rayleigh's principle (§§3.2.2, 3.2.5) to minimise the algebra, and to a sufficient approximation constructs dispersion curves giving H' in terms of c/β' for certain assigned values of μ/μ' and ρ/ρ'. Other early examples of dispersion curves of this type, with applications to investigations of the Earth's crustal structure, are to be found in work of Stoneley, Lee, Sezawa and Kanai. Also, as with Love waves, there is a minimum group velocity.

5.5. Surface waves in the presence of double and triple surface layers.

The first extension of Love wave theory to the case (see Fig. 19) in which two layers of uniform thickness bounded by plane horizontal surfaces rest on a medium M extending to an indefinitely great depth was carried out by Stoneley and Tillotson in 1928. Single and double dashes will be used to denote functions associated with the upper layers M' and M'', respectively. Stoneley and Tillotson assumed that $\beta'' < \beta' < \beta$, and showed that there are then two main cases which yield a solution. In the first of these cases, the surface wave velocity c lies between β'' and β'; the function $h''(x_3)$ (analogous to h' in § 5.1) gives a (real) amplitude factor periodic in x_3 inside M'', but its analogues inside both M'

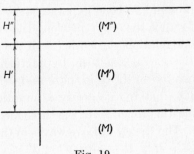

Fig. 19

and M give exponential amplitude factors. In the second case, c lies between β' and β, and the amplitude factors are periodic inside both M'' and M', but exponential inside M.

The boundary conditions are that the stress should be zero across the free surface, and that the displacement and stress should be continuous across each of the other two boundaries. These conditions lead to five equations from which the five arbitrary constants that are included in the general solution may be fairly readily eliminated to give the necessary equation connecting c and κ. For the first case mentioned above, this equation is

$$\mu'^2 s'^2 \tanh\left(-\iota s'\kappa H'\right) + \mu\mu' ss' - \mu\mu'' \iota s' s'' \tan\left(s''\kappa H''\right)$$
$$- \mu\mu'' \iota ss'' \tan\left(s''\kappa H''\right) \tanh\left(-\iota s'\kappa H'\right) = 0, \quad (26)$$

in which s'' is real and s' and s are imaginary; in (26), s and s' are as usual defined by (6), and s'' is analogously defined. If we make H' approach either zero or infinity, this equation, as expected, degenerates to a form equivalent to that for simple Love waves as given by equation (22). The equation (26) holds formally also for the second case above, but it is convenient to write it in a form adapted to the fact that s' is now real. If we then take H' or H'' zero, we again derive the equation for simple Love waves.

An intermediate case arises when $c = \beta'$, but this presents no special difficulty.

As with the simpler Love waves, it can be shown that nodal planes may exist in appropriate circumstances.

By an extension of the method described in § 5.3.2, it is possible to derive information about the Earth's crustal structure on the present two-layer hypothesis. As the equation (26) (or an equivalent form) is the only equation yielded by the theory, there is still only one relation yielded between the parameters necessary to describe the crustal structure. In practice, it has been the custom to assume a value for the ratio H''/H' and then determine H' or H'' by equation (26), making necessary assumptions concerning the densities and elastic properties of the three media involved.

The theory of Love waves in the presence of three surface layers M', M'', M''', with $\beta''' < \beta'' < \beta' < \beta$, was also first studied by Stoneley. There are now three main cases, namely, (i) $\beta''' < c < \beta''$, (ii) $\beta'' < c < \beta'$, (iii) $\beta' < c < \beta$, together with the intermediate cases $c = \beta''$ and $c = \beta'$. An equation connecting c and κ may be found after the manner described above, and contains terms of the type appearing in (26). This equation has been employed to estimate the value of H''' in cases where H'' and H' are assumed known.

5.6. Seismic surface waves.

The theory of the preceding sections applies to model conditions somewhat simpler than those in the actual Earth. We add here a few remarks on the circumstances with actual seismic waves. Further detail will be given in chapter 12.

We first note that the free surface of the Earth is curved and not plane. Allowance for the Earth's curvature introduces into the equations terms involving additional dispersion effects. The effects can be disregarded for ordinary seismic surface waves, with periods up to the order of 2–3 min, in which wave-lengths are small compared with the radius of the Earth; this applies in particular in surface-wave investigations of the Earth's crustal layers (see chapter 12). Latterly, however, it has become possible to record waves with considerably greater periods which are significantly influenced by structure below the crust, and for which curvature has to be taken into account (see §§ 5.9, 14.4).

In the preceding sections, all layers were assumed homogeneous. In 1928, Jeffreys investigated the effect on Love waves of allowing for heterogeneity below a single-layer crust, using data (see chapter 13) on the variation of rigidity below the crust. He found that for waves with periods of the order of a minute the group velocity is slightly diminished, but that estimates of the crustal thickness as made using the simpler theory are not appreciably affected. Stoneley examined the effect on Love waves of variation of density inside the crustal layer, and showed that Love waves can exist so long as the density variation is such that the Love wave velocity exceeds the S bodily wave velocity at all points of the layer. Stoneley was also the first to consider questions of the refraction of a surface wave group such as may occur at a margin between a continent and ocean (see § 6.7).

On the question of the mechanism of the generation of surface seismic waves, early investigators were Jeffreys, Sezawa and Kanai. For example, Jeffreys considered the case of Love waves in a two-layered crust, and an impulsive initial disturbance within the upper layer. He found that 'the disturbance transmitted through the lower layer consists of a series of overlapping pulses, each starting at an instant corresponding to the time of transmission of a pulse that has undergone an integral number of reflections inside the upper layer. The recovery after each pulse leads to a train of waves, the superposition of which gives the Love waves.'

It follows from § 3.5 that as surface waves spread out from an initially confined region, the amplitude will (neglecting dispersion effects) vary essentially inversely as the square root of the distance from this region. On the other hand, we have seen (see § 3.4.1) that with bodily seismic waves the amplitude is inversely proportional to the first power of the distance. Thus the more distant is a point of the Earth's surface from an initial earthquake disturbance, the relatively more prominent will be the surface waves compared with the bodily waves, a result that is well in accord with observations. Except near the region of the initial disturbance, the surface waves from an earthquake are (unless the focus is abnormally deep—see the last paragraph of § 3.2.5) indicated much more prominently than the bodily waves.

During the post-war years, the study of seismic surface waves has been greatly extended, notably at the hands of Ewing, Press, Oliver and others of the Lamont Observatory. One among many developments has been to show that the presence of oceans greatly increases Rayleigh wave dispersion and accounts for many of the long wave-trains found in the coda of seismograms.

5.7. *Lg* and *Rg* waves.

In 1952, Ewing and Press drew attention to shorter-period surface waves which they have called *Lg* and *Rg*, which are superposed on Love and Rayleigh waves over continental paths. The *Lg* waves have periods of order 1–6 sec and speed 3·5 km/sec; the *Rg* waves have periods of 8–12 sec and speed 3·1 km/sec. The precise mechanism of their transmission is not yet fully understood, but they have the remarkable property that they are entirely eliminated when the surface path from an earthquake source to an observatory includes 150 or more kilometres of ocean. The authors suggest that they are associated with higher-mode oscillations.

5.8. Damping of seismic surface waves.

The observed damping in the case of surface seismic waves is a little greater than in the case of bodily waves (§ 4.5.1). The amount of damping varies with the observed period, the effect being on the whole more marked with the shorter than with the longer waves. On the average, the damping factor in the amplitude is found to decrease in the ratio $1:e$ over a distance of order 5000 km on the Earth's surface. It is probable that scattering and reflection, when the waves cross regions where the structure of the Earth's crustal layers is significantly changing, are again responsible for at least part of this observed damping.

5.9. Long-period seismic waves. A most important modern development has been the construction of instruments designed to record waves with periods much in excess of the order of a minute. This has involved the extension of surface wave theory to applications to the structure of the Earth below the crust, and to the consideration of fundamental oscillations of the whole Earth, where periods up to the order of an hour are involved. Some details will be given in chapter 14.   124128

CHAPTER 6

REFLECTION AND REFRACTION
OF ELASTIC WAVES

As in §5.1, we consider two homogeneous media, M and M', in welded contact, separated by a plane boundary. We now proceed to investigate the laws of reflection and refraction for various types of plane waves incident through a medium M towards this boundary, which for convenience we again take to be horizontal. We take a frame of reference similar to that taken in §5.1; the origin O is any point of the boundary, Ox_3 points normally into the medium M', and Ox_1, Ox_2 are taken respectively perpendicular to and parallel to the line in which an incident wave front cuts the boundary. To begin with, we consider waves of simple harmonic form.

The relevant equations of motion are again the equations (4, (1)). Partial derivatives with respect to x_2 are again zero, and the general part of the analysis of §5.1, including the boundary conditions, will be relevant to the present problems. The principal modification is that we must in both media refer back to the more general solutions corresponding to (5, (7)), instead of using the particular solutions that were subsequently selected in §5.1 to fit the special requirements of particular types of surface waves. The essential effect of this modification is that an additional term has to be added to each of the equations (5, (8)); the form of the solution now obtained for the medium M is accordingly as in the equations (2) below.

6.1. Laws of reflection and refraction. It follows as in §5.1 that the relevant solutions of the equations of motion will contain no terms in x_2, and that x_1 will always enter only in a factor of the form $\exp\{\iota\kappa(x_1 - ct)\}$; this factor (see, for example, (2) and (3) below) will be common to every term that arises, whether associated with the incident or with reflected or refracted waves. It is important, however, to note that in the present problems the c in this factor is not the actual wave velocity, but the velocity of advance of the line in which a (plane) wave front cuts the plane boundary surface. An analogous interpretation holds for κ.

In a particular problem, let e be the (acute) angle between the normal to a wave front and the x_1-axis for any particular one of the waves involved (incident, reflected or refracted), and let i be the complement of e; we shall throughout this book take e, i to lie in the range from 0 to $\frac{1}{2}\pi$. Let v be the corresponding wave velocity. It follows from the property of c stated in the last paragraph that $v = c \cos e$. Hence we have

$$\frac{\sin i}{v} = \frac{\cos e}{v} = \text{constant} \tag{1}$$

for all the waves involved. (This relation may be alternatively inferred from a consideration of (3, (70)); or it may be deduced, using the calculus of variations, from Fermat's principle (§ 3.6.2).)

The relation (1) shows that laws of reflection and refraction hold

which are analogous to those applying to rays in geometrical optics. The present case is more general, however, since there are liable to be waves of the P as well as the S type (which alone occurs in optics), both reflected and refracted.

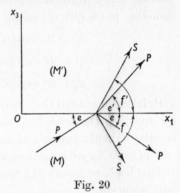

With an incident wave, i is called the *angle of incidence* and e the *angle of emergence*. In the sections that follow, we shall often in the one problem be concerned with

Fig. 20

two different directions of wave velocity in the same medium, associated respectively with the P and S reflections or refractions arising from a given incident wave. In such cases, we shall (see Fig. 20) denote the angles between the normals to wave fronts and the x_1-axis by e for P waves and by f for S waves in the medium M (i.e. for incident or reflected waves), and by e' and f' in the medium M' (i.e. for refracted waves).

6.2. General equations for the two media. In accordance with the remarks made at the beginning of this chapter, the solution for the medium M which replaces the less general solution (5, (8)) may be written in the form

$$\phi = A_0 \exp\{\iota\kappa(x_3 \tan e + x_1 - ct)\} + A \exp\{\iota\kappa(-x_3 \tan e + x_1 - ct)\},$$
$$\psi = B_0 \exp\{\iota\kappa(x_3 \tan f + x_1 - ct)\} + B \exp\{\iota\kappa(-x_3 \tan f + x_1 - ct)\},$$
$$u_2 = C_0 \exp\{\iota\kappa(x_3 \tan f + x_1 - ct)\} + C \exp\{\iota\kappa(-x_3 \tan f + x_1 - ct)\},$$

$$(2)$$

the coefficients $\tan e$ and $\tan f$ which replace the r and s of (5, (8)) being determined using (3, (70)). The first terms on the right-hand sides of (2) will correspond to incident waves, and the second terms to reflected waves. With separate incident P, SV and SH waves, we have, respectively,

$$B_0 = C_0 = 0, \quad C_0 = A_0 = 0, \quad A_0 = B_0 = 0.$$

For M', there will, of course, be no terms corresponding to the terms containing A, B, C in (2), since in M' the waves will all be moving away from the boundary. Hence for M' we may (corresponding to (5, (9)), replacing D', E', F' by A', B', C') write

$$\phi = A' \exp\{\iota\kappa(x_3 \tan e' + x_1 - ct)\},$$
$$\psi = B' \exp\{\iota\kappa(x_3 \tan f' + x_1 - ct)\},$$
$$u_2 = C' \exp\{\iota\kappa(x_3 \tan f' + x_1 - ct)\}.$$

$$(3)$$

Relations between the coefficients A, B, A_0, etc., are determined by applying the boundary conditions corresponding to the continuity of displacement and stress across the boundary at all times and places. As with surface waves, the application of these conditions leads to heavy algebra in general, and we shall here treat only some special cases.

6.3. Case of incident SH wave. When the incident wave is of the SH type, we have $A_0 = B_0 = 0$; also $\mu \neq 0$. The boundary conditions which involve ϕ and ψ then show that A, B, A' and B' have no dependence on C_0, and the relevant solution is accordingly of the form

$$u_2 = C_0 \exp\{\iota\kappa(x_3 \tan f + x_1 - ct)\} + C \exp\{\iota\kappa(-x_3 \tan f + x_1 - ct)\} \quad (4)$$

for the medium M, and

$$u_2 = C' \exp\{\iota\kappa(x_3 \tan f' + x_1 - ct)\} \quad (5)$$

for M'.

If $\mu' \neq 0$, continuity of the displacement at the boundary then gives

$$C_0 + C = C', \tag{6}$$

and continuity of the stress component p_{32} gives, by (5, (13)),

$$(C_0 - C)\,\mu \tan f = C'\mu' \tan f'. \tag{7}$$

From (6) and (7) we derive

$$\frac{C}{\mu \tan f - \mu' \tan f'} = \frac{C'}{2\mu \tan f} = \frac{C_0}{\mu \tan f + \mu' \tan f'}. \tag{8}$$

Also by (1) we have

$$\frac{\cos f}{v} = \frac{\cos f'}{v'}, \tag{9}$$

where v, v' are the velocities of S waves in M, M'. In the case of normal incidence ($f = f' = \tfrac{1}{2}\pi$), the formula (8) fails to determine the ratios of C and C' to C_0; but using (9) and taking limits, we derive for this case

$$\frac{C}{\mu v' - \mu' v} = \frac{C'}{2\mu v'} = \frac{C_0}{\mu v' + \mu' v}. \tag{10}$$

By (8), (9) and (10) we can for given media determine C and C' in terms of C_0 and f, and hence determine the amplitude ratios of the incident, reflected and refracted waves for any given angle of emergence.

The above solution shows that when the incident wave is of the *SH* type, then the reflected and refracted waves can only be also of the *SH* type. We notice that the coefficient C in (8) can be zero only for an angle of emergence which satisfies (9) and the equation $\mu \tan f - \mu' \tan f' = 0$. Apart from this possible value of f, there will always be a reflected wave. It may happen, moreover (depending on the particular values of μ, μ', ρ, ρ'), that the expression $\mu \tan f - \mu' \tan f'$ has no zero in the range $0 \leqslant f \leqslant \tfrac{1}{2}\pi$, in which case there is a reflected wave for every angle of incidence.

The question of the existence of a refracted wave conveying energy from the boundary into the medium M' is determined by equation (9). For if $v' > v$, $\cos f'$ exceeds unity for a range of real values of f. In this case, $\tan f'$ is pure imaginary and (5) takes the form

$$u_2 = C' \exp(-bx_3) \exp\{\iota\kappa(x_1 - ct)\}, \tag{11}$$

where b is a positive real number. This gives inside M', instead of a refracted wave, a surface movement whose amplitude diminishes exponentially with increasing distance from the boundary, and which travels along the boundary with the velocity of advance of the line in which the incident wave front cuts the boundary. When $\tan f'$ is imaginary, it follows from (8) that C/C_0 is equal to the ratio of two conjugate complex numbers; this entails that $|C/C_0| = 1$, and hence $C = C_0 \exp(-\iota\delta)$, where δ is a real number depending on f, μ/μ' and v/v'. Hence in the case under consideration, there is *total reflection* of the incident wave, the amplitude of the reflected wave is equal to that of the incident wave, and there is a change of phase given by δ. For the particular angle of emergence $\cos^{-1}(v/v')$ which gives f' a zero value, there is total reflection with zero change of phase.

If $\mu' = 0$, i.e. if M' is a fluid or vacuum, there is free slipping along the boundary and the condition which gives (6) no longer holds; also (5) is now irrelevant. But since p_{32} is now zero at the boundary, we have now that the left-hand side of (7) is zero, and so obtain $C = C_0$ in place of (6). The solution is therefore given entirely by (4) with C replaced by C_0. In this case there is complete reflection without change of type or phase.

6.4. P wave incident against a free plane boundary.

We next consider the case of a P wave incident through the medium M against a free plane boundary, the angle of emergence being e. Thus in (2) and (3), we put $B_0 = C_0 = 0$, $A' = B' = C' = 0$. Hence the relevant equations are

$$\left.\begin{aligned}
\phi &= A \exp\{\iota\kappa(-x_3 \tan e + x_1 - ct)\} \\
&\quad + A_0 \exp\{\iota\kappa(x_3 \tan e + x_1 - ct)\}, \\
\psi &= B \exp\{\iota\kappa(-x_3 \tan f + x_1 - ct)\}, \\
u_2 &= C \exp\{\iota\kappa(-x_3 \tan f + x_1 - ct)\},
\end{aligned}\right\} \tag{12}$$

holding in the medium M.

We shall in this problem assume that Poisson's relation holds in M. Since α is the velocity associated with ϕ, and β with ψ and u_2, we then have by (1) and (4, (7))

$$\cos^2 e = 3 \cos^2 f. \tag{13}$$

The boundary conditions are that the stress components p_{31}, p_{32}, p_{33} must vanish at the boundary. The condition involving p_{32} gives immediately by (5, (13)) that C is zero. Thus there can be no reflected SH waves in the present case.

The boundary conditions involving p_{33}, p_{31} then give, using (5, (11)), (5, (12)) and (4, (7)),

$$(A_0 + A)(1 + 3\tan^2 e) + 2B\tan f = 0,$$

$$(A_0 - A) 2\tan e + B(\tan^2 f - 1) = 0.$$

From these and (13) we derive

$$\frac{A}{4\tan e \tan f - (1 + 3\tan^2 e)^2} = \frac{B}{-4\tan e(1 + 3\tan^2 e)}$$

$$= \frac{A_0}{4\tan e \tan f + (1 + 3\tan^2 e)^2}. \quad (14)$$

By (13) and (14) we can determine A and B in terms of A_0 and e, and hence determine the amplitude ratios of the incident and the two reflected waves for any given angle of incidence.

For normal incidence we have $e = f = \frac{1}{2}\pi$, and for grazing incidence $e = 0$. It is readily deduced from (13) and (14) that B is zero in both these cases, but in no other case. Thus there exists a reflected disturbance of the SV type for all angles of incidence except zero and $\frac{1}{2}\pi$.

The coefficient A vanishes if $(1 + 3\tan^2 e)^2 = 4\tan e \tan f$. Using (13), we find that this equation has two relevant roots, namely, $e = 12°\cdot8, 30°$. For these angles of emergence, there are accordingly no reflected waves of the P type. Between them, A/A_0 is found to rise to a maximum of only $0\cdot058$ (at $e = 25°$). Thus over a fair range of values of e there is very little reflection in the P type. Jeffreys has pointed out that a small departure from Poisson's relation (e.g. when $\alpha = 1\cdot8\beta$) would prevent A from vanishing at all; nevertheless, the ratio A/A_0 would remain small over a similar range of values of e to that just indicated. Jeffreys points out further that for $2° < e < 63°$, at least half of the reflected energy is in the SV type; this result is relevant to an argument used in § 4.3.

6.5. SV wave incident against a free plane boundary. The formal solution for this case may be carried out after the manner shown in

§ 6.4. In (2) and (3), we put $A_0 = C_0 = 0$, $A' = B' = C' = 0$. We find again that C is zero for all angles of incidence, and hence that there are no reflected SH waves. Taking the angle of emergence of the incident wave as f, we have as the relevant equations for ϕ and ψ

$$\phi = A \exp\{\iota\kappa(-x_3 \tan e + x_1 - ct)\},\tag{15}$$

$$\psi = B \exp\{\iota\kappa(-x_3 \tan f + x_1 - ct)\} + B_0 \exp\{\iota\kappa(x_3 \tan f + x_1 - ct)\}.\tag{16}$$

If we assume again that Poisson's relation holds, we have (13) again, and we find that A and B are determined in terms of B_0 and f by means of (13) and the equations

$$\frac{A}{4 \tan f(1 + 3\tan^2 e)} = \frac{B}{4 \tan e \tan f - (1 + 3\tan^2 e)^2}$$

$$= \frac{B_0}{4 \tan e \tan f + (1 + 3\tan^2 e)^2}.\tag{17}$$

The resemblance between the forms (14) and (17) is an instance of a reciprocal theorem proved by Gutenberg.

We find, similarly to the case of § 6.4, that B is zero if $e = 12°\cdot 8$ or $30°$, i.e. (by (13)) if $f = 55°\cdot 7$ or $60°$. For a range of angles between these angles of emergence there is little reflection in the SV type.

There is the complication with incident SV waves that e is imaginary if $0 \leqslant f < \cos^{-1}(1/\sqrt{3}) = 54°\cdot 7$. For this range of values of f, (15) takes a form analogous to the right-hand side of (11), and we find (cf. the case described in § 6.3) that there is then complete reflection in the SV type, with a change of phase in general.

6.6. Reflection and refraction of seismic waves.

In seismology, the reflection and refraction wave problems are mostly concerned with the effects at a boundary of small curvature in regions at appreciable distances from an earthquake origin. In these circumstances, the plane-wave theory is again sufficiently accurate for most purposes. All the special cases described in §§ 6.3–5 are important in seismology, and are illustrative of types of solution arising from the equations set up in § 6.2. Other special cases corresponding to specific values of the parameters describing the properties of the two media M and M' need also to be considered in seismology; the values taken correspond to particular discontinuities within the Earth, as revealed in chapters 12 and 13. Early examples of solutions obtained in this way are to be found in work of Knott, Gutenberg, Jeffreys, Macelwane, Sezawa and Kanai. In these solutions, tables are presented giving values of ratios of expressions such as A/A_0, B/A_0, etc., in terms of values of e or f ranging from 0 to $\frac{1}{2}\pi$. Such tables are made the basis of comparisons with observational results, and are of use in connection with the energy considerations to be discussed in chapter 8.

In all the cases so far considered, the incident wave was taken to be a single simple harmonic wave. For more complicated forms of the incident wave, it is easy to deduce the relevant results by superposition of the effects of the separate simple harmonic constituents, provided there is no dispersion. The law of reflection and refraction continues to be given by (1), and formulae such as (8), (14) and (17) continue to hold, coefficients such as A_0, A, B, etc., being interpreted as indexes of the sizes of the displacement in the incident and derived waves.

The preceding theory is concerned with plane waves and plane boundaries. For more difficult cases, the reader is referred to work of Cagniard, Dix, Scholte, Blake and v.d. Waerden.

6.7. Refraction of dispersed waves.

We consider the refraction of waves, subject to dispersion, across an interface separating two homogeneous media M and M'. Stoneley pointed out that the direction of the refracted wave front is determined by the ratio of the velocities of wave propagation, while the velocities of transmission of energy in the two media follow the law of group velocity.

The following proof of this result is due to Jeffreys. Suppose a disturbance issues at time $t = 0$ from an assigned point O of the medium M, and consider the effect at time t at a point O' of the medium M'. For ease of exposition, the proof is given for the two-dimensional case; it is not difficult to extend the proof to the three-dimensional case. Consider (see Fig. 21) a pencil of rays which all pass from O to O' in the time t, the pencil cutting off a length ds of the interface near the point P say, and let the wave periods for the rays in this pencil all lie between $2\pi/\gamma$ and $2\pi/(\gamma + d\gamma)$. Let $OP = r$, $PO' = r'$, and let the wave and group velocities in the two media corresponding to the period $2\pi/\gamma$ be c, c', and C, C', respectively. By analogy with the form (3, (49)) (but taking γ as argument, instead of κ—cf. (8, (23))) it is seen that the displacement at O' at time t will be of the form

$$\iint f(\gamma)\, g(\theta) \exp\{\iota\gamma(rc^{-1}+r'c'^{-1}-t)\}\, d\gamma\, ds, \tag{18}$$

where $f(\gamma)$ is analogous to $\phi(\kappa)$ in (3, (49)), and $g(\theta)$ is a function of direction. The functions f and g will, like the function $\phi(\kappa)$, be in general slowly varying functions. It may then be shown (cf. § 3.3.5.2)

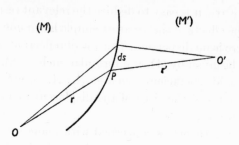

Fig. 21

that the predominant contribution to the integral (18) will in general arise from values of s and γ near those for which the integrand is stationary. The conditions for this (neglecting variation of f and g) are

$$\frac{1}{c}\frac{dr}{ds}+\frac{1}{c'}\frac{dr'}{ds}=0, \tag{19}$$

$$r\frac{d(\gamma c^{-1})}{d\gamma}+r'\frac{d(\gamma c'^{-1})}{d\gamma}-t=0. \tag{20}$$

Since dr/ds and dr'/ds are opposite in sign and equal in magnitude respectively to the sines of the angles which the pencil makes with the normal to the interface at P on the two sides, the equation (19) is equivalent to the usual law of refraction (1); thus the paths of the rays are determined by the wave velocities. Since $\gamma = \kappa c$, the equation (20) is by (3, (60)) equivalent to $t = r/C + r'/C'$, which shows that the travel-time of the predominant disturbance is determined by the group velocities.

CHAPTER 7

SEISMIC RAYS IN A SPHERICALLY STRATIFIED EARTH MODEL

We next consider questions concerning the transmission of bodily seismic waves in the interior of an Earth model assumed to be spherical and completely symmetrical about its centre in all its properties. We shall ignore diffraction effects and investigate properties of seismic rays. We shall be considering families of rays, each member of which has its end-points on the outer surface of the Earth model, and is refracted through any surface of discontinuity encountered. The P or S ray character will be taken to be assigned at all levels in any one family, and, on account of the symmetry of the model about its centre O, it will be sufficient for us to consider rays which all lie in the same plane through O and have their deepest points all on the same radius through O.

7.1. The parameter p of a seismic ray. We may regard the Earth model as composed of an indefinitely large number of thin homogeneous concentric spherical shells. Consider a portion $PP'P''$ of a seismic ray, where P, P', P'' are points on three consecutive boundaries between these shells. Let v', v'' be the ray speeds along PP', $P'P''$, respectively, and let the angles i', j', i'' be as in Fig. 22. Then, by (6, (1)),
$$\frac{OP'\sin i'}{v'} = \frac{OP'\sin j'}{v''}.$$

But $OP'\sin j'$ is equal to $OP''\sin i''$, these being both expressions for the perpendicular from O to $P'P''$. It follows that

$$p = \frac{r\sin i}{v}, \tag{1}$$

where r is the distance from O to any point P of the model, v is the ray speed at P, i is the (acute) angle between OP and the direction of the ray at P, and p is constant along the entire ray. The value of p, called the *parameter* of the ray, will differ from member to member of a given family.

7.2. Relations between p, Δ, T for a given family of rays. In the subsequent discussions, we shall make frequent reference to the particular values which r, v and certain other entities take at the outer surface of the model and also at the deepest point of the ray whose parameter is p. We shall use suffixes 0 and p, respectively, to denote such values.

7.2.1. The relation $p = dT/d\Delta$. Consider a family of rays of the type described at the start of this chapter. Let Δ be the angle subtended at O by the whole length of the particular ray whose parameter is p, and let T be the time of travel along this ray. Let

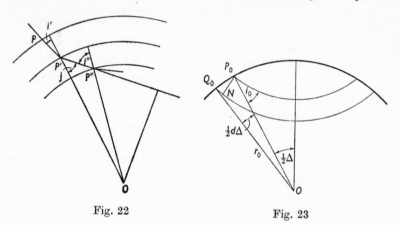

Fig. 22   Fig. 23

$p + dp$, $\Delta + d\Delta$, $T + dT$ be the corresponding values for an adjacent ray. Then if P_0, Q_0 be adjacent end-points of the two rays and $P_0 N$ be normal to the ray through Q_0, we have (see Fig. 23)

$$\sin i_0 = \frac{NQ_0}{P_0 Q_0} = \frac{v_0 \cdot \frac{1}{2} dT}{r_0 \cdot \frac{1}{2} d\Delta}.$$

Hence, by (1), $$p = \frac{dT}{d\Delta}. \tag{2}$$

(In connection with argument to be given in §8.1, we note here that the formula (2) is true also for the case of a family of rays which is of the type we have described except that each ray starts from some assigned point F in the interior of the Earth model. This is easily seen.)

7.2.2. Some integral expressions for T, Δ. Let P be any point of a ray whose parameter is p, let the polar coordinates of P be (r, θ) as indicated in Fig. 24, and let the arc-length $P_0 P$ be s. Then, by (1),

$$\frac{r^2}{v}\frac{d\theta}{ds} = p. \tag{3}$$

Eliminating ds between (3) and the polar relation

$$(ds)^2 = (dr)^2 + r^2(d\theta)^2, \tag{4}$$

we obtain

$$\frac{r^4}{p^2 v^2} = \left(\frac{dr}{d\theta}\right)^2 + r^2, \tag{5}$$

i.e.

$$d\theta = \pm p r^{-1}(\eta^2 - p^2)^{-\frac{1}{2}}\, dr, \tag{6}$$

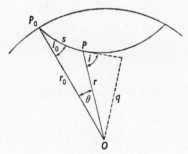

Fig. 24

where for convenience we have introduced η, defined by

$$\eta = r/v. \tag{7}$$

Integrating (6) between P_0 and the deepest point of the ray, we obtain a useful expression for Δ, namely,

$$\tfrac{1}{2}\Delta = p\int_{r_p}^{r_0} r^{-1}(\eta^2 - p^2)^{-\frac{1}{2}}\, dr. \tag{8}$$

If we eliminate $d\theta$ between (3) and (4) we obtain

$$\frac{p^2 v^2}{r^2} = r^2\left(\frac{d\theta}{ds}\right)^2 = 1 - \left(\frac{dr}{ds}\right)^2,$$

i.e.

$$ds = \pm r v^{-1}(\eta^2 - p^2)^{-\frac{1}{2}}\, dr. \tag{9}$$

Since the time T is equal to the integral $\int ds/v$ taken along the ray, we obtain from (9) a formula for T, analogous to the formula (8) for Δ, namely,

$$\tfrac{1}{2}T = \int_{r_p}^{r_0} \eta^2 r^{-1} (\eta^2 - p^2)^{-\frac{1}{2}} \, dr. \tag{10}$$

The following connection between T and Δ is sometimes useful. By (10), by elementary algebra,

$$T = 2 \int_{r_p}^{r_0} \{ p^2 r^{-1} (\eta^2 - p^2)^{-\frac{1}{2}} + r^{-1} (\eta^2 - p^2)^{\frac{1}{2}} \} \, dr.$$

Hence, by (8),

$$T = p\Delta + 2 \int_{r_p}^{r_0} r^{-1} (\eta^2 - p^2)^{\frac{1}{2}} \, dr. \tag{11}$$

Incidentally, we notice that since $dr/d\theta$ is zero at the deepest point of the ray, we have by (6) and (7)

$$p = \eta_p = r_p / v_p. \tag{12}$$

7.2.3. The functions ξ and ζ.

Let ξ and ζ be defined by

$$\zeta = \frac{d \ln v}{d \ln r} = \frac{r}{v} \frac{dv}{dr}, \quad \xi = \frac{2}{1 - \zeta} = \frac{2 d \ln r}{d \ln \eta}. \tag{13}$$

These functions of r are important because the simple condition $\zeta < 1$, or $\xi > 0$ (or $d\eta/dr > 0$), determines whether there can exist a ray of the family with its lowest point L at a given level r. This follows since, by (34) (to be derived in § 7.5.1) and (12), the downward curvature of a ray at L is $v^{-1} dv/dr$, while the curvature of the level surface through r is r^{-1}. Values of r at which ζ and ξ pass through the values 1 and ∞, respectively, are associated with discontinuous changes in the shapes of rays of a family; correspondingly, divergent integrals appear in the mathematical ray analysis.

7.2.4. Expressions for $d\Delta/dp$ and dT/dp.

By (8), (10) and (13),

$$\Delta = \int_{\eta_p}^{\eta_0} p \xi \eta^{-1} (\eta^2 - p^2)^{-\frac{1}{2}} \, d\eta, \tag{14}$$

$$T = \int_{\eta_p}^{\eta_0} \xi \eta (\eta^2 - p^2)^{-\frac{1}{2}} \, d\eta. \tag{15}$$

Integrating (14) and (15) by parts and using (12) gives

$$\Delta = [\xi \cos^{-1}(p/\eta)]_{\eta_p}^{\eta_0} - \int_{\xi_p}^{\xi_0} \cos^{-1}(p/\eta)\, d\xi$$

$$= \xi_0 \cos^{-1}(p/\eta_0) - \int_{\xi_p}^{\xi_0} \cos^{-1}(p/\eta)\, d\xi, \tag{16}$$

$$T = \xi_0(\eta_0^2 - p^2)^{\frac{1}{2}} - \int_{\xi_p}^{\xi_0} (\eta^2 - p^2)^{\frac{1}{2}}\, d\xi. \tag{17}$$

Differentiating (16) and (17) with respect to p, we have

$$\frac{d\Delta}{dp} = -\xi_0(\eta_0^2 - p^2)^{-\frac{1}{2}} + \int_{\xi_p}^{\xi_0} (\eta^2 - p^2)^{-\frac{1}{2}}\, d\xi = -X + Y, \quad \text{say,} \tag{18}$$

$$\frac{dT}{dp} = -p\xi_0(\eta_0^2 - p^2)^{-\frac{1}{2}} + \int_{\xi_p}^{\xi_0} p(\eta^2 - p^2)^{-\frac{1}{2}}\, d\xi. \tag{19}$$

It will be noticed that (18) and (19) entail (2). The formulae (16) to (19) assume that η, ξ and their derivatives are differentiable in the range $r_p \leqslant r \leqslant r_0$, and that ζ does not become equal to unity.

7.3. Features of the relations between Δ and T, corresponding to certain assigned types of variation of v with r.

We shall take the Earth model to be such that at most points of its interior, v is slowly increasing as r decreases, and the rate of change of v is changing only slowly; and that this set of circumstances holds in particular in the vicinity of the outer surface. By (16) it follows that for such behaviour of v which we shall call 'ordinary', ζ is negative and moderate in value, and $d\zeta/dr$ and $d\xi/dr$ small; in particular ζ_0 is negative; also $d\eta/dr$ is positive.

We shall examine the changes in Δ and T for a given family of rays as the angle of incidence i_0 at the outer surface decreases steadily between $\frac{1}{2}\pi$ and zero. Simultaneously, by virtue of the relation (see (1))

$$p = \eta_0 \sin i_0, \tag{20}$$

it follows that p decreases steadily between η_0 and zero. When $i_0 = \frac{1}{2}\pi$, Δ and T are of course both zero.

7.3.1. Since ζ_0 is negative and p is equal to η_0 when Δ is zero, it follows by (13) and (18) that for small values of Δ, X is large and positive. On the other hand, Y is found to be small for rays that do not penetrate deeply, owing to the smallness of $d\xi/dr$ and the small-ness of the relevant range of integration. Thus for small Δ, $d\Delta/dp$ is large and negative. Hence, by (2), $d^2T/d\Delta^2$ is negative, tending to 0 for small Δ; and hence (assuming a power series expansion to exist)

$$T = \eta_0\Delta - a\Delta^3, \tag{21}$$

approximately, where a is a positive constant.

A useful alternative to (21) comes directly from (18). If Y is small compared with X, we have approximately

$$\frac{d\Delta}{dp} = -\xi_0(\eta_0^2 - p^2)^{-\frac{1}{2}}.$$

Since $p = \eta_0$ when $\Delta = 0$, this gives

$$\Delta = \xi_0 \cos^{-1}(p/\eta_0);$$

and hence by (2) $$T = \eta_0\xi_0 \sin(\Delta/\xi_0). \tag{22}$$

Also, from (19), $$T = \xi_0(\eta_0^2 - p^2)^{\frac{1}{2}}.$$

The formula (22) is exact when $Y = 0$, i.e. by (18), when ξ is constant $(= \xi_0)$, and of course agrees with (21) so far as the third power in an expansion in powers of Δ. It is specially useful in that, by (13), it corresponds to a velocity distribution given by the simple law
$$v = ar^b, \tag{23}$$

where a and b are constants (actually $b = \zeta_0$).

7.3.2. When i_0 is zero, p is zero by (20). By (2) it then follows that for rays that pass near the Earth model's centre, for which by (1) p is a little greater than zero,

$$T = a - b(\pi - \Delta)^2, \tag{24}$$

approximately, where a and b are positive constants.

7.3.3. Now suppose that in the vicinity of a certain level there is a marked increase in the rate of increase of velocity with increase of depth. More precisely, suppose that (i) $X > Y$, i.e. $d\Delta/dp < 0$, for rays whose deepest points are just above the level in question; (ii) the behaviour of v is ordinary just above this level, while just below, the variation of v is such that ζ decreases rapidly as the depth increases, becoming rapidly large (and negative); (iii) as the depth further increases v soon resumes ordinary behaviour.

If the rate of change of ζ in connection with (ii) and (iii) is sufficiently great, it is evident from (18) that Y will exceed X for a range of values of p. Accordingly, $d\Delta/dp$ will become positive for this range, and circumstances will be as illustrated in Fig. 25 (a). The associated features of the (T, Δ) relation may then be inferred after the manner indicated in Fig. 25 (b) and (c); in (a), (b) and (c), the points A, A', A'', etc., correspond. The features include the

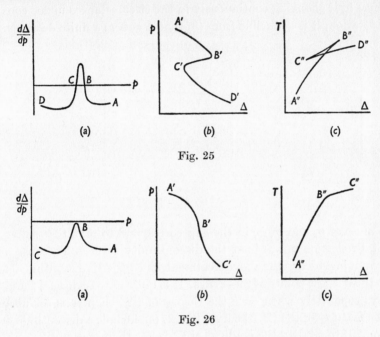

(a)   (b)   (c)

Fig. 25

(a)   (b)   (c)

Fig. 26

presence of cusps at B'' and C'', triplication of the pulse over a range of values of Δ, and upward curvature of the portion $B''C''$ of the travel-time curve (c).

7.3.4. If the velocity variation in the vicinity of another level is similar to that described in § 7.3.3, except that the rate of change of ζ falls just a little short of the amount needed to make Y exceed X, $d\Delta/dp$ nearly but not quite reaches the zero value. In this case, circumstances are as illustrated in Fig. 26. There is now no triplication, but the (T, Δ) curve has a considerable curvature in the vicinity of the appropriate value of Δ.

7.3.5. The case in which there is a discontinuity surface across which v increases by a finite amount from above to below, the behaviour on both sides of the surface being ordinary, may be deduced from the case of § 7.3.3. The forms of the corresponding curves are illustrated in Fig. 27. In the graph (b), Δ suffers a finite diminution in value from B' to C', owing to the finite decrease in r/v across the discontinuity surface, which entails a finite decrease in p; tince r_p is changing continuously in the circumstances under consideration, it is deducible from (8) that Δ suffers a finite decrease.

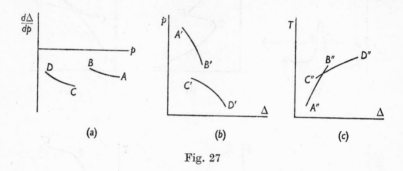

Fig. 27

(Values of p, and of i_0, in the gap correspond to rays that suffer sotal reflection upwards at the discontinuity surface. These rays are not included in the above treatment, since $dr/d\theta$ is discontinuous at the deepest points of these rays. It is quite easy to discuss these rays separately when once the theory of this chapter is set up.) The features of the (T, Δ) curve, Fig. 27 (c), include a discontinuity from B'' to C''; and the gradient at C'' is less than that at B''.

7.3.6. Next suppose that in the vicinity of another level the velocity decreases with increase of depth. More precisely, suppose that (i) $X > Y$, i.e. $d\Delta/dp < 0$, for rays whose deepest points are just above this level; (ii) the behaviour of v is ordinary just above this level, while just below, a decrease of velocity sets in which causes ζ to increase with increase of depth for some distance; (iii) as the depth further increases, ζ soon reaches a maximum and then rapidly decreases until the velocity resumes ordinary behaviour.

If the rate of decrease of velocity is such that ζ reaches the value $+1$, the integral in (18) diverges, and it is evident that there is a discontinuity in Δ as p continuously decreases. At the level, L_1 say, where ζ first passes through the value unity, $d\eta/dr$ is zero and decreasing (as the depth increases); just below this level η will therefore increase until, corresponding to (iii), ζ returns through the value $+1$; subsequently, if the further behaviour of v is ordinary, η will decrease in value until in due course it regains at some lower level, L_2 say, its value at L_1. On considering changes in the parameter p, i.e. η_p, it is evident from (12) that no ray of the family can have its deepest point between the levels L_1 and L_2, and that r_p, Δ and T suffer discontinuous changes.

On account of the divergence of the integral in (18) in this case, a full analytical discussion would require some modification of the formulae (18) and (19). Here we shall examine (in § 7.3.8) only the extreme case of discontinuity in the velocity.

7.3.7. If the velocity variation in the vicinity of some level is as n the case of § 7.3.6, except that the changes are not quite sufficient for ζ to reach the value $+1$, the effect is merely that $d\Delta/dp$ (which remains negative) is somewhat increased in magnitude for a range of values of p. It is easy to show, by inference similar to that in § 7.3.4, that this case entails a diminution in the curvature of the (T, Δ) curve for a range of values of Δ; the curve may become nearly straight.

7.3.8. We now discuss the case in which there is a discontinuity surface, $r = r_1$ say, across which v decreases by a finite amount from above or below. We now need to separate the contributions to $d\Delta/dp$ arising from the regions above and below this surface; we shall use the suffix a to indicate values of variables just above, and b for values just below. For rays that penetrate below the level $r = r_1$ we now obtain that $d\Delta/dp = -X + Y$, where

$$X = \xi_0(\eta_0^2 - p^2)^{-\frac{1}{2}} - \xi_a(\eta_a^2 - p^2)^{-\frac{1}{2}} + \xi_b(\eta_b^2 - p^2)^{-\frac{1}{2}}, \qquad (25)$$

$$Y = \int_{\xi_1}^{\xi_0} + \int_{\xi_p}^{\xi_1} (\eta^2 - p^2)^{-\frac{1}{2}} d\xi. \qquad (26)$$

Since $v_b < v_a$, we have $\eta_b > \eta_a$; if below the level $r = r_1$ the behaviour of v is ordinary for sufficient distance, η decreases as the depth increases until at a lower level, $r = r_2$ say, η regains the value

η_a. It follows that the given discontinuity in velocity entails a discontinuous increase in Y of amount

$$\int_{\xi_2}^{\xi_1} (\eta^2 - \eta_a^2)^{-\frac{1}{2}} d\xi. \tag{27}$$

The integral (27) is convergent and its value is moderate. On the other hand, the second term on the right-hand side of (25) is large for the highest rays which penetrate below the level $r = r_1$ (since p is nearly equal to η_a for these rays), while the first and third terms of (25) are moderate. It follows that as p decreases steadily through the value η_a, $d\Delta/dp$ changes suddenly to a large positive value. As p further decreases, the second term in (25) rapidly

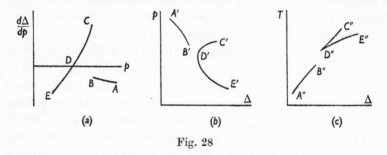

Fig. 28

diminishes to a moderate value, and so $d\Delta/dp$ soon returns to a value comparable with its value for rays just above the level $r = r_1$. If the behaviour of v below the level $r = r_1$ continues to be ordinary for a sufficiently large increase in depth, $d\Delta/dp$ will in due course become negative again. This follows from the fact that for rays of the family which pass near the centre of the model, p is small (and positive), and must by (24) obey the approximate relation

$$p = 2b(\pi - \Delta),$$

where $b > 0$.

The set of circumstances described is illustrated in Fig. 28, and the corresponding form of the (T, Δ) relation deduced. It will be noticed that there is a gap in the values of Δ, which would correspond to a 'shadow zone' on the surface of the Earth model. Also, as p continually decreases, the subsequent values of Δ pass through a minimum value at D'', analogously to the minimum deviation of a ray of light through a prism or lens.

For points near D in Fig. 28(a) we may write

$$\frac{d\Delta}{dp} \approx \alpha(p - \beta),$$

where α is the gradient and β the value of p at D. This relation gives

$$\Delta \approx \tfrac{1}{2}\alpha(p - \beta)^2 + \gamma,$$

where γ is constant; and using (2) we deduce that for points near D'' in Fig. 28(c),

$$T - T_1 = a(\Delta - \Delta_1) \pm b(\Delta - \Delta_1)^{\frac{3}{2}}, \tag{28}$$

where a and b are constants, and T_1, Δ_1 are the values of T, Δ at the point D''. Thus near D'', the form of the (T, Δ) curve approximates to a semicubical parabola.

7.3.9. The particular cases considered in §7.3.1–7.3.8 cover the principal features of the (T, Δ) relations that are met with in the actual Earth (see chapters 12 and 13).

We notice from Figs. 25–28 that $d^2T/d\Delta^2$ is mostly negative; correspondingly by (2), $dp/d\Delta$ is then negative; then by (20), $d\Delta/di_0$ is negative and $d\Delta/de_0$ positive, where $e_0 = \tfrac{1}{2}\pi - i_0$. But $d^2T/d\Delta^2$ may sometimes be positive, as, for example, in the branch $D''C''$ in Fig. 28(c); in such cases $d\Delta/de_0$ is negative.

7.4. Derivation of the P and S velocity distributions from the (T, Δ) relations. From readings of seismograms, it is possible to derive empirical tables connecting values of T and Δ for various families of seismic rays (details will be given in chapter 10). The theory in subsections of §7.3 then enables us to infer salient features of the P and S velocity distributions in the Earth. We now set up further theory by which the detailed P and S velocity distributions can be found.

We assume that the relation between T and Δ is known for a family of rays of prescribed type in a spherically symmetrical Earth model. By (2), Δ is thus a known function of p, and vice versa.

We assume further that η decreases monotonely as r decreases in the range $r_0 \geqslant r > r'$, where r' is a particular value of r less than r_0; dashes denote values of variables at the level $r = r'$.

Then by (8), provided $p > \eta'$, we may write

$$\Delta = \int_{\eta_p}^{\eta_0} 2pr^{-1}(\eta^2 - p^2)^{-\frac{1}{2}}\frac{dr}{d\eta}\,d\eta. \tag{29}$$

The equation (29) is a form of Abel's integral equation whose solution determines η as a function of r. The equation was first investigated in seismological contexts by Herglotz, Wiechert and Bateman. The following mode of solution is due to Rasch.

Let r_1 be a value of r such that $r_0 \geqslant r_1 > r'$, and let the suffix 1 be used to denote values of variables (e.g. v_1, η_1) at the level r_1. Incidentally, $\eta_1 > \eta'$. Also, let Δ_1 be the value of Δ for the ray whose deepest point is at the level r_1.

Apply the operation
$$\int_{\eta_1}^{\eta_0} dp (p^2 - \eta_1^2)^{-\frac{1}{2}}$$
to both sides of (29); this integration ranges over rays of the family from the highest, for which $p = \eta_0$, down to the ray for which $p = \eta_1$. We obtain

$$\int_{\eta_1}^{\eta_0} \Delta (p^2 - \eta_1^2)^{-\frac{1}{2}} dp = \int_{\eta_1}^{\eta_0} dp \int_{\eta_p}^{\eta_0} 2pr^{-1}\{(p_1^2 - \eta_1^2)(\eta^2 - p^2)\}^{-\frac{1}{2}} \frac{dr}{d\eta} d\eta$$

$$= \int_{\eta_1}^{\eta_0} d\eta \int_{\eta_1}^{\eta} 2pr^{-1}\{(p^2 - \eta_1^2)(\eta^2 - p^2)\}^{-\frac{1}{2}} \frac{dr}{d\eta} dp.$$

The last step, in which the order of integration is changed, is seen on drawing the relevant (triangular) domain of integration in a graph of η against p. Integrating by parts on the left side, and integrating with regard to p on the right, we obtain, since $\eta > \eta_1$,

$$\left[\Delta \cosh^{-1}\left(\frac{p}{\eta_1}\right) \right]_{\eta_1}^{\eta_0} - \int_{\eta_1}^{\eta_0} \frac{d\Delta}{dp} \cosh^{-1}\left(\frac{p}{\eta_1}\right) dp = \int_{\eta_1}^{\eta_0} \pi r^{-1} \frac{dr}{d\eta} d\eta.$$

The first term on the left side of this expression is zero, for Δ is zero when $p = \eta_0$, while $\cosh^{-1}(p/\eta_1)$ is zero when $p = \eta_1$. Hence

$$\int_0^{\Delta_1} \cosh^{-1}\left(\frac{p}{\eta_1}\right) d\Delta = \pi \ln \left(\frac{r_0}{r_1}\right). \tag{30}$$

Now we are given that p is a known function of Δ. Also η_1 is the known value of $dT/d\Delta$ at Δ_1. Hence r_1 is found from (30) in terms of Δ_1 and so in terms of η_1 or r_1/v_1; and this process can be carried out for any r_1 in the range $r_0 \geqslant r_1 > r'$. We have thus derived a method of finding v as a function of r in the range $r_0 \geqslant r > r'$.

If we use (T, Δ) data in this way for various ray families, we can find the P and S velocities at all points down to the level at which the η concerned first starts to increase with increase of depth.

For all the cases discussed in § 7.3, excepting those in §§ 7.3.6 and 7.3.8, η decreases as the depth increases, and so the corresponding departures of v from ordinary behaviour will not affect the success of the method. It must be noted of course that when there is a loop in the (T, Δ) curve, as in the case of § 7.3.3, $d\Delta$ must be reckoned negative on the upper branch in the use of (30).

The method fails to find v below any level at which a complication of the type discussed in §§ 7.3.6 or 7.3.8 sets in; in the former of these cases $d\eta/dr$ changes sign and reaches a turning value, while in the latter η suffers a discontinuous increase as the depth increases.

The method can easily be adapted to meet the case of § 7.3.8. Suppose there is a sudden (finite) increase in η from above to below the level $r = r'$, and that η decreases monotonely between this level and a lower level $r = r''$. The procedure determines v as a function of r for $r_0 \geqslant r > r'$. Using (8) and (10) with the lower limit of integration replaced by r', it is then possible to compute, for rays which go below the level $r = r'$, the contributions to T and Δ for the portions of the path above this level. By subtraction from values in the (assumed known) (T, Δ) table, a table of values of T' against Δ' can then be drawn up, where T' and Δ' apply to the sphere $r = r'$. The velocities for $r' > r > r''$ can then be determined as before. This process is called 'stripping the Earth'.

The theory of the case of § 7.3.6 is more troublesome. This case may arise in the outermost 200 km of the Earth and also near a depth of 5000 km. Nevertheless, the method leads to fairly precisely determined velocities throughout most of the Earth.

7.4.1. Alternative method. From (18), we have

$$Y = d\Delta/dp + \xi_0(\eta_0^2 - p^2)^{-\frac{1}{2}} = d\{\Delta - \xi_0 \cos^{-1}(p/\eta_0)\}/dp, \quad (31)$$

from which values of Y in terms of p can be deduced for a family of rays when the (T, Δ) relation is given. Also by (18), we have the integral equation

$$Y = \int_{\xi_p}^{\xi_0} (\eta^2 - p^2)^{-\frac{1}{2}} d\xi, \quad (32)$$

which can be solved to yield

$$\int_0^{Y_1} (p^2 - \eta_1^2)^{\frac{1}{2}} dY = -\tfrac{1}{2}\pi(\xi_1 - \xi_0). \quad (33)$$

Hence we can take the velocity law (23), or $\xi = \xi_0$, as a first approximation to a sought velocity distribution, and use (33) to compute corrections $\xi - \xi_0$ to ξ_0 at various depths, Y being a known function of p. The method is effective over wide ranges of depth in parts of the Earth, and is specially powerful where (22) gives a moderately good approximation to the (T, Δ) values. For details of this method, and further developments, see papers of Bullen (1960–1).

7.5. Special velocity distributions. We now obtain an expression for the curvature at any point of a seismic ray as a preliminary to considering useful model velocity distributions.

7.5.1. Curvature of a seismic ray. Let ρ be the upward radius of curvature at the point P of a seismic ray (see Fig. 24, p. 111). Then $\rho = -r\,dr/dq$, where q is the perpendicular from O to the tangent at P to the ray. Since, by (1), $q = pv$, we then have

$$\rho = -\frac{r}{p}\frac{dr}{dv}. \tag{34}$$

It is an immediate consequence of (34) that for a family of rays of given (i.e. P or S) type, the curvature at any fixed level is proportional to p. It follows further from (1) that $\rho \sin i$ is constant at a fixed level for a given family of rays, being equal to $-v\,dr/dv$.

From the formula for curvature in polar coordinates, or independently, using (1), (5) and (34), we can show that

$$\rho \sin^3 i = -\left\{\frac{d^2}{d\theta^2}\left(\frac{1}{r}\right) + \frac{1}{r}\right\}^{-1}. \tag{35}$$

7.5.2. Rays in a homogeneous medium. The particular case of (34) where v is constant for a range of values of r gives $\rho = \infty$, and hence (of course) that the rays are rectilinear in the corresponding region. Thus for a homogeneous Earth model, we have by (13) $\zeta = 0$, and thence, putting $\xi_0 = 2$ in (22), the (T, Δ) relation

$$T = 2\frac{r_0}{v_0}\sin\frac{\Delta}{2}; \tag{36}$$

the relation (36) is, of course, readily established directly.

7.5.3. Circular rays; the law $v = a - br^2$. By (34), it follows that if v satisfies the law

$$v = a - br^2, \tag{37}$$

the rays are circles of radii $(2pb)^{-1}$. The law (37) has frequently been used in approximate investigations concerning the region of the Earth just below the outer layers. The corresponding relation between T and Δ is most conveniently expressed in parametric form, the parameter used for this purpose being the angle i_0 used earlier in this chapter. In Fig. 29 we have drawn a particular ray of the series whose parameter is p say; K is the centre of the (circular) path of this ray. In the triangle OP_0K, we have $OP_0 = r_0$, $KP_0 = (2pb)^{-1}$, the angle $KOP_0 = \tfrac{1}{2}\Delta$, and the angle $OP_0K = \tfrac{1}{2}\pi + i_0$; hence the angle $OKP_0 = \tfrac{1}{2}\pi - \tfrac{1}{2}\Delta - i_0$. Therefore

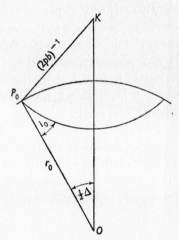

Fig. 29

$$2pb\sin\tfrac{1}{2}\Delta = r_0^{-1}\cos(\tfrac{1}{2}\Delta + i_0).$$

But by (20)

$$p = r_0 v_0^{-1}\sin i_0.$$

Eliminating p and using (37), we obtain

$$\Delta = 2\tan^{-1}(\cot i_0/\lambda), \tag{38}$$

where

$$1 + \lambda = 2a/v_0. \tag{39}$$

By (2), (1) and (38),

$$dT = p\,d\Delta$$

$$= -\frac{r_0\sin i_0}{v_0}\frac{2\lambda}{\lambda^2 + \cot^2 i_0}\operatorname{cosec}^2 i_0\,di_0.$$

Hence

$$T = \frac{r_0}{v_0\sqrt{(\lambda^2-1)}}\ln\frac{\lambda + \sqrt{(\lambda^2-1)}\cos i_0}{\lambda - \sqrt{(\lambda^2-1)}\cos i_0}. \tag{40}$$

By (38) and (40)

$$T = \frac{2r_0}{v_0\sqrt{(\lambda^2-1)}}\ln\left[\sqrt{(\lambda^2-1)}\sin\tfrac{1}{2}\Delta + \sqrt{\{(\lambda^2-1)\sin^2\tfrac{1}{2}\Delta + 1\}}\right]; \tag{41}$$

(39) and (41) connect T with Δ.

7.5.4. The law $v = ar^b$. This law is the relation (23), already established in § 7.3.1. It is specially powerful because of the simple form (22) of the corresponding (T, Δ) relation. It includes the case of constant v (§ 7.5.2), but is more flexible through having the two adjustable parameters η_0 and ξ_0, and in fact provides a close approximation to the actual velocity variation over particular ranges of depth in the Earth. Further, where the approximation is not adequate, corrections can be derived after the manner indicated in § 7.4.1. A limitation of the law is that it entails $v \to \infty$ as $r \to 0$ (assuming ζ_0 negative), so that the law is not serviceable where r/r_0 is small.

An important analysis of ray theory was made by Slichter in 1932, containing a quantity of information supplementary to that given above. Other authors who have made significant contributions include Lehmann and Gutenberg.

CHAPTER 8

AMPLITUDES OF THE SURFACE MOTION DUE TO SEISMIC WAVES IN A SPHERIC- ALLY STRATIFIED EARTH MODEL

We continue to set up theory relevant to an Earth model symmetrical about its centre. As in chapter 7, we let r denote the distance of any point from the centre, v the speed of a particular wave at this point and $\eta = r/v$ (equation (7, (7)); we shall again use the suffix 0 to denote values which variables take at the outer surface of the model.

We shall now investigate certain effects at the outer surface of the model following the occurrence of a disturbance initially confined to a small region inside the model; and shall for simplicity treat this region as a point F which we shall refer to as the focus. We shall assume that energy is sent out in all directions symmetrically from F, and proceed to investigate the amplitudes produced at the outer surface as a result of the bodily elastic waves transmitted from F. We shall assume that conditions permit us to make use of the ray theory set up in chapter 7, and that discontinuity surfaces inside the model will be sufficiently distant from F to permit us to use the plane-wave theory of reflection and refraction set up in chapter 6.

In the earlier sections of the present chapter, we shall give a simplified theory which ignores any energy losses that a particular wave may suffer between F and points of the outer surface of the model. The derivation of the necessary correcting factors arising from such energy losses will be discussed in §§ 8.5, 8.6.

In § 8.8 we shall refer to the amplitudes of surface seismic waves.

8.1. Energy per unit area of wave front in an emerging wave. Consider a wave of a particular type (e.g. dilatational) which leaves F and travels to the outer surface all the way in the same type. Let I denote the energy in this type emitted per unit solid angle from F, and let e_1 be the angle which any ray leaving F makes with the level surface of the model through F. Then the energy conveyed along all the rays for which e lies in a particular range, e_1 to $e_1 + de_1$ say, is $2\pi I \cos e_1 de_1$; we take de_1 to be positive.

Now the area of that part of the outer surface of the model containing points whose angular distances (i.e. angles subtended at the model's centre) from F lie between Δ and $\Delta + d\Delta$ is

$$2\pi r_0^2 \sin \Delta \, |d\Delta|.$$

(The modulus of $d\Delta$ is used in this formula since $d\Delta$ and de_1 can sometimes be of opposite signs—see §7.3.9.) It follows that the area of that part of a particular wave front which emerges at the outer surface between these distances is $2\pi r_0^2 \sin \Delta \sin e_0 \, |d\Delta|$, where e_0 is the angle of emergence.

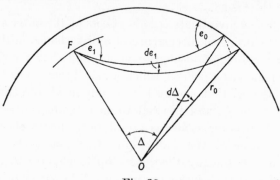

Fig. 30

We deduce therefore that arising from the above disturbance leaving F, the energy $E(\Delta)$ per unit area of the portion of the wave front emerging at the angle e_0 is given by

$$E(\Delta) = \frac{I}{r_0^2} \frac{\cos e_1}{\sin \Delta \sin e_0} \left| \frac{de_1}{d\Delta} \right|, \tag{1}$$

where the range e_1 to $e_1 + de_1$ corresponds to the range Δ to $\Delta + d\Delta$.

If T is the travel time from F corresponding to the distance Δ, we have by (7, (1)) and (7, (2))

$$\eta_1 \cos e_1 = \eta_0 \cos e_0 = dT/d\Delta, \tag{2}$$

where η_1 and η_0 are the values of η at F and at the outer surface. By (2) we have

$$-\eta_1 \sin e_1 \frac{de_1}{d\Delta} = \frac{d^2T}{d\Delta^2}.$$

Hence $$\frac{\cos e_1}{\sin e_0}\left|\frac{de_1}{d\Delta}\right| = \frac{\cot e_1}{\eta_1 \sin e_0}\left|\frac{d^2T}{d\Delta^2}\right|$$

$$= \frac{\eta_0}{\eta_1}(\eta_1^2 \tan^2 e_0 - \eta_0^2 \sin^2 e_0)^{-\frac{1}{2}}\left|\frac{d^2T}{d\Delta^2}\right|, \qquad (3)$$

using (2) again.

We shall shortly be taking into account reflections which the wave must suffer at the outer surface of the model, and shall quote formulae obtained in chapter 6. It will therefore be convenient for us now to denote the angle of emergence at the outer surface of the model by the symbol e instead of e_0. We may then by (1) and (3) express $E(\Delta)$ in the form

$$E(\Delta) = \frac{I\eta_0}{r_0^2 \eta_1 \sin \Delta}(\eta_1^2 \tan^2 e - \eta_0^2 \sin^2 e)^{-\frac{1}{2}}\left|\frac{d^2T}{d\Delta^2}\right|. \qquad (4)$$

8.2. Relation between energy and amplitude. Consider an advancing P or S wave, and let w be the energy per unit volume over a region such that the material can be treated as uniform within it (we exclude complications due to diffraction). Then by (3, (65))

$$\frac{\partial w}{\partial t} + \frac{\partial}{\partial x_j}(wv_j) = 0, \qquad (5)$$

where v_j is the wave velocity. By (2, (47)) we may to sufficient accuracy, neglecting the external forces X_i, write

$$\frac{\partial w}{\partial t} = \frac{\partial}{\partial x_j}\left(p_{ij}\frac{\partial u_i}{\partial t}\right). \qquad (6)$$

By (5) and (6) we have

$$\frac{\partial}{\partial x_j}\left(wv_j + p_{ij}\frac{\partial u_i}{\partial t}\right) = 0. \qquad (7)$$

For a plane wave advancing parallel to the x_1-axis, we find from (7) that at any particular instant

$$wv_1 = -p_{i1}\frac{\partial u_i}{\partial t}, \qquad (8)$$

the integration constant being taken as zero.

We shall apply (8) to the particular case in which the waves are plane simple harmonic SH waves, the displacement being given by

$$u_i = (0, C\cos\{\kappa(x_1 - \beta t)\}, 0),$$

where C is the amplitude, $2\pi/\kappa$ is the wave-length and β is the wave velocity; thus $v_i = (\beta, 0, 0)$. By $(2, (32))$ and $(2, (13))$ we have

$$p_{12} = p_{21} = 2\mu e_{21} = \mu \frac{\partial u_2}{\partial x_1} = -\mu\kappa C \sin\{\kappa(x_1 - \beta t)\},$$

all the other p_{ij} being zero. Substituting into (8) we obtain

$$w = \mu\kappa^2 C^2 \sin^2\{\kappa(x_1 - \beta t)\}. \tag{9}$$

(We note that (9) can be independently derived using $(2, (54))$ and the fact (§ 3.3.6) that w is twice the strain energy per unit volume.) Integrating (9) over one wave-length, i.e. over the range

$$0 \leqslant x_1 \leqslant 2\pi/\kappa,$$

we find that the energy E, per unit area normal to the x_1-axis, in one wave-length is equal to $\pi\mu\kappa C^2$; i.e. by $(3, (40))$ and $(4, (5))$,

$$E = 2\pi^2 \rho\lambda C^2/\tau^2, \tag{10}$$

where λ is the wave-length, τ is the period of the wave, and ρ is the density of the medium.

It follows from (10) that the mean energy per unit length in a train of waves is proportional to the square of the amplitude, and inversely proportional to the square of the period.

Formulae similar to (10) may be likewise derived for the case of P and SV simple harmonic plane waves.

8.3. Movements of the outer surface arising from an incident wave of given amplitude.

We now consider the amplitudes of the vibrations of surface particles of the Earth model arising from various waves incident from below. It will be sufficiently accurate here to neglect the curvature of the outer surface, and so to make direct use of formulae obtained in chapter 6 for cases of plane waves incident against a plane boundary. We shall again assume that Poisson's relation holds for the material just below the outer surface, and so have e and f (as defined in chapter 6) connected by the relation $(6, (13))$, namely,

$$\cos^2 e = 3 \cos^2 f. \tag{11}$$

We shall first consider the case of an incident P wave emerging at the angle e. We may represent this near the outer surface (using the notation of § 6.4) by

$$\phi = A_0 \exp\{\iota\kappa(x_3 \tan e + x_1 - ct)\}, \tag{12}$$

and the reflected P and S waves by

$$\phi = A \exp\{\iota\kappa(-x_3 \tan e + x_1 - ct)\}, \tag{13}$$

$$\psi = B \exp\{\iota\kappa(-x_3 \tan f + x_1 - ct)\}, \tag{14}$$

respectively. The ratios A/A_0, B/A_0 are then obtained from (6, (14)), f being determined from e using (11). By (12), (13), (14) and (5, (1)) we see that the components of the incident and the two reflected waves are given at the surface by

$$u_i = (\iota\kappa A_0, 0, \iota\kappa A_0 \tan e) \exp\{\iota\kappa(x_1 - ct)\},$$
$$u_i = (\iota\kappa A, 0, -\iota\kappa A \tan e) \exp\{\iota\kappa(x_1 - ct)\},$$
$$u_i = (-\iota\kappa B \tan f, 0, -\iota\kappa B) \exp\{\iota\kappa(x_1 - ct)\},$$

respectively. Hence the ratio of the horizontal component, A_h say, of the amplitude of the motion of the outer surface to the amplitude, A_k say, of the incident wave alone is $(A_0 + A - B \tan f)/A_0 \sec e$. By (6, (14)) we then deduce that

$$\frac{A_h}{A_k} = \frac{12 \sin e \sec^2 e \tan f}{4 \tan e \tan f + (1 + 3 \tan^2 e)^2}. \tag{15}$$

Similarly, the corresponding ratio for the vertical component, A_v say, is found to be given by

$$\frac{A_v}{A_k} = \frac{6 \sin e \sec^2 e (1 + 3 \tan^2 e)}{4 \tan e \tan f + (1 + 3 \tan^2 e)^2}. \tag{16}$$

If the ratio $A_v : A_h$ be denoted by $\tan \bar{e}$, we have by (15) and (16)

$$\tan \bar{e} = \frac{A_v}{A_h} = \frac{1 + 3 \tan^2 e}{2 \tan f}. \tag{17}$$

The angle $\bar{e}$ has been called the *apparent angle of emergence*, and from (11) and (17) we find by elementary trigonometry the relation

$$2 \cos^2 e = 3(1 - \sin \bar{e}), \tag{18}$$

connecting the actual and apparent angles of emergence of P waves incident at the outer surface. In obtaining (18) we have, for ease of

9

calculation, assumed Poisson's relation (4, (7)) to hold. But it is not difficult to show that in the general case

$$2\cos^2 e = \frac{\alpha^2}{\beta^2}(1 - \sin \bar{e}),$$

where α, β are the relevant P, S velocities; this relation was first obtained by Wiechert.

In a similar way, using formulae in § 6.5, we may derive formulae corresponding to (15), (16), (17) and (18) for the case of SV waves incident at the outer surface.

In the case of incident SH waves, the amplitude of the surface earth movement is twice that of the incident waves. This follows immediately from (6, (4)) and the last paragraph of § 6.3.

8.4. Amplitude as a function of Δ.

If, following a particular initial disturbance, A_h and A_v were sufficiently accurately estimated as functions of Δ (for a particular pulse, assumed simple harmonic), we could by (17) and (18) compute $\bar{e}$, and then e, as functions of Δ. Since $\eta_0 \cos e = dT/d\Delta$ (i.e. equation (2) written in the present notation), we could then compute $(\eta_0)^{-1} dT/d\Delta$ in terms of Δ.

Moreover, from (4), (10), (15) and (16), we may derive

$$A_h^2 \propto \frac{4I \tan^2 e \sec^2 e \tan^2 f}{\eta_1 \sin \Delta (\eta_1^2 \tan^2 e - \eta_0^2 \sin^2 e)^{\frac{1}{2}} \{4 \tan e \tan f + (1 + 3 \tan^2 e)^2\}^2} \left|\frac{d^2T}{d\Delta^2}\right|,$$

$$\tag{19}$$

$$A_v^2 \propto \frac{I \tan^2 e \sec^2 e (1 + 3 \tan^2 e)^2}{\eta_1 \sin \Delta (\eta_1^2 \tan^2 e - \eta_0^2 \sin^2 e)^{\frac{1}{2}} \{4 \tan e \tan f + (1 + 3 \tan^2 e)^2\}^2} \left|\frac{d^2T}{d\Delta^2}\right|;$$

$$\tag{20}$$

in (19) and (20) the constant of proportionality depends on the properties of the material at the outer surface of the Earth model and on the wave-length λ and period τ of the particular pulse when approaching this outer surface. With the use of (19) or (20), it would be theoretically possible, knowing A_h or A_v as a function of Δ, and knowing η_0, to estimate η_1, i.e. the value of r/v near the focus F.

Again, the proportionality of A_h^2 and A_v^2 to $|d^2T/d\Delta^2|$ gives a possible means of using amplitude observations to check values of $|d^2T/d\Delta^2|$ as estimated from the (T, Δ) relations.

It is evident, therefore, that studies of the observed amplitude variations following earthquakes have the possibility of providing useful information on features of the P and S velocity variations within the Earth, to some extent independently of the method indicated in chapter 7. In practice, there are a number of complications in the way of applying the amplitude method to actual earthquake problems, and because of these the amplitude method gives far less precise results than the method based on direct use of travel-time data. The chief complications arise from the heterogeneous character of materials near the Earth's outer surface, and from the need for estimating energy losses associated with internal discontinuity surfaces (see § 8.5.2). Nevertheless, progress has been made in the use of amplitude observations, particularly by Gutenberg and Richter; amplitude considerations first drew attention to the existence of a discontinuity surface inside the Earth's central core (see § 13.1.3).

As simple applications of the amplitude theory, we notice by (19) and (20) that in general A_h and A_v are relatively small when $d^2T/d\Delta^2$ is small, and relatively large when $d^2T/d\Delta^2$ is large. It is easy to show that these results are in accord with results indicated from the theory of chapter 7. Thus smallness of $d^2T/d\Delta^2$, i.e. smallness of curvature in the corresponding (T, Δ) curve, was seen in § 7.3.7 to be associated with a (not too great) decrease of velocity with increase of depth over a range of depth inside the Earth model; this circumstance was in turn seen to be associated with an increased spread of values of Δ against p (and therefore against e), and therefore to imply diminished amplitudes of the surface movements for a range of values of Δ. Again, largeness of $d^2T/d\Delta^2$ was seen in § 7.3.4 to correspond to a fairly rapid increase of velocity with increase of depth over a range of depth, and this was seen to be associated with a decreased spread of values of Δ against p, and hence with increased surface amplitudes for a range of values of Δ. Thus when markedly increased amplitudes are detected over a particular small range of values of Δ, there is a likelihood that the velocity increases markedly over a corresponding small range of depth. Because of the complexities mentioned, it is, however, necessary to check from other evidence that this is in fact the cause of the increased amplitudes.

8.5. Loss of energy during transmission through the medium.
So far we have ignored possible energy losses during wave transmission. There will be some loss due to possible departures from
perfect elasticity, but, as pointed out in § 4.5.1, such losses are very
slight in the case of the actual Earth. The main energy losses will
arise from heterogeneity of the medium, including particularly
the effects of energy partitioning at discontinuity surfaces.

8.5.1. We consider first the case in which the three parameters
specifying the elastic properties and density of a (perfectly elastic)
medium vary fairly gradually; more precisely, we suppose that there
is a large number n of thin homogeneous layers, the fractional
changes in the parameters from layer to layer being of the order of
$1/n$. By the use of formulae obtained in chapter 6, Jeffreys has
shown that in general, for any particular wave (P, SV, or SH)
encountering a boundary between a pair of the layers, all but the
order of $1/n^2$ of the incident energy is transmitted in the same type.
For instance, in the case of SH waves incident at the angle $\frac{1}{2}\pi - f$
against a boundary separating a pair of layers M, M', whose
properties are as defined in § 5.1, we have by (6, (8))

$$\frac{C}{C_0} = \left(1 - \frac{\mu' \tan f'}{\mu \tan f}\right)\left(1 + \frac{\mu' \tan f'}{\mu \tan f}\right)^{-1}. \tag{21}$$

If we put $\mu' = (1+\delta)\mu$ and $\tan f' = (1+\epsilon)\tan f$, and take δ and ϵ
to be of the order of $1/n$, we obtain

$$C/C_0 \approx \{1 - (1+\delta+\epsilon)\}\{1 + (1+\delta+\epsilon)\}^{-1}$$
$$\approx \tfrac{1}{2}(\delta+\epsilon);$$

hence $(C/C_0)^2 = O(1/n^2)$. Thus the energy loss in the transmitted
wave of the same type after passing through the n layers is in
general only of the order of $1/n$ of the original energy, which is
quite trifling when n is large.

A first exception formally arises where the wave makes nearly
grazing incidence with one of the boundaries. (In the case of SH
waves, f is then nearly equal to $\frac{1}{2}\pi$ and it no longer follows that we
can write $\tan f' = (1+\epsilon)\tan f$ with ϵ of the order of $1/n$.) A second
exception arises if the wave-length is so great as to be comparable
with the distance over which there is an accumulated finite change
in the values of the parameters describing properties of the medium;

there will then be an appreciable fraction of energy lost to derived waves. (The second exception approximates to the circumstances at a single surface of finite discontinuity.)

8.5.2. We now consider the effect of a single finite discontinuity surface inside the Earth model, and take first the case of an incident SH wave. With our usual notation, it then follows that the transmitted energy is $\{1 - (C/C_0)^2\}$ times the incident energy, where C/C_0 is given by (21). A factor of the form $\{1 - (C/C_0)^2\}$ is called an energy *transmission factor*, and will need to be applied for each discontinuity surface that the wave traverses. Such factors will therefore in practice need to be applied to the right-hand sides of expressions such as (19) and (20) before these formulae may be used to interpret the actual amplitude variations observed at the outer surface.

The case of an incident P wave is more complicated than that of an incident SH wave. Consider a P wave incident at the angle $\frac{1}{2}\pi - e$ against the (plane) discontinuity surface separating two media M and M'. By an extension of the argument in § 6.4, it is possible to derive an expression for the ratio A/A_0 in terms of e, where A_0 and A are relevant to the medium M and analogous to the A_0 and A in (12) and (13). (This involves the use of equations analogous to (13) and (14) for the medium M', in addition to the first two of the equations (6, (12)) of § 6.4.) The precise result is algebraically complicated, but use may be made of the experience of Knott who computed numerical values of the ratio A/A_0 for various given values of e for particular media whose parameters have certain assigned values not greatly different in the two media. The results of Knott indicate that when the media are not greatly different, an incident P wave is reflected and refracted mainly into P waves, the reflected and refracted SV waves containing only a small fraction of the total energy involved (an analogous result holds also for an incident SV wave). Jeffreys has accordingly assumed that a satisfactory first approximation to A/A_0 may be obtained by disregarding the reflected and refracted SV waves, and on this assumption obtained the approximate formula

$$\frac{A}{A_0} \approx \left(\frac{\rho'}{\rho} - \frac{\tan e'}{\tan e}\right) \bigg/ \left(\frac{\rho'}{\rho} + \frac{\tan e'}{\tan e}\right). \tag{22}$$

The appropriate transmission factor in this case is thus approximately given by $\{1 - (A/A_0)\}^2$, where A/A_0 is given by (22).

The corresponding formula for an incident SV wave is less simple than (22), but certain particular numerical calculations of Knott indicate broadly similar results to the P case.

In practice, a further transmission factor is sometimes applied to the amplitude formulae in order to allow for possible energy losses through friction and scattering (see § 4.5.1).

It may be remarked that there are special difficulties connected with the study of amplitudes of waves arising from 'near earthquakes' (see § 9.8), for which the distance Δ does not exceed about 10°. These difficulties are associated with present inadequate knowledge of features of the transition from layer to layer in the outer part of the Earth (see § 12.2). The effects of varying degrees of sharpness of discontinuities on the transmission and reflection of seismic waves in relation to the incident wave-lengths have been discussed in some detail by Jeffreys and by Sezawa and Kanai.

8.6. Waves which suffer reflection or change of type.

In all the preceding sections, we have investigated the energy conveyed only in waves which have been transmitted without change in type from a focus F to the outer surface of the Earth model, and which have not been reflected at any discontinuity surface. There will, of course, be other waves arriving at the outer surface which have suffered reflection at one or more surfaces of discontinuity (including both internal discontinuity surfaces and the outer free surface itself), and which may have changed type when reflected or refracted. The formulae (19) and (20) are still relevant to the case of a wave finally emerging in the P type, if I and η_1 be taken now to correspond to the energy and velocity (P or S) in the type which the wave in question had on leaving F. It is necessary as before to work out transmission factors corresponding to each encounter with a discontinuity surface, and to apply these transmission factors to the right-hand sides of (19) and (20). The method follows the same principles as in the preceding sections, but it is evident that the results will be much more complicated. Similar remarks apply to waves emerging in the SV type. In the case of a

wave emerging as *SH*, the algebra is rather simpler, since an *SH*
wave does not change in type on reflection or refraction

8.7. Amplitudes corresponding to cusps in (T, Δ) curves.

Rapid or sudden changes in the variation of the velocity v with the
depth z can result in cusps in the corresponding (T, Δ) curves,
examples being the curves shown in Figs. 25(c) and 28(c) of §§ 7.3.3,
7.3.8. It has commonly been assumed that such cusps are associated
with abnormally large amplitudes, but the writer (1960) has shown
that this is by no means always the case.

For the case of § 7.3.3, where v is a continuous function of z
while dv/dz increases markedly in the vicinity of a certain depth,
let C'', D'', as in Fig. 25(c), denote the cusps at the smaller and
greater Δ, respectively. It transpires that when the change in
dv/dz takes the form of a simple discontinuous increase, there will
be large amplitudes at C'' but not at D''. The reason is that while
C'' corresponds to an ordinary minimum in p (i.e. $dT/d\Delta$) against
Δ, it is found that D'' corresponds to a node-point maximum.
Abnormally large amplitudes occur where $d\Delta/de$ is abnormally
small, and therefore where $d\Delta/dp$ is abnormally small, since by
$(7, (1))$ p is proportional to $\cos e$, e being the angle of emergence at
the surface. Since $d\Delta/dp$ vanishes at C'', but not at D'', the cusp
C'' is associated with large amplitudes, while in general D'' is not.

On the other hand, it is possible to have large amplitudes at
both cusps, if there is fairly sudden change in dv/dz spread over a
small but finite range of depth. In this case, v and dv/dz are continuous, but d^2v/dz^2 may be discontinuous.

In the case of § 7.3.5, where v increases discontinuously with z,
the (T, Δ) curve (Fig. 27(c)) takes the form shown in Fig. 25(c) if
the branch $C''D''$ be added to include rays totally reflected at the
discontinuity surface. For this case, it can be shown that in
general the amplitudes are not abnormally large at either cusp.

These various results show that what may appear to be quite
minor changes in details of a velocity distribution can affect the
associated variation of amplitude with Δ at the surface quite
radically. The results emphasise the dangers in attempting to
infer velocity values from amplitude data alone.

For the case of § 7.3.8, where there is a sudden diminution in v at a certain depth, the theory gives large amplitudes at the cusp D'' (Fig. 28 (c)).

8.8. Amplitudes of surface seismic waves.

We have seen that when a focus F is not too deep, sizeable surface waves will be generated and will spread outwards over the outer surface. It is sufficiently accurate for ordinary problems on surface waves to neglect the curvature of the Earth's outer surface, and we have seen in § 3.5 that when there is no dispersion the amplitudes will then be inversely proportional to the square root of the distance from the source when the distance is appreciable. There is, however, the further effect of dispersion to be taken into account.

In § 3.3.5.1 we obtained the approximate formula (3, (57)) for the displacement, in the vicinity of a given place x and time t, due to the passage of a wave disturbance subject to dispersion of the type that occurs with surface seismic waves (in § 3.3.5 only the case of plane waves was discussed, but this is sufficiently indicative of dispersion effects at appreciable distances from the source). In seismology, observations are made of the whole train of local earth movements (following any earthquake) at particular observing stations, and it is convenient, following Jeffreys, to replace (3, (57)) by a related asymptotic approximation which is better suited to these circumstances, namely,

$$y_r(x, t) = \frac{f(\gamma_r)}{\sqrt{[\tfrac{1}{2}\pi \,|\, (d^2\kappa/d\gamma^2)_r|\, x]}} \cos (\kappa_r x - \gamma_r t \pm \tfrac{1}{4}\pi), \qquad (23)$$

where $f(\gamma_r)$ is analogous to $\phi(\kappa_r)$. The coefficient of the cosine factor in (23) indicates the amplitude to be expected on the theory here given. The distance x appears only in the factor $x^{-\frac{1}{2}}$, which is common to all the wave groups. Thus the ratios of the amplitudes of waves of given periods would on this theory be the same at all places on the Earth's outer surface. Apart from the factor $x^{-\frac{1}{2}}$, the amplitude would vary from wave group to wave group in a way depending on the form of the initial disturbance and on the detailed character of the dispersion.

CHAPTER 9

THE PRINCIPLE OF THE SEISMOGRAPH

The purpose of the seismograph is to record as many useful details as possible concerning the nature of the earth movement in the vicinity of a particular point of the Earth's surface following an earthquake.

The most general type of local movement in a material body is represented by the form (2, (11)), the terms in which correspond to translation, rotation and strain, respectively. In the case of the earth movement following an earthquake, the translation movement usually receives most attention. (Local rotation effects are sometimes significant in regions close to the region of origin of an earthquake, and are of interest in the study of earthquake effects on buildings.) Seismographs are usually constructed to record details from which translational components of the local earth movement may be inferred. As a rule, the components taken are the two horizontal components, north–south and east–west, and the vertical, or 'Z', component.

In §§ 9.1, 9.2, we shall describe ideal seismographs for measuring horizontal and vertical components, respectively, of a local earth movement. The constructional details are rather different in the two cases, but it will be seen that the same type of differential equation representing the motion of the seismograph relative to the ground is inherent in both. In later sections, we shall use this differential equation as a basis for discussing the connection between the relative motion of a seismograph and the actual motion of the ground. Finally, we shall offer some brief comments on certain other types of instruments.

Since, in a book on the theory of seismology, we are chiefly interested in the broad principle of the seismograph rather than in practical instrumental details, we shall assume that the angular displacement of the seismograph is always small, and shall ignore all small quantities of the second order. A more complete discussion of seismographs would require consideration of higher-order terms;

but we may note that as a result of such studies, it is often possible to design a seismograph in such a way that the first-order theory gives very accurate results for purposes for which the instrument is employed.

9.1. The horizontal component seismograph.

This consists in principle of a so-called horizontal pendulum, i.e. a pendulum swinging about an axis which is at a small inclination i to the

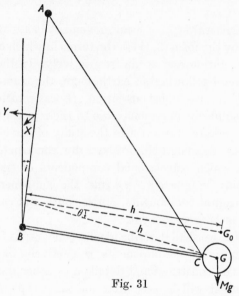

Fig. 31

vertical and which is attached to the earth as rigidly as possible. The pendulum has the form of a bar BC with a heavy mass at the end C which is connected to the axis AB at A by a light support AC (see Fig. 31); this pendulum, free to swing about AB, is the *boom*. Let M be the mass of the boom, and h the distance from AB of its centre of mass, G. The equilibrium position ABG_0 of the plane ABG is called the *neutral plane*.

During the passage of an earthquake disturbance, let the component, denoted by u, of the displacement of the ground (and hence of AB) in the direction perpendicular to the neutral plane be given by $u = f(t)$, where t denotes the time and f is any function. At any particular instant, let θ be the (assumed small) angle between the plane ABG and the neutral plane. Let X be the component, perpendicular to the neutral plane, of the resultant reaction force exerted by the axis on the pendulum, and Y the component in the neutral plane perpendicular to AB. Correct to the first order of small quantities, the horizontal displacement of G is $u + h\theta$. Hence we have

$$X = M(\ddot{u} + h\ddot{\theta}). \tag{1}$$

The weight of the boom is equivalent to $Mg \cos i$ parallel to BA, together with $Mg \sin i$ in a direction perpendicular to BA and parallel to the neutral plane. The component of the acceleration of G in the direction of Y is of the second order, and so we have, correct to the first order,

$$Y = Mgi. \tag{2}$$

Considering the rate of change of angular momentum about an axis through G parallel to AB, we have, neglecting friction forces,

$$M\kappa^2 \ddot{\theta} = -Xh - Yh\theta, \tag{3}$$

where κ is the radius of gyration of the boom about this axis. Eliminating X, Y we have

$$\kappa^2 \ddot{\theta} + ghi\theta + h\ddot{u} + h^2 \ddot{\theta} = 0,$$

i.e.

$$\ddot{\theta} + \omega^2 \theta = -\ddot{u}/l, \tag{4}$$

where $l = (\kappa^2 + h^2)/h$, the *reduced pendulum length*, and $\omega^2 = gi/l$.

As will be seen in § 9.4, it is usually desirable to arrange (by fluid or electromagnetic damping) that the pendulum of a seismograph will be subject to an appreciable friction force. We take this force to be proportional to the first power of the speed of the pendulum. The equation (4) will then need to be modified by the inclusion of a corresponding damping term, so that the equation of relative motion of the seismograph will take the form

$$\ddot{\theta} + 2\lambda\omega\dot{\theta} + \omega^2 \theta = -\ddot{u}/l, \tag{5}$$

where λ is an index of the extent of damping.

9.2. The vertical component seismograph. The principle of the seismograph used for measuring the vertical component of an earth movement is indicated in a study of the following arrangement shown in Fig. 32. A pendulum ABG can rotate about a horizontal axis through A rigidly attached to the ground. The bulk of the mass of the pendulum is in the vicinity of the centre of mass G; AB, BG

and GA are members of a light frame. We assume that adjustments have been made whereby G is level with A in the equilibrium position. The pendulum is supported at B by means of a spring BC, of natural length d say, which is rigidly attached to the ground at C, in the plane ABG. We shall for ease of calculation here neglect the mass of the spring.

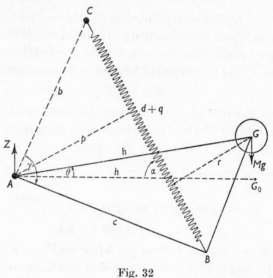

Fig. 32

Let $AB = c$, $AC = b$, $CAB = \gamma$, $AG = h$, and let p be the perpendicular from A to BC. The tension of the spring will be βq, where β is a constant of the spring and q is the extension. During the passage of the disturbance, let $u = f(t)$ be the upward vertical component of the earth displacement, let θ be the (assumed small) upward angular displacement of AG, and let Z be the upward vertical component of the resultant force exerted by the axis on the pendulum at any particular instant.

Since the vertical displacement of G is then $u + h\theta$, correct to the first order, we have on resolving vertically

$$Z + \beta q \sin \alpha - Mg = M(\ddot{u} + h\ddot{\theta}),$$

where α is the angle BC makes with the horizontal. The angular momentum principle then gives

$$M\kappa^2 \ddot{\theta} = -\beta q r - Zh,$$

approximately, where κ is the radius of gyration of the pendulum about an axis through G parallel to the axis of rotation, and r is the perpendicular from G to BC. Eliminating Z, we then obtain

$$M\kappa^2\ddot{\theta} = -Mh(\ddot{u} + h\ddot{\theta}) - Mgh + \beta q(h\sin\alpha - r)$$

$$= -Mh(\ddot{u} + h\ddot{\theta}) - Mgh + \beta pq. \tag{6}$$

Using the suffix 0 to correspond to the equilibrium position, we have, from (6), $Mgh = \beta(pq)_0$. Also, correct to the first order in θ, we have

$$pq = (pq)_0 - \left(\frac{d(pq)}{d\gamma}\right)_0 \theta.$$

Hence (6) becomes

$$M(\kappa^2 + h^2)\ddot{\theta} + \beta\left(\frac{d(pq)}{d\gamma}\right)_0 \theta = -Mh\ddot{u}.$$

If l be the reduced pendulum length, we may rewrite this equation in the form

$$\ddot{\theta} + \omega^2\theta = -\ddot{u}/l,$$

which is the same as the equation (4) obtained for the horizontal seismograph, except that ω is now a function of constants special to the vertical component seismograph. The inclusion of the frictional effect then gives the equation (5) again.

9.3. The indicator equation. In practice, the angle θ giving the relative motion of the seismographs in §§ 9.1, 9.2 is often so small that one could not measure its variation without some further instrumental device. In some seismographs this device is a system of levers attached to the pendulum which magnifies up the relative displacement θ. The magnified motion is then recorded by a pen on smoked paper on a drum which is made to rotate as uniformly as possible about an axis rigidly attached to the earth. In other seismographs use is made of a beam of light which is reflected from a mirror attached to the pendulum, and records on photographic paper on the rotating drum. The record containing the trace made by the indicator is called a *seismogram*.

The displacement, x say, of the indicator from its zero position will in simple circumstances be proportional to the angle θ, and in this case we introduce the *statical magnification* V_s, defined as the ratio $x/l\theta$. By (5) we then have

$$\ddot{x} + 2\lambda\omega\dot{x} + \omega^2 x = -V_s\ddot{u} = -V_s f''(t) \qquad (7)$$

as the indicator equation.

It may be noted that the development of seismographs has now reached a stage in which any further increase in the sensitivity can, on account of the general unrest of the ground (see § 18.5), give no additional help in the recording of ordinary earthquakes.

9.4. Damping of seismographs.

It would obviously be a convenience if a seismograph could be designed so that its seismograms would give fairly close pictures of the relevant components of the actual earth movements, and we shall discuss the question as to how far this may be realised in practice.

We first note that the left-hand side of (7) is identical with that of the equation (3, (3)). Therefore the complementary function of the solution of (7) takes one of the forms given in (3, (8)), and so depends on constants of the seismograph and not on parameters describing the earth motion (unless the latter is impulsive). This makes it desirable to arrange the instrumental constants so that the complementary function will be as insignificant as possible; this factor is taken into account especially in deciding the amount of damping to be introduced. If the damping coefficient λ is less than unity, in which case the complementary function has the form of (3, (8a)), i.e.

$$C \exp(-\lambda\omega t)\cos(\sqrt{[1-\lambda^2]}\,\omega t + \epsilon), \qquad (8)$$

then clearly the larger λ is, the less important is the complementary function; thus it is evident that unless there is some appreciable damping, the indicator could by no means give a close record of the actual earth movement. If $\lambda > 1$, the complementary function has by (3, (8c)) the form

$$A\phi(t) + B\psi(t), \qquad (9)$$

where A and B are constants, and

$$\phi(t) = \exp(-\alpha t), \quad \psi(t) = \exp(-\beta t), \quad \alpha, \beta = (\lambda \pm \sqrt{[\lambda^2 - 1]})\,\omega. \qquad (10)$$

Since $\beta < \alpha$, the term $B\psi$ of (9) becomes increasingly more important than the term $A\phi$ as time goes on, and this accordingly makes it desirable that β should be as large as possible, i.e. that any excess of λ over unity should be as small as possible. We conclude that a desirable feature of a seismograph is that the damping should be fairly near the critical value, $\lambda = 1$.

Some seismographs are in fact designed so that λ is as close to unity as possible; the corresponding form of the complementary function of the solution of (7) is then given by (3, (8b)). It is to be noticed that the damping affects the complementary function and does not otherwise interfere with the response to the ground motion.

In other seismographs there are practical reasons for having λ somewhat less than unity (though still appreciable). In illustrations to follow we shall sometimes take $\lambda = 1/\sqrt{2}$, which is a useful representative value. We have already pointed out (§ 3.1.2) that (*ceteris paribus*) the magnitudes of the ordinates of the graphs of the complementary functions in the cases $\lambda = 1/\sqrt{2}$, $\lambda = 1$ are not greatly different. Hence if the value of λ is in (or near) the range

$$1/\sqrt{2} \leqslant \lambda \leqslant 1,$$

the damping will be reasonably satisfactory.

In the case of a seismograph for which $\lambda < 1$, the damping is frequently described in terms of the damping ratio ϵ, defined as the ratio of the amplitudes of x in two successive swings of the seismograph when it is allowed to swing freely (the Earth being at rest). By (3, (8a)) it is easy to deduce that

$$\log \epsilon = \pi \lambda (1 - \lambda^2)^{-\frac{1}{2}} \tag{11}$$

(ϵ as here defined and used in (11) is not to be confused with the phase constant ϵ appearing in (3, (8a))). Knowledge of the damping ratio ϵ and of the free pendulum period $2\pi/\omega$ is sufficient to determine the constants in the indicator equation (7).

9.5. Solution of the indicator equation. We now proceed to examine the nature of the solution of the indicator equation (7) corresponding to certain prescribed types of earth movement.

9.5.1. Simple harmonic earth motion. Suppose that the relevant component of the earth motion takes the form $u = a \cos pt$, where a, p are constants. Then (7) becomes

$$\ddot{x} + 2\lambda \omega \dot{x} + \omega^2 x = V_s p^2 a \cos pt. \tag{12}$$

By (3, (11)) and (3, (12)) a particular solution of (12) is

$$x = aV_d \cos{(pt - \delta)}, \tag{13}$$

where $$\tan{\delta} = 2\lambda\omega p/(\omega^2 - p^2) \tag{14}$$

and $$V_d = V_s p^2 \{(\omega^2 - p^2)^2 + 4\lambda^2\omega^2 p^2\}^{-\frac{1}{2}}. \tag{15}$$

The right-hand side of (13) is, apart from the phase difference δ, equal to V_d times the earth movement in this case, and for this reason V_d is called the *dynamical magnification*.

When the earth movement is accurately simple harmonic with unchanging period $2\pi/p$, the dynamical magnification is constant and the seismogram will be an accurate record of the earth movement (neglecting the effect of the complementary function). But the dependence of V_d on p shows that the magnification is different for different periods in the earth movement. Hence in general the seismogram will not be expected to be a precisely accurate picture of the actual earth movement.

We notice from (15) that if there were no damping, there could be resonance if $p = \omega$. This gives a further reason for having seismographs damped; for if λ were very small, there would be abnormal exaggeration of earth movements with periods near the natural period of the seismograph.

It needs to be noted that when the earth movement is not approximately simple harmonic, direct applications of the dynamical magnification factor will fail to indicate the true amplitudes of the earth movement.

9.5.2. Impulsive earth motion. Suppose next that in the vicinity of the seismograph the earth is at rest prior to the instant $t = 0$, and that an impulsive disturbance then arrives which causes the relevant component $\dot{u}$ of the earth velocity to jump suddenly from zero to a fixed value, $\dot{u}_0$ say. The solution of (7) in these circumstances is found, for $t > 0$, to be

$$x = -V_s \dot{u}_0 t \exp{(-\omega t)} \tag{16}$$

if $\lambda = 1$, and

$$x = \frac{-V_s \dot{u}_0}{\omega\sqrt{(1 - \lambda^2)}} \sin{(\sqrt{[1 - \lambda^2]}\,\omega t)} \exp{(-\lambda\omega t)} \tag{17}$$

if $\lambda < 1$.

We notice that the onset of the motion of the indicator is sharp in both cases. For the case $\lambda = 1$, we deduce from (16) that the maximum displacement on the seismogram occurs when $t = 1/\omega$. For the case $\lambda < 1$, we deduce from (17) that the maximum occurs when $\tan(\sqrt{[1 - \lambda^2]}\,\omega t) = \sqrt{(1 - \lambda^2)}/\lambda$; taking the representative case $\lambda = 1/\sqrt{2}$, the last formula gives $t = 1\cdot 1/\omega$. In the case $\lambda < 1$, x passes through its first zero after the time $t = 0$ when $\omega t = \pi/\sqrt{(1 - \lambda^2)}$; for the case $\lambda = 1/\sqrt{2}$, this gives $t = 4\cdot 4/\omega$. After this time the displacement is always small compared with the first maximum for all cases where λ is in or near the range $1/\sqrt{2} \leqslant \lambda \leqslant 1$.

9.5.3. General earth motion. We now derive a solution of the indicator equation (7) for a general earth motion $u = f(t)$, using the method of variation of parameters. We take as a trial solution of (7) the form

$$x = A(t)\,\phi(t) + B(t)\,\psi(t), \tag{18}$$

where ϕ and ψ are given by (10). In the trial solution (18) the right-hand side is the same as (9) except that A and B are now taken as functions of t and not as constants. By (18) we have

$$\dot{x} = A\dot{\phi} + B\dot{\psi}$$

and

$$\ddot{x} = A\ddot{\phi} + B\ddot{\psi} - V_s f''(t),$$

provided

$$A\phi + B\psi = 0 \left.\rule{0pt}{12pt}\right\}$$

and

$$A\dot{\phi} + B\dot{\psi} = -V_s f''(t). \tag{19}$$

It follows (since $x = \phi$ and $x = \psi$ make the left-hand side of (7) zero) that (18) is a solution of (7) if $\dot{A}$ and $\dot{B}$ are given by (19), i.e. if

$$\dot{A} = \frac{V_s \psi f''}{\phi\dot{\psi} - \dot{\phi}\psi}, \quad \dot{B} = \frac{-V_s \phi f''}{\phi\dot{\psi} - \dot{\phi}\psi}.$$

Hence a particular solution of (7) is seen to be

$$x = V_s \phi \int \frac{\psi f''}{\phi\dot{\psi} - \dot{\phi}\psi}\,dt - V_s \psi \int \frac{\phi f''}{\phi\dot{\psi} - \dot{\phi}\psi}\,dt, \tag{20}$$

where ϕ, ψ satisfy (10).

Combining this solution with the relevant complementary function, we obtain an exact formula for the response of the seismograph to any given earth movement $u = f(t)$.

9.6. Deduction of the actual form of the earth movement from a given seismogram. The important problem of inferring precise details of the earth movement from the trace on a given seismogram is the converse of that discussed in § 9.5, and we now look at the equation (7) again with this problem in view. Integrating (7) with respect to t, we obtain, using the suffix 0 for values at time $t = 0$,

$$\dot{u} = \dot{u}_0 - V_s^{-1}\left\{\dot{x} - \dot{x}_0 + 2\lambda\omega(x - x_0) + \omega^2\int_0^t x\,dt\right\}. \tag{21}$$

Integrating again, and using the fact that

$$\int_0^t dt \int_0^t x\,dt = t\int_0^t x\,dt - \int_0^t xt\,dt,$$

we obtain

$$u = u_0 + V_s^{-1}x_0 + (\dot{u}_0 + V_s^{-1}\dot{x}_0 + 2\lambda\omega V_s^{-1}x_0)\,t - V_s^{-1}x$$
$$- (2\lambda\omega + \omega^2 t)\,V_s^{-1}\int_0^t x\,dt + \omega^2 V_s^{-1}\int_0^t xt\,dt. \tag{22}$$

The equation (22) expresses the relevant component of the earth motion in terms of constants of the seismograph, the time t, and values of x which can be measured on the seismogram; and so gives a formal solution of the problem. In using equations like (22), recourse is had to mechanical integration. Auxiliary experiments are made to test the reliability of the results; seismographs are placed on shaking tables to which known irregular motions are applied, and the results of the integration compared with these known motions.

On account of the numerical difficulties of treating equations such as (22), pains are taken in practice to design seismographs in such a way that certain important aspects of the earth movements may be fairly rapidly inferred from seismograms. We proceed now to consider this matter.

9.7. Displacement meters and accelerometers. If the natural undamped period $2\pi/\omega$ of a seismograph were very great compared with the predominant period of the earth movement (assuming the existence of a predominant period), the indicator equation (7) would approximate to the form

$$\ddot{x} = -V_s\ddot{u}. \tag{23}$$

Thus, if the seismograph were in equilibrium and at rest just prior to the onset of the disturbance, x as read from the seismogram would in this case be approximately proportional to the actual component u of the earth displacement. A seismograph in which this feature was realised would be a *displacement meter*. Actually there are practical limitations to the extent to which this accurate proportionality may be realised, on account of the difficulty of constructing satisfactory instruments with very long periods.

If, on the other hand, the natural period $2\pi/\omega$ were very short compared with the predominant period of the earth motion, the indicator equation would approximate to the form

$$\omega^2 x = -V_s \ddot{u}. \tag{24}$$

A seismograph for which this equation holds approximately is called an *acceleration meter* or *accelerometer*. In this case, a practical limitation arises from the fact that the smaller $2\pi/\omega$ is, the smaller x is (by (24)), for a given component $\ddot{u}$ of the earth acceleration (assuming that V_s is assigned); and so the less sensitive is the seismograph.

In view of the great simplicity of these two cases as compared with the general case of § 9.6, it is often desirable that seismographs should approximate as far as possible to one or other of these two types.

9.8. Seismographs for near and distant earthquake studies.

The Earth's internal constitution is such that the earth movements at points of the outer surface which are near the source of an earthquake are different in character in certain respects from those at points a great distance away. The reasons for this will be seen when we come to discuss the Earth's constitution in chapters 12 and 13. Separate types of seismographs have accordingly been constructed for measuring the earth movements arising from *near earthquakes*, originating within about 10 degrees from the location of the seismograph, and those arising from distant earthquakes, originating at greater distances away.

9.8.1. Near-earthquake instruments.

In near earthquakes, waves of periods of less than 0·01 sec may be significant, and the longest periods are not as a rule much greater than about 0·5 sec. In accordance with § 9.7, this would suggest using a seismograph approximating to a displacement meter, with natural period of at least several seconds. It transpires, however, that the amplitudes of the motions to be assessed cover a wide range and may be very small (sometimes of an order less than 10^{-3} cm), and it would not always be practicable to arrange for adequate magnification with a displacement meter.

On the other hand, the accelerations are relatively high (the periods being short), and will be expected to be more easily measurable. If an accelerometer were used, however, the necessary period would theoretically need to be less than 0·01 sec, and by (24) the magnification would again need to be impossibly high.

In addition, there are often complications arising from extraneous effects such as the presence of microseisms (see § 18.5), and the seismograph needs to be designed to minimise the intrusion of these effects on the record.

It is therefore clear that there are difficulties in the way of obtaining seismograms from near earthquakes that will approximate to accurate pictures of the earth movements. In elementary practice, seismographs of periods somewhat less than a second are commonly used, the magnifications being as high as possible. The seismograms then give some indication of the acceleration changes, but of course fall short of being accurate representations of the earth acceleration.

9.8.2. Distant earthquake instruments. With earthquakes recorded at distant stations, the amplitudes of the earth movements at these stations may reach an order of 0·1 cm, and periods up to the order of 40 sec are common. In this case the accelerations are small, and it transpires that an accelerometer would not be sensitive enough to record a distant earthquake well.

The use of a displacement meter would at first sight appear to be unsatisfactory, since an instrumental period of the order of several times 40 sec would appear to be necessary. But it happens that the longer periods arise from the dispersion of surface waves, the corresponding earth movement being roughly simple harmonic. In these circumstances, the equations of § 9.5.1 may be used. Thus in practice a seismograph whose natural period is of the order of 15–30 sec is commonly used. By § 9.7 such a seismograph will act approximately as a displacement meter for the shorter earth periods, and by (13) for the longer earth periods as well, subject of course to the variation of the magnification factor V_d as given by (15).

In order to derive the fullest information concerning the earth movements, it is of course desirable to use an assembly of seismographs with natural periods spread over a considerable range.

9.9. Other types of seismograph.
The theory of the seismograph as discussed in the preceding sections is relevant to a number of seismographs used in practice, and in particular to the Milne–Shaw seismograph. We now refer briefly to some other types.

Wiechert designed a seismograph in which the pendulum is vertical and inverted, being maintained thus by small springs pressing against supports rigidly attached to the ground. The mass of the pendulum is large (sometimes several tons), and the seismograph records both horizontal components at once.

A useful instrument for near earthquake purposes is the Wood–Anderson; the principle of this instrument rests on the use of a vertical fibre which is under tension with a small attached mass and which suffers torsion during the passage of an earthquake wave.

9.9.1. The electromagnetic type.
A cardinal development took place when Galitzin introduced the idea of recording the seismogram by means of a ray of light from the mirror of a galvanometer through which passes an electric current generated by electromagnetic induction when the pendulum of the seismograph moves. The current is induced in a set of coils that are attached to and move with the pendulum in an independently set up magnetic field. If u is the relevant component of the earth displacement, the pendulum displacement θ and galvanometer displacement x (which is proportional to that shown on the seismogram) satisfy equations of the form

$$\ddot{\theta} + 2\lambda\omega\dot{\theta} + \omega^2\theta = -\ddot{u}/l + h\dot{x}, \tag{25}$$

$$\ddot{x} + 2\mu\Omega\dot{x} + \Omega^2 x = k\dot{\theta}, \tag{26}$$

where λ, μ, ω, Ω, h, k and l are all instrumental constants.

In earlier instruments, the 'feed-back' term $h\ddot{x}$ in (25) was small and commonly neglected, in which case (25) and (26) are readily solvable for simple forms of the earth displacement u. We shall indicate solutions for the cases of (a) simple harmonic, (b) impulsive, earth motion, taking $\lambda = \mu = 1$ (critical damping) and $\Omega = \omega$ (equal galvanometer and pendulum periods), in addition to neglecting the term in h.

For case (a), we take $u = a \cos pt$, for which (25) takes the form of (12) and so has a particular (the 'steady state') solution $\theta = aV' \cos(pt - \delta')$, where V' and δ' depend on ω, l and p. Substitution into (26) then gives

$$x = aV'' \cos(pt - \delta''), \tag{27}$$

where V'' and δ'' depend on ω, l, k and p, showing (cf. § 9.5.1) that the galvanometer response is similar to that of the indicator in the simpler type of seismograph.

For case (b), taking an impulsive earth motion as in § 9.5.2, the solution for x is found to be

$$x = -\frac{k}{l}\dot{u}_0(\tfrac{1}{2}t^2 - \tfrac{1}{6}\omega t^3)\exp(-\omega t). \tag{28}$$

It follows from (28) that the galvanometer does not here start with a finite velocity as does the indicator in the case of § 9.5.2 (equation (16)). Nevertheless, the initial acceleration of the galvanometer is appreciable, the first maximum of x being reached after time $1\cdot3/\omega$, which is not greatly different from the corresponding time in § 9.5.2.

When the term in h in (25) is not negligible, the solution of (25) and (26) is more complicated. There are, however, great practical advantages to be derived from the presence of seven adjustable constants in these equations, in contrast to the three constants in the form (5). In part for this reason, electromagnetic seismographs have very largely superceded the simpler mechanical types. Various instrumental devices have been brought to bear with a view to realising optimum values of the seven constants for particular purposes. For example, instruments may be designed to produce seismograms in which the dynamical magnification is nearly constant over a wide range of earth periods, to reveal earth motions of unusually short or unusually long periods, or to enable specific parts of the seismic spectrum to be closely studied. Outstanding contributors in these developments include Benioff, Willmore and Kirnos. Mention should also be made of an extensive modification of the Galitzin-type seismograph by Press and Ewing, resulting in instruments capable of recording earth periods up to 10 min; with these, the pendulum is operated at a 30 sec period, with a galvanometer period of 90 sec.

A useful discussion of the equations (25) and (26) at some length has been given by Willmore (1961).

9.9.2. Strain seismograph. In 1935, Benioff made an important innovation by designing an instrument to measure a component of ground strain, instead of the usual ground displacement. During the passage of seismic waves, this instrument records variations in the distance between two points of the ground some 20 m apart. The variations are measured against a standard-length tube, originally of steel, but later replaced by a fused quartz extensiometer. The recording is electromagnetic, the original galvanometer period being 40 sec, subsequently increased at various stages to 8 min. The equation for the galvanometer deflection has the same form as (5). Benioff's strain seismograph was the first to record earthquake periods up to the order of 1 h.

Benioff has also investigated properties of a seismograph designed to measure ground dilatations directly.

9.9.3. Portable seismographs. In addition to seismographs intended for the recording inside observatories of natural earthquakes, other instruments, commonly called 'seismometers', have been designed to record seismic waves in the field at short distances from artificially produced explosions. The original purpose of the latter instruments was to make seismic surveys which would assist in revealing immediate subsurface rock structures (see §§ 12.1.5, 18.6). These seismometers had short periods and usually worked in conjunction with electronic amplifiers.

In 1950, Willmore designed an intermediate type of instrument capable of recording seismic waves at distances of several degrees from a source, yet retaining the robustness and portability of field instruments. Willmore's instruments have galvanometric recording and the performance equals or surpasses that of many existing observatory instruments. The Willmore and other portable seismographs have the great advantage that they can be set up at short notice at strategic places in the field to record waves from large artificial explosions or from sustained aftershocks of natural earthquakes. With their help it becomes possible to provide quantities of improved data on the structure of the Earth's outer layers.

9.9.4. Other developments. Instruments called *tiltmeters* have been developed in Japan to measure slow angular displacements of large earth blocks extending over considerable periods of time (of the order of days and more). Records from tiltmeters are checked against local earthquake occurrence, with a view to finding correlations which might throw light on future earthquake occurrence.

Earthquake motions are sometimes detected on instruments designed for completely different purposes. A notable instance occurred when Ness, Harrison and Slichter recorded long-period earth motions on a LaCoste–Romberg tidal gravity meter following the main Chilean earthquakes of 1960 May 22, the periods ranging from 3 to 55 min (see § 14.5.1).

Over the past few years, attention has been given to the development of mechanical filtering procedures designed to separate out a pulse of interest on a record where there is a complicated background. For this purpose, records are taken on magnetic tape on each of an array of seismometers which are spread over a distance comparable with the wave-length of the pulse and may be in two lines in the form of a cross. The separate tape records are weighted and combined according to definite procedures, the tapes being displaced relatively to one another before superposition to ensure that the particular pulse is in phase on all of them. Cross-correlation techniques are commonly employed in the process. Research on these lines carries with it the prospect of greatly improved precision in the determination of arrival times of seismic phases, especially arrivals after the first.

For further information on related instrumental trends, the reader is referred to a Report of the United States Panel on Seismic Improvement on *The Need for Fundamental Research in Seismology*, U.S. Department of State, July 1959.

CHAPTER 10

THE CONSTRUCTION OF
TRAVEL-TIME TABLES

The circumstances of an earthquake's occurrence (unless the earthquake be due to an artificially produced explosion) are entirely beyond control and so investigations of the detailed physical characteristics of earthquakes must allow for a much bigger influence of unknown factors affecting the recorded observations than is the case with a well-designed laboratory experiment. The indications of a small set of earthquake observations thus necessarily fall short of the precision commonly attained in purely laboratory experiments in physics.

What the science of seismology loses through absence of design of experiment (that is, apart from the recording side), however, is in part made up by the large quantity of observational data available. There are more than a thousand seismological observatories distributed over the Earth's surface, each possessing one or more seismographs, and in the course of a single year some hundreds of thousands of earthquake records are obtained from these seismographs. The best treatment of this material is necessarily to be made through the careful use of statistical theory, in conjunction with the theory discussed in the preceding chapters. The need for the use of statistical theory is more imperative than in some other branches of physics, and this is so whether use is made of the extensive routine observations of observatory workers or whether an intensive study of original earthquake records is made by an individual. In particular, it is specially important in practical seismology that some indication of the extent of error (the standard error when relevant) should accompany every numerical result.

10.1. Parameters of earthquakes. The initial disturbance connected with an earthquake, or at least that part which sends out the main waves (see § 4.3), is confined to a limited region of the Earth's interior whose linear dimensions do not ordinarily exceed the order of a few kilometres (see chapter 15). The centre of this confined region is called the *focus* (sometimes the *hypocentre*) of the particular earthquake. The point of the Earth's outer surface vertically above the focus is the *epicentre*. Quantitative description of earthquake phenomena must be in terms of parameters whose particular values indicate the chief features of an earthquake. In the early development of the necessary theory, it is convenient to take into account just four such parameters, namely the time of origin, two coordinates (usually taken as the colatitude θ and the east longitude ϕ) giving the position of the epicentre, and the depth of the focus. To begin with, we shall assume the Earth to be spherically symmetrical about its centre.

10.2. Calculation of the epicentral distance and azimuth of an observing station from an epicentre.

As a preliminary to making use of seismograms, it is desirable that we should be able to connect suitably the cordinates θ, ϕ of an epicentre Q (say), with the corresponding coordinates θ', ϕ' of an observing station O (say).

Following Turner, we let A, B, C, D, E, G, H, K be defined by

$$A = \sin\theta \cos\phi, \quad B = \sin\theta \sin\phi, \quad C = \cos\theta; \tag{1}$$

$$D = \sin\phi, \qquad E = -\cos\phi; \tag{2}$$

$$G = \cos\theta \cos\phi, \quad H = \cos\theta \sin\phi, \quad K = -\sin\theta; \tag{3}$$

and let $A', B', \ldots,$ be corresponding constants for the station O. (A, B, C are direction-cosines of the line joining the Earth's centre to Q; etc.) As checks on the magnitudes and signs of numerical values, we note that

$$A = KE, \quad B = -KD, \quad G = -CE, \quad H = CD.$$

Tables giving A', B' and C' for all observatories have been computed by the staff of the *International Seismological Summary*; these tables further give the heights of the observatories above mean sea-level, and also the heights above the surface of the standard (spherical) model Earth defined in § 10.6.3.

We now introduce the *epicentral distance* Δ of O from Q, measured sometimes as the arc-length QO in kilometres, and sometimes (as will be the case in this book) as the angle subtended by QO at the

Earth's centre; and also the *azimuth* Z which is the angle (measured from north through east) between the meridian line through Q and the arc QO. It is easily deduced from (1), (2) and (3) that

$$\cos \Delta = AA' + BB' + CC', \tag{4}$$

$$2 \operatorname{vers} \Delta = 2(1 - \cos \Delta) = (A - A')^2 + (B - B')^2 + (C - C')^2, \tag{5}$$

$$2(1 + \cos \Delta) = (A + A')^2 + (B + B')^2 + (C + C')^2, \tag{6}$$

$$2 + 2 \sin \Delta \sin Z = (A' - D)^2 + (B' - E)^2 + C'^2, \tag{7}$$

$$2 + 2 \sin \Delta \cos Z = (A' - G)^2 + (B' - H)^2 + (C' - K)^2. \tag{8}$$

From (4), (5) or (6), Δ may be determined from knowledge of the coordinates of Q and O; and then from (7) or (8), Z.

It is important in practice to know the extent of error in the computed values of Δ, including (in precise work) allowance for the error introduced by the actual process of computation involved in using (4), (5) or (6). The formula (5) is distinctly the best to use for $0° < \Delta < 20°$; if θ, ϕ, θ', ϕ' are known correct to the nearest minute, and four-figure tables are used, the standard error in the value of Δ calculated using (5) ranges from $0°·05$ at $1°$ to $0°·007$ at $20°$; for very short distances, the error is much reduced by using six-figure tables for $2 \operatorname{vers} \Delta$. The formula (6) is similarly the best to use for $160° < \Delta < 180°$. The formula (4) is the faster to use when a multiplying machine is available, and the standard error of the computed Δ (using four-figure tables) is then $0°·01$ or less for $20° < \Delta < 160°$.

Instead of (4) or (5), the approximate formula

$$\Delta^2 \approx (\theta - \theta')^2 + (\phi - \phi')^2 \sin^2 \tfrac{1}{2}(\theta + \theta') \tag{9}$$

is sometimes used when Δ is small. This gives a maximum error not exceeding about $0·0004\Delta^3$ degrees when Δ is not too great, provided Q and O are not within about $20°$ of the Earth's north or south pole. The formula (9) is sufficiently accurate for most work on near earthquakes (see chapter 12), the error being ordinarily less than $1 \mathrm{km}$ if $\Delta < 6°·5$.

10.3. Features of seismograms. Following the occurrence of an earthquake, the seismogram traced at any observing station is usually rather complicated in appearance. Fig. 33 is a copy of a typical seismogram traced at Melbourne by waves from a New Zealand earthquake. The displacements shown in the earlier part of the record are due to the arrival of bodily elastic waves that have travelled by various routes from the earthquake's focus through the Earth's interior; the later part of the record is formed predominantly by surface waves which travel more slowly than the bodily waves. Except close to the epicentre, the surface waves usually have greater amplitudes than the bodily waves because of the slower rate of amplitude diminution with distance (see §§ 3.5, 5.6). (An exception occurs (see §§ 3.25, 15.5.1) when the focus is abnormally deep, for then the surface waves are abnormally small.) When the earthquake is a strong one, a seismogram at a distant

Fig. 33

station reveals the arrival of disturbances over a long period of time (sometimes several hours); the term *coda* has been used to denote that part of the record which follows the earlier surface waves.

It is to be expected that a seismogram will show more or less prominent displacements corresponding to the onsets of a number of specific pulses, including those due to the direct P and S waves (whose rays follow paths of least time from the focus to the observatory), and also possibly other pulses connected with waves that have suffered reflection or change of type at any discontinuity surfaces within the Earth, including the outer surface. Such displacements on the seismogram as can be associated with specific types of ray mark the *phases* of the seismogram. In practice, the complicated appearance of a seismogram makes it often difficult or even impossible to discern many of the phases that are expected to be present. Through long effort on countless seismograms, it has, however, become possible to construct empirical travel-time tables which give the times for many particular families of rays in terms of an earthquake's focal depth and a station's epicentral distance.

The question of the derivation of these tables is a basic problem in seismology to which we shall devote some attention.

In this connection, special importance attaches to the fact that the P wave that has travelled from an earthquake focus to a station by the path of least time is recorded by a seismograph that (apart from microseisms—see chapter 18) is usually in a relatively undisturbed state. This does not apply to any pulse arriving later, and so it is usually possible both to identify and to estimate the instant of onset of the first P pulse much more precisely than is possible with other pulses. The construction of the main P travel-time tables is therefore of prime importance.

10.4. Theory of the evolution of the main P travel-time tables.

The construction of the P travel-time tables is interlocked with the determination of values of the four main parameters (§ 10.1) for each earthquake used. The special statistical procedures required have been developed by Jeffreys.

10.4.1. Equations of condition between earthquake and table parameters. Suppose that, following successive approximations from crude beginnings, a provisional P travel-time table has been constructed. Let R be the radius of the Earth stripped of its crust, and let hR denote the depth below the crust of an earthquake focus. Suppose that the table gives values $T(h, \Delta)$ of the P travel-times in terms of h and Δ, and let $\xi(h, \Delta)$ denote the errors in the T, the correct times being thus $T + \xi$.

For an earthquake used in improving the table, take a tentative focus F and a tentative origin-time. Let hR now apply to this F, and take the tentative origin-time as zero. Let Δ apply to the angular distance from F to an observing station O, and let Z be the azimuth of O from F. (Uncertainty in the position of O, which will here be ignored, can be allowed for separately as in § 10.2.) The suffix 0 will denote values of T, ξ, etc., which correspond to these particular values of h and Δ.

Let τ, zR and $\delta\Delta$ be the corrections needed to give the accurate origin-time, focal depth and epicentral distance from O. Thus

$$\delta\Delta \approx -x \sin Z - y \cos Z, \tag{10}$$

where x and y are the east and north angular displacements which F needs.

Let t be the measured arrival-time of the first P onset at O, and ϵ the error in this measurement; t is also the 'observed' (O) travel-time of the pulse. The table value T_0 which corresponds to h and Δ will be called the 'calculated' (C) travel-time. Let

$$\mu = t - T_0 \tag{11}$$

denote the 'residual' (O − C).

On forming two expressions for the accurate travel-time from the true focus to O, we have, correct to the first order (provided $(\partial T/\partial \Delta)_0$ and $(\partial T/\partial h)_0$ exist),

$$t + \epsilon - \tau = T_0 + \xi_0 - (x \sin Z + y \cos Z)\left(\frac{\partial T}{\partial \Delta}\right)_0 + z\left(\frac{\partial T}{\partial h}\right)_0, \tag{12}$$

and hence

$$\xi_0 - (x \sin Z + y \cos Z)\left(\frac{\partial T}{\partial \Delta}\right)_0 + z\left(\frac{\partial T}{\partial h}\right)_0 + \tau - \mu = \epsilon. \tag{13}$$

(13) is an equation of condition between the five parameters x, y, z, τ and ξ_0, the quantities Z, $(\partial T/\partial \Delta)_0$, $(\partial T/\partial h)_0$ and μ being computable from explicit data. Similar equations can be formed for other observing stations and other earthquakes.

10.4.1.1. In the earlier stages of evolution of the P travel-time table, only 'normal' earthquakes (whose foci lie within 50 km of the Earth's surface) were used. For these, the effect of focal depth on the travel-times is relatively slight and the presence of sharp changes in seismic velocities in the outer part of the Earth makes it expedient to drop the term in z from (13), and instead work provisionally in terms of a conventional 'origin-time' for each normal earthquake. The convention chosen is that for small Δ (but exceeding $1°{\cdot}5$) the P travel-time will be as nearly as possible proportional to Δ.

As detailed knowledge of the crustal layering becomes available, it becomes possible, with the help of the methods of chapter 12, to estimate the position of the focus and the actual origin-time of each earthquake more precisely.

At an appropriate stage, earthquakes with foci deeper than normal are brought into the discussion, and with the help of the unabridged form of (13) and various other devices, tables adapted to all focal depths are set up.

10.4.2. Application of least-squares theory. When equations of the type (13) are formed for a set of earthquakes and observatories, the parameters of the earthquakes and the corrections ξ_0 for representative values of h and Δ can be estimated by least squares.

Let m be the total number of earthquakes used, n the average number of recording stations, and p the number of parameters needed to determine the P table to satisfactory accuracy. The total number of parameters would then be $4m+p$, and the number of equations of condition like (13) would be mn.

As a preliminary to discussing the use of the least squares method, we shall write the set of equations of condition like (13) in the form

$$\sum_{k=1}^{q} (a_{ik}x_k) - b_i = \epsilon_i \quad (i = 1, 2, ..., r), \tag{14}$$

where $r = mn$, $q = 4m+p$, x_k is a typical one of the $4m+p$ parameters, and a_{ik}, b_i are known quantities. The normal equations corresponding to (14), as derived according to the least squares theory, namely

$$\sum_{i=1}^{r} \left\{ \left(\sum_{k=1}^{q} a_{ik}x_k - b_i \right) a_{ij} \right\} = 0 \quad (j = 1, 2, ..., q),$$

may be written as

$$\sum_{k=1}^{q} (c_{jk}x_k) = f_j \quad (j = 1, 2, ..., q), \tag{15}$$

where $\qquad c_{jk} = \sum_{i=1}^{r} (a_{ij}a_{ik}), \quad f_j = \sum_{i=1}^{r} (a_{ij}b_i).$

The formal solution of the set of linear equations (15) is

$$Cx_l = \sum_{j=1}^{q} (C_{jl}f_j) \quad (l = 1, 2, ..., q), \tag{16}$$

where C is the determinant of the c_{ij}, and C_{jl} is the cofactor of the element c_{jl} in C.

10.4.3. Jeffreys's method of successive approximation. Now in practice n is of the order of 100, p of order 50, while m must be considerable to achieve good results. The direct process of reducing the formal solution (16) to a useful numerical result is therefore prohibitively laborious (without the aid of electronic computers, which were not available in earlier days when much of the basic work was done), and Jeffreys has derived an effective method of successive approximation.

We first rewrite (15) in the form

$$c_{ll}x_l = f_l - \sum_k{}' (c_{lk}x_k) \quad (l = 1, 2, ..., q), \tag{17}$$

where $\sum_k{}'$ denotes summation for all relevant values of k except the particular value l. First approximations to the x_l in the form

$$x_l = f_l/c_{ll} \quad (l = 1, 2, ..., q) \tag{18}$$

may then be obtained by taking the parameters on the right-hand sides of each of the equations (17) as all zero. Second approximations to the x_l may then be obtained by substituting the values (18) into the right-hand sides of (17) and solving the resultant equations. Proceeding by iteration, a satisfactory solution of the equations (15) may be obtained, provided the process is convergent. This process is equivalent to expanding the C_{jl}/C in descending powers of the elements of the leading diagonal of C, and will clearly converge if other elements of C are sufficiently small.

In our problem, there is the special feature that (in addition to a table correction ξ_0) each of (13) contains the x, y, z, τ for just one particular earthquake and no parameters for any other earthquake. This feature persists into the normal equations, with the result that the great majority of the elements of the determinant C (apart from those in the leading diagonal) are zero.

For the remainder of this subsection, we shall drop the term in z in (13) and follow the earlier stages of the procedure as described in § 10.4.1.1. Provided the needed table corrections ξ_0 are not too great, it can then be shown that, as a result of the special feature mentioned above, the following will be a convergent process:

(i) Find by least squares from equations of the type (13) first approximations to the x, y, τ for each separate earthquake considered, taking all the other parameters as zero; this is equivalent to ignoring all errors in the provisional travel-time table, and so solving by least squares a set of equations of the type

$$(x \sin Z + y \cos Z)(\partial T/\partial \Delta)_0 - \tau + \mu = 0. \tag{19}$$

(ii) Using these first approximations to x, y, τ, determine from (13) (putting $\epsilon = 0$) preliminary estimates of ξ_0 for various values of Δ for each earthquake.

(iii) Combine these preliminary estimates of ξ_0 by a suitable process (to be described shortly), obtaining a first set of corrections to be applied to the travel-time table.

(iv) Proceed by iteration.

In practice, the question of deciding whether the errors in the provisional table are sufficiently small for the process to be valid is not a source of serious trouble, because the process being iterative is self-checking. It can be shown, moreover, that even when some of the table errors are quite appreciable, there will be convergence with the use of earthquakes for which the P arrival-times are available at three groups of stations which are at roughly the same epicentral distance and are in widely different azimuths. At an early stage of the approximation, it may be necessary to ignore the readings of earthquakes which do not fulfil this condition, lack of rapid convergence being the criterion.

The process of solving the hundred or so equations like (19) for any one earthquake may be shortened by replacing these equations by a small number of equations in each of which the values taken for Δ, Z and μ are the mean values for a group of stations having roughly the same Δ and Z. In practice, it is sufficiently accurate to solve by least squares a set of about five (sometimes even fewer equations.

In treating the preliminary estimates of ξ_0 obtained during the process (ii), it is convenient to arrange these estimates, which we shall denote as ξ, in groups corresponding to suitable ranges of values of Δ; the size of a range depends on the number and consistency of the observations and on the apparent curvature of the travel-time curve in the vicinity of the particular Δ.

The process (iii) of finding the best values of the corrections to be applied to the travel-time table is complicated by the circumstance that the distribution of the ξ for any given range of values of Δ is found to depart somewhat from the normal law of errors. Jeffreys has taken this into account by expressing the distribution in terms of a probability function given by

$$f(\xi) = (1-s)\,\pi^{-\frac{1}{2}}h\exp\{-h^2(\xi-\xi_0)^2\}+sg(\xi);\qquad(20)$$

in this expression, h and s are constants, the latter being fairly small, and $g(\xi)$ is a function of which the only prior knowledge is that it varies slowly with ξ within a range of values up to a few times $1/h$ on either side of ξ_0, and that its integral over all values of ξ is unity. The law (20) thus corresponds to the presence of an abnormal error occurring with probability s in addition to a normal error distributed about the true value with precision constant h.

10.4.3.1. The method of uniform reduction. Jeffreys has derived a useful method for determining the parameters in (20). He has further shown that when the number of observations is large enough, it is frequently sufficiently accurate to subtract from each frequency total in the distribution of values of ξ a constant number just sufficient to result in the isolation by zeroes of a central frequency group, to which normal error theory may be applied. This method is called the method of uniform reduction, and has been successfully applied in the present and in other problems in seismology.

For example, the following table shows the distribution of values of ξ obtained from a certain set of Japanese earthquakes (at one stage of the general process of successive approximation) for $0° < \Delta < 20°$; the first row gives the values of ξ in seconds, and the second row the corresponding frequencies. By inspection, a uniform reduction of 2 may be made to each entry in the second row, giving the third row, to which the normal theory may then be applied:

-9	-8	-7	-6	-5	-4	-3	-2	-1	0	1	2	3	4	5	6	7	8	9
0	2	2	1	3	4	7	6	13	22	14	12	11	4	3	2	0	2	1
0	0	0	0	1	2	5	4	11	20	12	10	9	2	1	0	0	0	0

For more difficult cases, Jeffreys has further evolved a method of ascertaining weights to be attached to the preliminary ξ, giving modified ξ to which normal error theory may be applied to determine the best estimates of the ξ_0 and the precision constant h. Such weights are readily estimated from a large number of observations in a sizeable range of values of Δ, and may be applied without change to the residuals for various subranges of Δ (the subranges actually taken in work connected with the above cases were $0° \leqslant \Delta < 3°$, $3° \leqslant \Delta < 6°$, etc.).

When the best estimates of ξ_0 are separately obtained in this way for certain specific values of Δ (the centres of the subranges), it is finally necessary to evolve and apply a suitable method of smoothing. This has also been carried out by Jeffreys, including special attention to places where the slope of the (T, Δ) curve changes rapidly or abruptly.

For more complete details of the various methods introduced by Jeffreys in this section of seismology, the reader is referred to Jeffreys, *On Travel Times in Seismology* (Publications du bureau central séismologique international, série A, fasc. 14, 1936) and to Jeffreys, *Theory of Probability* (Oxford, Clarendon Press, 1961).

10.4.4. Further matters relevant to the construction of the P travel-time tables. An important early question is how far the assumption of spherical symmetry in the Earth is reliable. The two main sources of deviation are the Earth's ellipticity of figure (to be considered separately in § 10.7), and differences in subsurface structure in different geographic regions. The latter make it desirable first to group together earthquakes with epicentres in particular regions (e.g. Europe, North Atlantic, North America, etc.) and later combine the results for the whole Earth. (For the needed statistical theory, see Jeffreys and Bullen, *Times of Transmission of Earthquake Waves* (Bur. centr. séism. internat., série A, fasc. 11, 1935).)

When allowance is made for ellipticity, it transpires that for epicentral distances exceeding 20° the travel-times are to a considerable degree independent of the locations of epicentres and observing stations. The greatest systematic differences are between the times for paths under the Pacific and under continental regions for distances of the order of 50°. In continental regions, there also appear to be some differences between shield and mountainous regions. With P waves for $\Delta > 20°$, the time differences do not appear to exceed 2 sec or so in travel-times up to 10 min, although the effects may be more marked in $dT/d\Delta$. The lateral variations in structure responsible for the differences are likely to be largely confined to the outermost 200–400 km of the Earth. Thus apart from its ellipticity, the Earth is, broadly speaking, remarkably close to spherical symmetry, and the theory of chapters 7 and 8 is relevant to good approximation.

Further refinements include the investigation of systematic errors and the spread of random errors in arrival-time data from particular observing stations. These errors may be due to local geological structure, the height of a station above mean sea level, poor time service, microseisms, or other cause. The application of statistically determined weights to the data from different stations, taken in conjunction with knowledge of the types of seismographs in use, leads to a higher precision in the final tables obtained.

In order to take account of layering in the crust, recourse is had to theory of § 7.3.5, which treats the case of a velocity jump downwards across a single discontinuity surface concentric with the outer surface. For the case of two such surfaces the (T, Δ) curve takes the form shown in Fig. 34, and various standard travel-time tables have

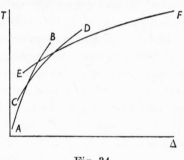

Fig. 34

assumed this model representation of conditions in the crust. Geographic regional variations are, however, specially marked in the crust and contribute substantially to uncertainties in the tables.

Towards examining effects of focal depth, let E and F be the epicentre and focus of an earthquake, and O an observing station at distance Δ, where Δ is sufficiently great for the ray EO to penetrate below the crust. Let v denote the P velocity at depth z below the Earth's surface, let $z = f$ at F, and let H be the crustal thickness. Let T be the travel-time along the ray FO, and $T + \delta T$ along EO.

When $f < H$, i.e. when the focus is inside the crust, the dependence of T on f is best indicated by formulae to be developed in

§§ 12.1.1, 12.1.2 (where h is equal to the present f). For comparison with the case $f > H$, it is useful to note that, to a first approximation in which squares of f/R are neglected, it can be shown that

$$\delta T \approx \int_0^f \phi(v, \Delta)\, dz, \tag{21}$$

where
$$\phi(v, \Delta) = \{v^{-2} - (dT/R\, d\Delta)^2\}^{\frac{1}{2}}. \tag{22}$$

When F is below the crust, let $f = H + hR$ (h being here defined as in § 10.4.1). For this case, it can be shown that

$$\delta T \approx \int_0^H \phi(v, \Delta)\, dz + hR\phi(v_0, \Delta), \tag{23}$$

where v_0 is the P velocity just below the crust. (Similar theory of course also applies to S.) The integral in (23) (like that in (21)) ranges only inside the crust, and its total fluctuation for varying Δ is found to be less than 2 sec. On the other hand, the term in h, through its dependence on $dT/d\Delta$, can vary markedly with Δ. For example, for $h = 0\cdot05$ (see the first table in § 10.9.1), $\delta T = 9, 36, 41$ sec when $\Delta = 10°, 50°, 100°$, respectively; for $h = 0\cdot10$, the corresponding δT are 8, 60, 71 sec.

Thus significant depth of an earthquake focus can be readily detected from the fact that the residuals μ (of § 10.4.1), taken against table-times for a surface focus, show systematically increasing negative values as Δ increases. This result provides one of the principal practical methods of estimating focal depths, and of evolving tables giving focal depth allowances. The unabridged equations (13) serve for further refinements.

Another complication in setting up the tables arises from the fact that in many earthquakes the principal P movement at the focus is rather small compared with the principal S movement. Thus a wave may ascend from the focus to the outer surface in the S type, and after the reflection there (near the epicentre) the reflected P wave may sometimes be recorded at a station some distance away as the first P movement. The significance of this phenomenon was first noticed by Stechschulte and Scrase, who introduced the notation sP to denote the corresponding phase on the seismogram. The notations sS, pP, pS, have analogous meanings; thus, for instance, pP corresponds to a wave which ascends from the focus to the outer surface in the P type, and then after reflection travels in the P type to the recording station.

When the phases P and pP (or S and sS, etc.) are both recorded, the differences between their arrival-times for various Δ provide a further important means of estimating focal depths.

We finally mention the possibility of using amplitude theory to check various features of the tables. For instance, we have pointed out (§ 8.4) that the occurrence of abnormal amplitudes for a range of values of Δ may assist in assessing corresponding values of $d^2T/d\Delta^2$. Amplitude data need to be used, however, with extreme caution, since amplitudes are very dependent on conditions near an observatory site, and, further, are sensitive to small changes in d^2v/dz^2 and even d^3v/dz^3 (see § 8.7).

10.5. Use of electronic computers. The iterative character of many of the foregoing procedures makes them eminently suited to the use of electronic computers, and a number of steps have already been taken in this direction.

Bolt, for example, in 1960 devised a programme based on (13) (with the term in ξ_0 omitted) whereby successive approximations to trial origin-times, epicentres and focal depths are derived at high speed. With Willmore's co-operation, the programme was adapted in 1961 for use in preparing the *International Seismological Summary* (§ 11.2.1). Electronic computing has also been introduced into epicentral determination by the *Bureau Central Séismologique International* at Strasbourg (§ 11.2) and the United States Coast and Geodetic Survey. Another instance is a programme devised by Flinn for treating local earthquakes.

10.6. Evolution of travel-time tables for phases (due to bodily waves) other than the P. As pointed out in § 10.3, the times of onset on seismograms are in general much more precisely determined for P than for other phases. In consequence, the P travel-time tables are by far the best determined and are ordinarily used in all origin-time and epicentral determinations. The process of constructing travel-times for other phases is therefore not usually complicated by having to take account of uncertainties in origin-times and epicentres.

Nevertheless, there is the possible complication that the main S wave may leave a focus at a different instant from the main P wave, so that the origin-time found for P may not necessarily be the same as that for S. This complication has been referred to as the ' Z phenomenon', and demands the use of a special parameter in the course of the construction of tables for phases where the waves leave the focus in the S type. (Actually the Z phenomenon is less important than it was at one stage thought to be.)

The greater uncertainties in the tables other than the P are accentuated by difficulties in identifying onsets after the first P. An apparently prominent onset is sometimes the result of a fortui-tous reinforcement of a number of relatively unimportant ground movements. Also it is often difficult to decide which phase is associated with a particular onset among the many genuine ones to be expected. Thus in practice there is inevitable misidentification of a proportion of onsets after the first. Efforts are made to reduce misidentifications both by statistical treatment of data and by various instrumental procedures.

There are, however, other factors which help to reduce the table uncertainties. For instance, among the many different significant earthquake phases observed, the results for one phase can often be used to check and improve the results for another phase; in-stances of the interdependence of different travel-time tables are given in § 10.6.2. Again, readings of deep-focus earthquakes can be used with advantage to improve certain of the tables. In addition, much help can be obtained from the use of specific travel-time formulae produced in chapter 7, such as $(7, (21), (22), (24), (28))$. For instance, the formula $(7, (28))$ has been used in connection with the phases PKP, PKP_2 (these are defined in the immediately following subsection), for which there is a cusp in the corresponding (T, Δ) curve.

10.6.1. Notation used for phases read on seismograms. We have already referred to the phases P, S, and the group pP, pS sP, sS.

Phases corresponding to waves that have suffered reflection a the Earth's outer surface (or possibly at one of the crustal discontinuity surfaces), the wave initially leaving the focus in a direction away from the outer surface (in contrast to pP, etc.), are denoted as PP, PPP, SS, SSS, PS, SP, PPS, etc. For instance, PS corresponds to a wave which is of P type before the reflection and of S type afterwards. In addition, there are phases such as pPP, sPP, sPS, etc. A few cases are illustrated in Fig. 35.

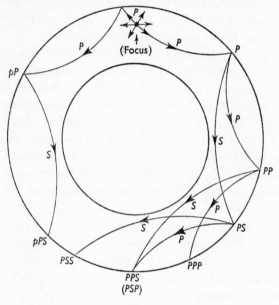

Fig. 35

Further important phases are associated with the presence of a discontinuity surface which occurs at a depth of about 2900 km below the outer surface, separating the 'central core' of the Earth from the 'mantle' (see chapter 13). The symbol c is used to indicate an upward reflection at this discontinuity. Thus if a P wave travels down from a focus to the discontinuity surface in question, the upward reflection into the S type is recorded at an observing station as the phase PcS; and similarly with PcP, ScS, ScP. A phase such as $ScSP$ would correspond to the reflection into the P type, at (or near) the outer surface, of a wave that had before reflection approached the outer surface as ScS. Phases such as $pScS$ are also significant, the symbol p corresponding as before to an initial ascent to the outer surface in the P type.

The symbol K is used to denote the part (of P type) of the path of a wave which may lie inside the central core. Thus the phase PKS corresponds to a wave that starts in the P type, is refracted into the central core into the P type, and refracted back into the mantle in the S type in which it finally emerges. Phases such as $PKKP$, etc., correspond to waves that have suffered an internal reflection at the boundary of the central core. Some cases of phases

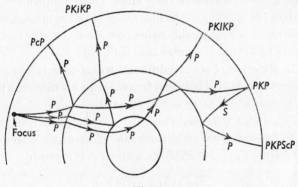

Fig. 36

corresponding to waves that have penetrated into the central core are indicated in Figs. 36, 37. In cases where the travel-time is a two-valued function of the distance (see Fig. 28(c)) the suffix 2 is sometimes used for the upper branch; this is the case, for instance, with PKP, the phase corresponding to the upper branch being denoted as PKP_2. (For more precise details concerning PKP, see §§ 10.9.1 and 13.8.3.)

Lehmann's discovery of the existence of a further discontinuity surface inside the central core (see chapter 13) made it necessary to introduce further basic symbols. For paths of waves inside the central core, the symbols i and I are used analogously to c and K for the whole Earth; thus i indicates reflection upwards at the boundary between the outer and inner portions of the central core, and I corresponds to the part (of P type) of the path of a wave which lies inside the inner portion. Thus, for instance, discrimination now needs to be made between the phases PKP, $PKiKP$ and $PKIKP$; the first of these corresponds to a wave that has entered the outer and not reached the inner portion of the central core, the second to one that has been reflected upwards at the boundary between the two portions, and the third to one that has penetrated into the inner portion.

By combining the symbols p, s, P, S, c, K, i, I in various ways, we can set down notation for all the main phases associated with bodily earthquake waves. The symbol J has been introduced to correspond to S waves in the inner core, following evidence (§ 13.8.5) on the solidity of the inner core. (The symbol Z was once proposed for S waves in the outer core, but there is now strong evidence (§ 13.3) that the outer core is fluid.)

10.6.2. Relations between different travel-time tables. We now show some connections between travel-times for different phases.

A very simple instance is the connection between the travel-times of P, PP, PPP, etc. Thus, if we consider foci at the outer surface and assume that reflections take place at the outer surface, the travel-time T_{PPP} for PPP for a given Δ is given by

$$T_{PPP}(\Delta) = 3T_P(\tfrac{1}{3}\Delta), \tag{24}$$

where T_P is taken from the P travel-time table.

A case such as PS is dealt with by using the fact that the parameter p of a seismic ray is by (6, (1)) and (7, (1)) the same before and after a reflection. Hence by (7, (2)) the travel-time T_{PS} for a given distance Δ is given by

$$\left.\begin{aligned}
T_{PS}(\Delta) &= T_P(\Delta_1) + T_S(\Delta_2), \\
\text{where} \qquad \Delta_1 + \Delta_2 &= \Delta \quad \text{and} \quad dT_P/d\Delta_1 = dT_S/d\Delta_2.
\end{aligned}\right\} \tag{25}$$

Use of the last of these equations involves matching gradients in the P and S travel-time tables.

The equations (24) and (25) are actually used in preparing theoretical travel-time tables for PPP and PS; and similarly with PP, SS, PPS, etc. We note, however, that there are discrepancies between these theoretical tables and the indications of seismogram readings; the latter show considerable scatter. This is to be expected, since reflections are liable to occur at any of the discontinuities in the Earth's upper layers, and such reflections will (depending on the angles of incidence, etc.) sometimes carry more energy than a wave reflected right from the outer surface.

Another instance of a relation between travel-times is that for the phases ScS, SKS and $SKKS$, which incidentally has proved useful in evolving tables for them. Thus, if $T_{ScS}(\Delta)$ be the travel-time for ScS for the distance Δ, etc., we have, neglecting focal depth,

$$\left.\begin{array}{c} T_{ScS}(\Delta_1) + T_{SKKS}(\Delta_3) = 2T_{SKS}(\Delta_2), \\ \Delta_1 + \Delta_3 = 2\Delta_2 \\ dT_{ScS}/d\Delta_1 = dT_{SKKS}/d\Delta_3 = dT_{SKS}/d\Delta_2. \end{array}\right\} \quad (26)$$

where and

The derivation of (26) is easily seen from a study of Fig. 37.

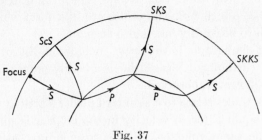

Fig. 37

It is clear that many other relations similar to those exhibited in (24), (25) and (26) can be set down.

10.6.3. Available travel-time tables of bodily waves. As a result of the quality of the early Milne seismograph, useful instrumental records of earthquakes began to accumulate towards the end of the nineteenth century, and the beginning of the present century saw the introduction of travel-time tables by Oldham. The first widely used tables were constructed by Zöppritz in 1907. Oldham in 1906 drew attention to the existence of the central core, and in 1914 Gutenberg prepared a comprehensive set of tables, including tables for a number of phases corresponding to waves that penetrate into the central core.

The Zöppritz tables were later adapted by Turner for use in the

International Seismological Summary for earthquakes occurring between 1918 and 1929.

In 1930, Jeffreys, starting from the Zöppritz–Turner tables, inaugurated a series of successive approximations towards improved tables, and was joined by the writer in 1931. In 1935 the first Jeffreys–Bullen tables were produced. Substantial refinements were incorporated in a new set of 'J. B.' tables first published in 1940. These tables give travel-times for the phases P, S, pP, sS, PP, PPP, PS, SP, PPS, SPP, PSP, SS, SSP, PSS, SPS, SSS, PcP, PcS, ScP, ScS, $ScSP$, PKP (sometimes denoted P'), PKS, SKP, SKS, $PKKP$, $PKKS$, $SKKP$, $SKKS$, $SKKKS$, $PcPPKP$, $PcSPKP$, $ScSPKP$, $SKSP$, $PKPPKP$, $PKPPKS$. Auxiliary tables are given for sP, $sPKP$, $sPcP$, $sPKS$, $sSKP$ and $pPKP$. Tables are included for K, KIK and I, corresponding to paths within the central core. Compatible tables for near-earthquake phases are also included. The tables are in a form which enables focal depth to be readily taken into account.

The last paragraph incidentally includes a list of the more important earthquake phases due to bodily waves. Additional phases are, however, observed.

The J. B. tables relate to a standard model Earth in which each surface of equal P (or S) velocity in the interior is spherical and encloses the same volume as the corresponding surface of the actual Earth. The aim of the tables is to serve as a standard for the 'average' global earthquake.

The next step is to evolve auxiliary tables containing allowances for regional geographic deviations from the average. Auxiliary tables allowing for the Earth's ellipticity of figure are already available (see §§ 10.7, 10.9.2), and progress, as yet far from final, has been made in assembling data to determine allowances for further regional differences.

Travel-time tables and charts have been independently constructed by Gutenberg and Richter, Byerly, Macelwane, Miss Lehmann, Hodgson, Brunner and a number of other seismologists. With the exception of Gutenberg and Richter, most authors have used a much less extensive set of data than was used in preparing the J. B. tables; many tables are special to intensive studies of the seismograms of relatively small sets of earthquakes. Such tables have, however, directed attention to special points of interest; for example, Byerly's tables for the Montana earthquake of 1925 June 28 gave the first indication of peculiarities in the P travel-times near 20° (see chapter 13). The tables of Gutenberg and Richter are in the main in good accord with the J. B. tables.

With the large increase of first-class seismological observatories since World War II, there has been a big increase in reliable arrival-time data. The application of nuclear explosions to seismic problems has further provided a quantity of valuable data directly on travel-times (see chapter 16). The newer data already show the J. B. tables to be in need of some correction, although (see § 13.2) there are reasons for not applying unfinished corrections at the present stage.

An essential feature of the work of Jeffreys has been the consistent use of statistical procedures, including χ^2 and other significance tests. The procedures, many of which were newly evolved by Jeffreys for the purpose, are indispensable in combining large quantities of arrival-time data, as well as in assessing the reliabilities of results. It is only through these procedures that meaning can be attached to the notion of 'average earthquake', and the procedures will accordingly be needed when the J. B. tables are amended.

10.7. Effect of the Earth's ellipticity. In 1933, Comrie, and Gutenberg and Richter, pointed out that the use of geocentric instead of geographic latitudes (which had always been used previously) would reduce errors in travel-time tables due to neglect of the Earth's ellipticity. (The *geographic latitude* of a place is the angle between the normal to the level surface at the place and the plane of the equator; the *geocentric latitude* is the angle between the radius vector from the Earth's centre to the place and the plane of the equator.) These errors were becoming increasingly important with the increasing accuracy of the travel-time tables, and Jeffreys subsequently obtained a formula for the ellipticity effect.

We introduce spherical polar coordinates (r, θ, ϕ), the origin being at the Earth's centre, and take $\theta = 0$ at the focus of a particular earthquake. To begin with we take the focus to be at the outer surface, and we consider the travel-time along any ray. For the model Earth defined in § 10.6.3, we have, using notation in chapter 7,

$$T = \int ds/v,$$
$$\left(\frac{ds}{d\theta}\right)^2 = \left(\frac{dr}{d\theta}\right)^2 + r^2 + r^2 \sin^2\theta \left(\frac{d\phi}{d\theta}\right)^2.$$

For the actual Earth, we write correspondingly

$$T' = \int ds'/v,$$
$$\left(\frac{ds'}{d\theta}\right)^2 = \left(\frac{dr'}{d\theta}\right)^2 + r'^2 + r'^2 \sin^2\theta \left(\frac{d\phi'}{d\theta}\right)^2,$$

and we assume v to be known as a function of r. (This will be the case, to sufficient accuracy, using travel-times as determined neglecting ellipticity and using the theory of § 7.4.)

Since for the model we have $d\phi/d\theta = 0$ along a ray, it follows that for the actual Earth $d\phi'/d\theta$ is small. Hence, writing

$$\delta r = r' - r, \quad \delta T = T' - T,$$

we have, correct to the first order of small quantities,

$$\delta T = \int_0^\Delta v^{-1}\left\{\left(\frac{dr'}{d\theta}\right)^2 + r'^2\right\}^{\frac{1}{2}} d\theta - \int_0^\Delta v^{-1}\left\{\left(\frac{dr}{d\theta}\right)^2 + r^2\right\}^{\frac{1}{2}} d\theta$$
$$= \int_0^\Delta \tfrac{1}{2}v^{-1}\left\{\left(\frac{dr}{d\theta}\right)^2 + r^2\right\}^{-\frac{1}{2}} \left\{2\frac{dr}{d\theta}\frac{d\delta r}{d\theta} + 2r\,\delta r\right\} d\theta$$
$$= p\int_0^\Delta r^{-2}\left(\frac{dr}{d\theta}\frac{d\delta r}{d\theta} + r\,\delta r\right) d\theta,$$

where in obtaining the last line, use has been made of the relation (7, (5)). This gives the formula obtained by Jeffreys, namely,

$$\delta T = p\left[r^{-2}\frac{dr}{d\theta}\delta r\right]_0^\Delta + p\int_0^\Delta \left(\frac{d^2 r^{-1}}{d\theta^2} + r^{-1}\right)\delta r\,d\theta. \tag{27}$$

The first term in (27) is readily seen (using (7, (1)) and the relation $|r\,d\theta/dr| = \tan i$—see Fig. 24, p. 111) to be equal to $[v^{-1}\delta r \cos i]_{0,\Delta}$; this represents the time along the extra lengths at the two ends of the actual ray projecting outside the outer boundary of the model (such an extra length and time will of course be negative if δr is negative). The second term involves an integration along the whole length of the ray. On expressing the second term in the form

$$-p\int_0^\Delta (\rho \sin^3 i)^{-1}\,\delta r\,d\theta$$

(see (7, (35))), where ρ is the radius of curvature of the ray, we see that if for a particular ray δr everywhere has the same sign, this second term will be opposite in sign to the first (assuming, which is sufficiently near to the actual circumstances, that ρ is always positive). This result is to be expected from the fact that where δr is positive the internal layers of higher velocities are displaced outwards slightly, and so cause an increase in velocity along the corresponding part of the actual ray, above that pertaining to the Earth model.

The equation of a surface of equal velocity within the actual Earth is given to sufficient accuracy by

$$r' = r\{1 + \epsilon(\tfrac{1}{3} - \cos^2\theta')\}, \tag{28}$$

where ϵ is the ellipticity of the surface, and θ' denotes the geocentric colatitude of a point. Hence

$$\delta r = \epsilon r(\tfrac{1}{3} - \cos^2\theta'). \tag{29}$$

By (27) and (29), it is possible, using formulae in chapter 7, to express the ellipticity correction in the form

$$\delta T = \epsilon_0[(\tfrac{1}{3} - \cos^2\theta')\,(\eta^2 - p^2)^{\frac{1}{2}}]_{0,\,\Delta} + p^{-1}\int_0^\Delta \epsilon(\tfrac{1}{3} - \cos^2\theta')\,\eta^3\frac{dv}{dr}d\theta, \tag{30}$$

where ϵ_0 is the ellipticity of the Earth's outer surface.

In chapter 13 we shall indicate a method of estimating values of ϵ throughout the Earth. Hence, using (30), it is possible to construct tables giving values of the ellipticity correction δT to be applied for any particular ray.

The above theory assumes the focus to be at the outer surface of the Earth. The ellipticity corrections are small, however, and it has been shown that the tables for surface-focus earthquakes give the corrections to sufficient accuracy for all deep-focus earthquakes as well.

10.8. Travel-times of surfaces waves. Seismic surface waves with periods up to the order of a minute, unlike bodily waves, are largely confined to the vicinity of the Earth's outer surface. The records of surface waves are thus much influenced by crustal structures and may vary very much with the azimuth from the epicentre. In addition they are subject to marked dispersion (see chapter 5). Hence in most respects they do not lend themselves to the construction of global travel-time tables as in the case of bodily waves, and require special consideration as set down in chapters 5 and 12.

In routine observatory work, it has been the custom to denote the onset on a seismogram of the first surface waves (recognised by their longer periods) by the symbol L. (The symbol M has been used to denote the time of arrival of maximum amplitudes, but does not serve a useful physical purpose.)

Stoneley showed that the frequency distributions of travel-times of L for given ranges of Δ are strongly double-humped, and pointed out that the two peaks would correspond to the onsets of Love and Rayleigh waves, respectively. The onsets are denoted as LQ and LR (Q for *Querwellen*, an alternative name for Love waves) and Stoneley found the corresponding travel-rates to be about 4·43 and 3·97 km/sec, respectively. The travel-rates are fairly independent of the paths traversed and so it is useful to take these phases into account along with bodily wave phases.

10.9. Numerical results. We now give a number of typical travel-times from the Jeffreys–Bullen tables. For more complete details, the reader is referred to Jeffreys and Bullen, *Seismological Tables* (Brit. Assoc. for Adv. of Science, Gray-Milne Trust, 1958). In § 10.9.2 an indication will be given of the ellipticity corrections; and in § 10.9.3, of the times for LQ and LR.

10.9.1. The Jeffreys–Bullen seismological tables. The J. B. tables apply to the model Earth as defined in § 10.6.3.

The P tables give the travel-time T in terms of the epicentral distance Δ for $0° \leqslant \Delta \leqslant 105°$ for fourteen different focal depths, corresponding respectively to foci at the level of the outer surface and at the levels $h = 0·00, 0·01, ..., 0·12$, where h denotes fractions of the distance between the base of the crustal layers and the centre of the model. Typical results are:

Δ	Surface focus		$h = 0\cdot00$		$h = 0\cdot05$		$h = 0\cdot10$	
	min	sec	min	sec	min	sec	min	sec
$10°$	2	28·0	2	24·4	2	18·8	2	19·9
$50°$	8	58·0	8	53·1	8	21·6	7	58·1
$100°$	13	48·4	13	43·1	13	7·1	12	37·3

There is a complication in the vicinity of $\Delta = 20°$, due to the (T, Δ) relation being of the form indicated in Fig. 25 (c). The main P tables apply to the branch giving the smallest value of T for a given Δ, separate tables being included for the other branches; the notation P_d, P_u, P_r is used for phases corresponding to the three branches $A''B''$, $C''B''$, $C''D''$, respectively (the letters d, u, r being initial letters of the words *direct*, *upper* and *refracted*). Auxiliary tables are given for special use with short epicentral distances, and also for foci at specific levels within the crustal layers.

Similar remarks apply to the S tables (including the same complication near $\Delta = 20°$). Typical results for S are:

Δ	Surface focus		$h = 0\cdot00$		$h = 0\cdot05$		$h = 0\cdot10$	
	min	sec	min	sec	min	sec	min	sec
$10°$	4	22·2	4	16·6	4	8·6	4	11·9
$50°$	16	8·6	16	0·3	15	4·4	14	22·2
$100°$	25	20·4	25	11·5	24	6·9	23	13·2

The P and S tables are supplemented by tables giving the excesses of the travel-times of pP over P and of sS over S. For the case $pP - P$, typical results are:

Δ	$h = 0\cdot00$	$h = 0\cdot05$		$h = 0\cdot10$	
	sec	min	sec	min	sec
$30°$	10	1	6		—
$50°$	10	1	12	1	58
$100°$	11	1	23	2	22

These tables are useful in the study of deep-focus earthquakes.

Tables for other phases are given in detail for a surface focus, and there are auxiliary tables giving sufficiently accurate allowances for focal depth. The following results illustrate this in the case of the phase PPP:

		Surface focus			
Δ	$10°$		$100°$		$200°$
	min	sec	min	sec	min	sec
T	2	43	20	5	32	44

Focal depth allowances (to be subtracted)

Δ	$h = 0·00$ sec	$h = 0·05$ sec	$h = 0·10$ sec
10°	3	—	—
100°	5	34	53
200°	5	39	65

With phases such as the group PSS, SSP, SPS, the travel-times for a surface focus are, of course, the same in each case, but separate tables for the focal depth allowances have to be used for PSS on the one hand, and SSP, SPS on the other.

The following are extracts from the tables for certain other important phases, corresponding to a surface focus (focal depth allowances are given as with PPP):

Δ	PcP min sec	ScS min sec	PKP min sec	PKP_2 min sec	SKS min sec
0°	8 34·3	15 35·7	—	—	—
10°	8 39·0	15 44·6	—	—	—
50°	10 18·3	18 47·8	—	—	—
100°	13 48·5	25 20·7	—	—	{24 27·0 ⎰ 25 24·9
143°	—	—	19 33·5	19 33·5	26 43·9
180°	—	—	20 12·2	22 10·6	27 13·5

We note incidentally from the PKP table that a disturbance will travel from a surface focus F to the *anticentre* (the point on the opposite side of the Earth cut by the diameter through F) in a little more than 20 min.

The travel-time curve for the type PKP is rather complicated in the vicinity of $Δ = 143°$. Near this value of $Δ$ there is a cusp of the type indicated in the curve $C''D''E''$ of Fig. 28 (c); this cusp is a consequence of a sudden diminution in the P velocity across the boundary of the central core. The upper branch, (i) say, corresponding to $D''C''$ runs from $Δ = 143°$ to $Δ = 180°$, and is the one commonly denoted as PKP_2. The lower branch, (ii) say, corresponding to $D''E''$ runs continuously only from $Δ = 143°$ to about $Δ = 147°$; this is because of the velocity jump between the outer and inner parts of the central core (see chapter 13), which results in there being another branch, (iii) say, corresponding to $C''D''$ of Fig. 27 (c), which runs from about $Δ = 110°$ to $Δ = 180°$. (It is possible that there may be also a fourth branch corresponding to

$C''B''$ of Fig. 25 (c); whether this is the case or not depends on whether the boundary between the outer and inner core is sharp enough to produce detectable reflections.) The branch (iii) crosses the branch (i) near $\Delta = 144°$ and the branch (ii) near $\Delta = 145°$. Thus three phases occur very close together for $143° \leqslant \Delta \leqslant 147°$. Separate notation for the branches (ii) and (iii) has not as yet been introduced, the symbol PKP being generally used to denote the earliest arrival in the PKP type. (For still further complications, see § 13.8.3.)

The two values in the above table for SKS at $\Delta = 100°$ correspond to two branches in the travel-time curve. These two branches are due to the excess of the P velocity near the outer boundary of the central core over the S velocity near the base of the mantle (see chapter 13), and the circumstances are as in Fig. 27 (c). One branch runs from about $\Delta = 62°$ to $\Delta = 133°$, and the other from about $\Delta = 99°$ to $\Delta = 180°$. The two branches meet near $\Delta = 133°$, so that there is only one SKS phase for $133° \leqslant \Delta \leqslant 180°$. The first branch crosses the main S curve at $\Delta = 83°$; when $\Delta > 83°$, SKS precedes S.

There are similar complications with a number of other phases. But the above cases illustrate the main features.

The following tables apply to portions of paths within the central core:

Δ	K		KIK		I	
	min	sec	min	sec	min	sec
10°	1	14·6	—		0	19·5
50°	5	48·2	—		1	34·6
100°	9	39·7	9	59·8	2	50·8
140°	—		11	9·7	3	29·0
180°	—		11	37·9	3	42·1

In these tables, the K times correspond to paths in the outer but not the inner part of the central core, the KIK times to paths terminating at the outer boundary of the core but penetrating the inner part, and the I times to paths in the inner part of the core alone.

10.9.2. Ellipticity tables. The following table gives values of the ellipticities of internal strata of equal (P or S) velocity within the Earth as calculated by the method to be indicated in § 13.7.

In this table, d denotes the depth in kilometres below the Earth's outer surface and ϵ the ellipticity; values are also given for η, where

$$\eta = \frac{d(\log \epsilon)}{d(\log r)}, \qquad (31)$$

where r denotes the distance from the Earth's centre (η as here defined is, of course, distinct from the η we have used in previous sections). This parameter η is useful in a number of problems in geophysics:

d	0	1000	2000	3000	4000	5000	6000
η	0·56	0·48	0·46	0·16	0·21	?	0·00
ϵ	0·00337	0·00309	0·00280	0·00257	0·00242	0·0021	0·0021

The values of ϵ are probably accurate within 0·00002 for $d \leqslant 3000$ km, but may have errors up to about 0·0004 below this level.

Ellipticity corrections to the travel-time tables have been prepared for the phases P, S, PKP, PKS, SKP, SKS, $SKKS$, PcP, PcS, ScP, ScS, corresponding to the use of geocentric latitudes in calculating values of Δ. Tables are also available for the first five of these phases when geographic latitudes are used. The tables give the corrections in terms of the colatitude of an epicentre, and the epicentral distance and azimuth of an observing station.

For P waves, the ellipticity corrections corresponding to the use of geocentric latitudes range from -0.9 to $+1.0$ sec, and with geographic latitudes from -1.7 to $+2.7$ sec. The corresponding ranges for S are -1.7 to $+1.7$ and -3.3 to $+5.1$ sec.

When geocentric latitudes are used, the application of the ellipticity corrections is facilitated by use of the approximate formula

$$\delta T = f(\Delta)(h_0 + h_1), \qquad (32)$$

where h_0, h_1 are the values of δr at the epicentre and at the observing station, and $f(\Delta)$ is a function of Δ alone given by auxiliary tables (δT and δr are as defined as in § 10.7). The values of δr range from -14 km at the Earth's poles to $+7$ km at the equator. In the case of P, $f(\Delta)$ ranges from zero at $\Delta = 0°$ to 0·07 sec/km at $\Delta = 105°$; in the case of S, from zero to 0·13 sec/km.

Formulae of the form (32) may also be used in the case of the following phases, the numbers in brackets giving the range of variation of $f(\Delta)$ in sec/km: PKP (0·07 to 0·10); SKS and $SKKS$ (0·10 to 0·14); PcP (0·05 to 0·07); PcS and ScP (0·08); ScS (0·09 to 0·13).

For PKS and SKP, the forms

$$\delta T = f(\Delta)\,(h_0 + h_1 + \tfrac{1}{4}h_1), \qquad (33)$$

$$\delta T = f(\Delta)\,(h_0 + h_1 + \tfrac{1}{4}h_0), \qquad (34)$$

respectively, are necessary, with $f(\Delta)$ varying from 0·08 to 0·11 sec/km.

The maximum errors in the ellipticity corrections obtained using the approximate formulae (32), (33) and (34) are within 0·3 sec for P, and within 0·5 sec for most of the other phases.

In earlier work in seismology, geographic latitudes were always used in calculations of epicentral distances, and earlier tables giving the constants A', B', C' (§ 10.2) for the world's observatories were computed using geographic latitudes. Tables are available which enable the conversion from geographic to geocentric angular distances to be made (British Ass. for the Adv. of Science, Gray-Milne Trust, 1938). In 1938, Comrie recomputed the constants A', B', C', using geocentric latitudes, and geocentric latitudes are now regularly used in seismic calculations.

In 1937, the writer showed that if a special 'seismological latitude' β, defined by $\beta = 1 \cdot 1\beta_1 - 0 \cdot 1\beta_2,$ (35)

where β_1 and β_2 are the geocentric and geographic latitudes, were used in place of β_1 in computing epicentral distances, the formula (32) would give the P and S ellipticity corrections within the remarkably small maximum errors of 0·07 and 0·13 sec, respectively, for all Δ and Z.

Another point of interest, noted by Jeffreys, is that seismological data alone would enable the ellipticity of the Earth's outer surface to be estimated within an uncertainty of one-sixth.

10.9.3. Stoneley's tables for LQ and LR. The following are extracts from Stoneley's tables for the surface wave phases LQ and LR:

Δ	60°	100°	140°	180°
	min	min	min	min
LQ	25·1	42·0	59·0	76·1
LR	28·1	47·0	66·0	85·0

CHAPTER 11

THE SEISMOLOGICAL OBSERVATORY

Since the greater part of the data used by the theoretical seismologist emerges from readings made of seismograms traced inside observatories, it is desirable that we should include a short account of the organization of observatory work.

A typical seismological observatory has three main functions to fulfil, namely, (i) the satisfactory recording of local earth movements due to distant and also (ii) to near earthquakes, and (iii) attending to special aspects of local earthquake problems. In the following sections we shall comment briefly on the equipment and routine procedure in observatories, and on the process of compilation of data on local and world-wide earthquakes.

11.1. Inside the observatory. A well-equipped seismological observatory has seismographs that record the vertical and two horizontal (usually the N.–S. and E.–W.) components of the local ground motion, and has several instruments for each component.

The ground motions which can be measured cover a vast spectrum with periods ranging from fractions of a second to the order of an hour. For a simple ground motion of the form $u = a \cos pt$, equations such as $(9, (13\text{--}15))$ show that the response of a particular seismograph varies very much with the period $2\pi/p$ of the motion. Hence it is desirable to have a variety of seismographs each concerned primarily with a different section of the spectrum. Seismographs were classified at an early stage into 'short', 'intermediate' and 'long', according as the effective instrumental periods $2\pi/\omega$ are between about 0·1 and 2 sec, 2 and 12 sec, and 12 sec and 1 min, respectively. Latterly 'ultra-long' period instruments capable of measuring ground-motion periods much in excess of a minute have been developed.

In general working practice, short-period seismographs are most useful for recording near earthquakes, where the predominant periods are normally less than a second. Long-period seismographs are better for more distant earthquakes which generally produce surface waves with periods in excess of 10 sec. Many observatories have only short- and long-period seismographs; when only a single instrument can be afforded, the chosen period is commonly about 6–8 sec. The better observatories contain instruments with at least three widely separated periods.

When the observatory is in a seismically active region, it usually has in addition a strong-motion seismograph (§ 18.8), of low sensitivity, which will not ordinarily be put out of action by a strong local earthquake.

A limited number of observatories contain ultra-long-period seismographs which are used to investigate less routine aspects of the recording of earthquakes. Special instruments such as Benioff's strain seismograph may be set up under observatory control at sites well removed from the observatory proper.

The selection of the site for a seismological observatory is a matter of some importance. It is desirable that seismographs should be firmly set up on a hard rock foundation if possible, since extraneous local 'noise' is more readily introduced through soft ground. Some observatories are seriously troubled with microseisms (see § 18.5), which are superposed on and may mask important parts of the record of an earthquake. When the microseisms have a prevailing period, it is sometimes possible to reduce their effects by making adjustments to instrumental constants.

It is very evident from the theory given in chapter 10 that a highly accurate time service is necessary in conjunction with the running of the seismographs. Much importance attaches to having the absolute time available, and the data from observing stations in which only time-intervals can be measured are of relatively low utility. One method of indicating the time on a seismogram is to have the pen raised from the paper, or the light shut off in the case of photographic recording, during the sixtieth second of each minute, this signal being omitted at every exact hour. The error in the clock giving these signals is recorded at regular intervals of a day or less. Accuracy to 0·1 sec in reading seismograms is now commonly sought for some phases, and accuracy to at least a second is required in the reading of most bodily wave phases.

Sometimes allowance is made for variation of the rate of rotation of the drum as revealed by different lengths of the trace in different minute intervals.

Since the times of occurrence of natural earthquakes are not known in advance, seismographs have to be in operation continuously. In routine work the rate of rotation of the drum is generally between 0·8 and 6 cm/min; the faster rates are desirable in near-earthquake recording.

Seismograms are removed from the drums when complete, developed in the case of photographic recording, and read. Various measuring devices are used in the process of reading, which involves noting the Greenwich civil time of each onset on the seismogram that is judged to be significant. The development of the necessary judgment is a matter involving long experience. After the readings have been made, travel-time tables, and charts and diagrams derived from the tables, are used to identify phases. Usually there remain some unidentified phases which should be reported as such and may later prove to be important in the further development of seismology.

It is imperative that travel-time tables, or devices derived from them, should not be brought to bear until after the seismograms have been read. Prior to the production of the J.B. tables, this was not a serious matter because the earlier tables contained so many large errors that they could be used only as a general guide; in fact the unidentified readings of earlier days, when subjected to appropriate statistical tests, provided some of the most valuable data used in evolving the J.B. tables. The very reliability of modern tables, however, sometimes tempts a routine reader of seismograms to record apparent onsets near the expected arrival-times of particular pulses and to disregard equally prominent onsets arriving at other times. The result is lack of objectivity which can impede the task of finding further improvements to the tables.

The readings when made are transmitted to various centres (see § 11.2) which co-ordinate the readings of particular earthquakes at different stations, and make estimates of epicentres, origin-times, focal depths and other features of the earthquakes. In the transmitted details, the symbols i and e (corresponding to *impetus* and *emersio*) are commonly prefixed before the times for individual phases, indicating respectively a sharp and a gradual onset.

11.1.1. Interpretation of seismograms. An experienced reader of seismograms will usually be able to decide quickly whether the trace made by a particular earthquake is due to a normal or a deep-focus earthquake. A deep-focus earthquake is detected by the (usually) relatively small amplitudes of the surface waves, by observations of phases such as pP, sS, $sScS$ (see § 15.5.1), and by marked deviations in the arrival-times of particular pulses from those for a normal earthquake (see tables in § 10.9.1).

We have already mentioned that the identification of particular phases on a seismogram requires some skill. Moreover, the appearance of a seismogram depends to a considerable extent on characteristics of the recording seismograph; for example, Gutenberg and Richter have identified the phases PcP, ScS on records of normal earthquakes made by short-period vertical component seismographs incapable of recording long surface waves.

There are, however, a number of guiding principles which help in general in the reading of seismograms of normal earthquakes. The following selection of results derived from travel-time and amplitude data and based on experience of Lee and of Gutenberg and Richter is of help in this connection:

(i) Except close to the epicentre, the first movement for distances up to $105°$ corresponds to the main P phase; movements corresponding to the main S phase are fairly large up to about $100°$.

(ii) If $\Delta > 83°$, the phase SKS precedes S; but if $\Delta < 100°$, SKS is weaker than S.

(iii) PS, SP, PPS, PSP, SPP cannot appear unless $\Delta > 40°$; but if $\Delta > 80°$, PS and PSP are stronger than P.

(iv) For $105° < \Delta < 142°$, the first prominent phase is PP, and the second is PPP or PKS (depending on the particular value of Δ); PS, PSP are large; SKS is weaker than $SKKS$.

(v) For $130° < \Delta < 140°$, PKS is usually the largest phase in the earlier part of the seismogram; after PKS, a fairly large number of phases arrive at close intervals and close comparison with travel-time tables is usually necessary.

(vi) Near $\Delta = 142°$, PKP appears strongly; for $143° < \Delta < 180°$, the first phases correspond to two branches of PKP.

(vii) Near $\Delta = 160°$, it is frequently difficult to pick out distinct phases, the motion often appearing very complicated but without clear signs of new onsets; SS and sometimes SSS may be large.

(viii) Near $\Delta = 180°$, there is an appreciable interval between the earth movements due to bodily waves and those due to surface waves, and the seismogram may have the appearance of being a record of two separate disturbances.

Gutenberg and Richter have drawn attention to three specific errors that are the most frequently made in the reading of seismograms. These are:

(i) the identification of PP and PS as P and S when Δ is about 115–120°, leading to a false estimate of about 80° for Δ;

(ii) the identification of SKS as S when $\Delta > 83°$;

(iii) in the case of a deep-focus earthquake, the identification of pP or some similar phase as S, leading to a too small estimate of Δ, the earthquake being possibly falsely interpreted as a local shock.

As pointed out by Lehmann and Plett, the error (ii) may be avoided by noting that SKS must, due to its path in the P type in the central core, arrive polarised in the SV type; whereas S arrives in general in both SH and SV types.

The foregoing remarks apply in the main to seismograms of distant earthquakes. Phases of near-earthquake seismograms will be discussed in chapter 12.

11.1.2. Preliminary determination of epicentres. With some single observatories and small groups of observatories, it is the custom to make provisional estimates of the epicentres, etc., of the more important earthquakes. These estimates serve to give early information locally about particular earthquakes, and they serve also as first approximations in the calculations subsequently made by the large co-ordinating centres.

In the case of a single observatory, an earthquake's epicentre can often be estimated from the readings of two (perpendicular) horizontal component seismograms. For example, for a normal earthquake the epicentral distance if less than 105° is indicated by the interval between the arrival-times of P and S; the azimuth (subject to an ambiguity of 180°—but there are usually prior reasons for accepting one of the two thus indicated locations as the more probable) is indicated by a comparison of the sizes and directions of the first movements shown in the seismograms. It should be noted, however, that Richter and others have observed that in certain regions the first movement at some stations has arrived from a direction differing slightly from the direction towards the epicentre.

When data from more than one observatory are available, an earthquake's epicentre may be estimated from the indicated epicentral distances.

In the process of these provisional determinations, use is made of various devices such as globes and map projections. At Kew, there is a globe of diameter about 46 cm (4 cm of arc correspond to an angular distance of 10°) on which distances and azimuths are directly measured to good accuracy. The azimuths determined in this way are in fact usually adequate for most seismological purposes, and recourse to formulae such as (10, (7)) and (10, (8)) is often unnecessary. A commonly used map projection is the stereographic projection to which we shall now refer briefly.

11.1.3. Use of stereographic projection. Let V be a fixed point on the surface of a given sphere of centre O, and let π be the plane through O perpendicular to OV. Then the stereographic projection of any point P of the sphere's surface, corresponding to the vertex of projection V and the plane π, is the point in which VP (produced if necessary) meets the plane π.

An important property of this stereographic projection is that any circle on the sphere's surface is projected into a circle on the plane π.

In seismological applications, V is commonly taken at the south pole of a sphere (of radius r_0 say—in practice r_0 is often taken equal to 10 cm) representing the Earth (taken spherical). Thus the plane π passes through the equator, the north pole is projected into the point O, and meridian lines are projected into straight lines radiating from O.

Now suppose that, as a result of readings of seismograms, the angular distances of the epicentre Q of a particular earthquake from a set of given observatories are known approximately. Let θ, ϕ be the colatitude and (east) longitude of any one, R say, of the observatories, and let Δ be approximately the angular distance RQ. Then the epicentre Q must lie near the circumference of a small circle of the sphere with centre on OR and of angular radius Δ. It may be shown by elementary trigonometry that the stereographic projection of this small circle on to the plane π is a circle whose centre is at a distance $r_0 \sin \theta / (\cos \theta + \cos \Delta)$ from O along the projection of the meridian line corresponding to ϕ, and whose radius is $r_0 \sin \Delta / (\cos \theta + \cos \Delta)$. The circles on the plane π obtained in this way for the set of observatories will then intersect near the projection of the epicentre Q, which is thus approximately determined.

11.2. International seismological organisations.

11.2. International seismological organisations. From 1841 onwards, reports on earthquake investigations appeared intermittently in the *General Reports* of the British Association, and from 1881 were prepared regularly by Milne. Milne subsequently (at Shide in the Isle of Wight) produced the 'Shide circulars' which dealt with earthquakes from 1899. The earliest known list of instrumentally recorded earthquakes with computed origin-times and epicentres is that for the period 1899–1903.

An International Association of Seismology was founded in 1905 at a meeting of representatives of 23 sovereign States in Berlin, and met in Rome in 1906 where it was decided to establish an international station at Strasbourg. After difficulties caused through World War I, a Central Bureau was re-established at Strasbourg (now in France) under the direction of E. Rothé, and arrangements were made for the preparation and publication at Oxford of the *International Seismological Summary* (*I.S.S.*) in succession to the Shide circulars and British Association Reports. The first *I.S.S.*, that for earthquakes of 1918, appeared in 1923. The Central Bureau at Strasbourg (B.C.I.S.), now directed by J.-P. Rothé, and the *I.S.S.*, directed initially by Turner and later by Jeffreys and Stoneley, have closely collaborated over the years.

In 1951, the International Association became the International Association of Seismology and the Physics of the Interior of the Earth (I.A.S.P.I.E.).

The B.C.I.S. issues provisional bulletins giving epicentres, origin-times, etc., and a selection of station readings, for all main earthquakes; the bulletins appear within about twelve months of the earthquake occurrence. The *I.S.S.* waits until fairly complete station readings have been received from most of the world's observatories before starting to carry out computations on an earthquake, and its coverage is wide and detailed. A short description of the *I.S.S.* is given in § 11.2.1.

International seismological services are also provided by other organisations. Specially valuable are the services of the United States Coast and Geodetic Survey, which receives readings by telegram from a world-wide selection of stations, and issues, within a fortnight of the occurrence, cards giving rapidly estimated origin-times and focal locations of all larger earthquakes. The U.S.C.G.S. and the Jesuit Seismological Association also issue global earthquake bulletins. The Dominion Observatory at Ottawa issues a *Bibliography of Seismology*.

In addition, there are various regional centres which control networks of stations and which act as intermediaries between individual stations and the international organisations. A regional centre normally undertakes the estimation of epicentres, origin-times and focal depths of local earthquakes. By long-standing tradition, individual stations and regional centres make their readings, and copies of their seismograms where desired, available to stations and research centres throughout the world. This is the raw material from which much of the knowledge of the Earth's interior ultimately emerges.

11.2.1. The *International Seismological Summary*. The *I.S.S.* is the most comprehensive publication on earthquake occurrence. By the use of methods described in chapter 10, the *I.S.S.* has until recently determined origin-times, epicentres and the constants A, B, C, D, E, G, H, K (see § 10.2) for all earthquakes sufficiently well read to make determinations possible. For earthquakes since 1953, the growing quantity of data has, however, forced a restriction in the determinations to earthquakes of magnitudes (see § 15.2) 6 and more. Estimates of focal depth are given whenever this is greater than normal.

For earthquakes from 1918 to 1929, the Zöppritz–Turner travel-time tables were used in preparing the *I.S.S.*; from 1930 to 1936, the preliminary J. B. tables of 1935; and from 1937 onward, the J. B. tables of 1940. For each earthquake treated, there are columns showing for each recording station the epicentral distance Δ and azimuth, and the *P* and *S* arrival-times referred to the estimated origin-time as zero, together with the residuals (O–C) giving the excesses of these times over the times in the tables. *PKP* residuals are shown in square brackets for values of Δ beyond those at which the normal *P* is recorded; *SKS* and *SKKS* residuals are likewise indicated by special brackets. Times for a limited number of supplementary phases are entered, and another column gives the onset time of *L*. The letters E, N and Z after a station name indicate that the reading relates to a particular component of the ground motion; *i* and *e* indicate that an onset is of *impetus* or *emersio* type (see § 11.1); *a* and *k* indicate anaseismic and kataseismic *P* or *PKP* onsets (§ 15.7.3).

Various other features have been included in the past. Examples are the very valuable 'additional readings' which were given from 1918 to 1951, and the classification of earthquake epicentres into *N*1, *N*2, *N*3, *R*1, *R*2, *R*3, *X* (*N* = new, *R* = repeated, *X* = 'adopted' epicentre; 1, 2, 3 = good, moderate, poor determination). The *I.S.S.* has also supplied index catalogues listing locations and origin-times of earthquakes, and providing important source information on earthquake distribution. It is of interest to note that the *I.S.S.* grew from a modest 220 pages in 1918 to 1250 pages in 1952 (a year in which 'additional readings' were excluded).

11.3. Current trends. At the present time, re-organisation of the treatment of global seismological data on a large scale is being contemplated.

With the trend towards automatic computation of epicentres, etc. (see § 10.5), it is being proposed that the world's observatories supply details of their seismogram readings on special standard cards in place of the present bulletins; investigations are at present being carried out on the most suitable type of card to use, and the most suitable information to be entered on the cards. The idea is that the cards be fed into an electronic computer at an International Centre, which will compute epicentres, origin-times and other principal characteristics of the world's earthquakes, and print the results, with estimates of precision, along with further selected data. The envisaged result is a publication that will ultimately supersede the present *I.S.S.*, the whole process being mechanical from the stage where numerical data are entered on the cards to the production of the publication.

It is envisaged that the International Centre should also be responsible for such matters as compiling statistical information on earthquakes, with special reference to geographical distribution, frequency, magnitude and focal depth; compiling and maintaining a list of world stations, including precise station locations and also giving pertinent information on personnel, instruments, etc., as a function of the time; preparing special tables that can be readily processed by an electronic computer; and compiling and publishing a bibliography of seismology.

A measure of standardisation of procedures in individual observatories is also under consideration. It has been suggested that the sensitivities of all existing seismographs be determined as continuous functions of the ground period inside the range of period from 0·1 sec to at least 100 sec, and that, where feasible, instrumental constants be adjusted so to conform as closely as possible with one of a number of standard calibration curves (subject to some choice of sensitivity to suit local recording conditions).

The setting up of a limited number of Regional Centres covering large areas is also envisaged. These Centres would act as links between existing smaller centres and the International Centre, and publish epicentres, magnitudes, etc., of local earthquakes below the level treated at the International Centre. They would store copies of local records and also publish regional catalogues, including summaries of macroseismic observations (see § 18.2). A limited number of stations would be asked to include measurements of amplitudes and periods to facilitate estimates of earthquake magnitudes.

Consideration is being given to the copying of seismograms on to standard microfilm which can be sent to research centres for special study. Once a standard had been adopted, research centres would use standard projectors specially designed to enable them to scrutinise enlargements of the microfilm with the minimum of difficulty. It is envisaged that microfilm copies of all seismograms be deposited at the International Centre, and of local seismograms at Regional Centres.

Another recommendation is that seismological stations be set up in all land regions at distances apart not exceeding 1000 km. (For special studies and in many particular regions the intervals of course need to be much less than this.)

These and further proposals were considered at meetings of the International Seismological Summary Committee in 1961 and subsequently. Although it is not to be expected that the proposals will all come to pass before some years have elapsed, they reveal the present trend of thinking on organisational matters, and already some of the proposals have been translated into action. In 1963, a new International Centre was set up under the direction of Willmore in Edinburgh, where a start is being made to meet the new aspirations.

CHAPTER 12

SEISMOLOGY AND THE EARTH'S UPPER LAYERS

From the theory and the numerical results discussed in earlier chapters, it is possible to derive much information concerning the Earth's interior. In the present chapter we shall confine our attention to the outermost 40 km of the Earth. It was once thought that the Earth was composed of a comparatively thin crust resting on material in a fluid or near-fluid state. We shall see in chapter 13 that this is not the case, but the terms *crust* and *crustal layers* continue to be used in connection with the outer part of the Earth; we shall here use these terms to refer to the part of the Earth above the Mohorovičić discontinuity (see § 12.2.1).

Seismological data on the structure of the crust come from several sources, including studies of bodily waves in near earthquakes (see § 9.8) and explosions, of phases such as pP in deep-focus earthquakes, and of the dispersion of surface waves from distant earthquakes. We proceed to discuss these sources of evidence.

12.1. Theory of travel-times in near earthquakes
12.1.1. Special form of the (T, Δ) relation for near earthquakes.
For the model Earth described in chapter 7, the travel-time T and the epicentral distance Δ in the case of a surface focus are, by $(7, (7))$ and $(7, (11))$, connected by the relation

$$T = p\Delta + 2\int_{r_p}^{r_0} \left(\frac{1}{v^2} - \frac{p^2}{r^2}\right)^{\frac{1}{2}} dr, \tag{1}$$

where v is the ray speed at distance r from the centre of the model, p is the parameter of the ray, and the suffixes 0 and p are used to denote values at the outer surface and at the lowest point of the ray, respectively. By $(7, (1))$ we have $p = r_p/v_p$. Introducing $z = r_0 - r$, we may rewrite (1) in the form

$$T = \frac{r_p \Delta}{v_p} + 2\int_0^{z_p} \left\{\frac{1}{v^2} - \left(\frac{r_p}{r}\right)^2 \frac{1}{v_p^2}\right\}^{\frac{1}{2}} dz. \tag{2}$$

If the focus instead of being at the outer surface is at the depth h below this level, we need to replace the operation $2\int_0^{z_p}$ in (2) by $\left(\int_0^{z_p}+\int_h^{z_p}\right)$; this is seen on considering separately the portions of the ray on either side of the lowest point. (We are here considering rays which leave the focus in a downward direction.)

In the case of near earthquakes, a simplification arises from the fact that the rays do not penetrate to a great depth, so that r_0-r_p is small compared with r_0. In this case, we have approximately

$$T = \frac{r_0\Delta}{v_p} + \left(\int_0^{z_p}+\int_h^{z_p}\right)(v^{-2}-v_p^{-2})^{\frac{1}{2}}\,dz. \qquad (3)$$

The formula (3) may be more directly derived by neglecting the curvature of the Earth and assuming horizontal stratification from the outset. Take Ox horizontal and in the plane containing a ray whose focal depth is h, and Oz vertically downwards. Let i be the (acute) angle between the ray and the vertical at any point of its path. Since $T=\int ds/v$ taken along the path, and, by (7, (1)),

$$v = v_p\sin i, \qquad (4)$$

we have
$$T = \int v_p^{-1}\operatorname{cosec}^2 i\,dx$$

$$= \int v_p^{-1}\,dx + \int v_p^{-1}\cot^2 i\,dx$$

$$= \frac{r_0\Delta}{v_p} + \int \frac{\cot i}{v_p}\,dz, \qquad (5)$$

where $r_0\Delta$ is the epicentral distance measured as an arc-length. By (4) and (5) we immediately have (3).

In specific near-earthquake problems, it is convenient to write (3) in the form
$$T = r_0\Delta/v_p + a_p, \qquad (6)$$

noting that a_p depends only on the focal depth h and the velocity distribution down to the depth z_p.

It has already been pointed out (§ 4.3) that the extent of oscillatory movement in the earlier parts of seismograms is evidence of marked heterogeneity in the outer part of the Earth. This conclusion is confirmed in detailed studies of near earthquakes and waves from explosions, and makes it desirable to consider theory for a layered crust.

12.1.2. Application to a layered crustal structure. We shall now apply (3) and (6) to the case of a model crust consisting of a limited number m of homogeneous layers whose boundaries are parallel to the outer surface (see Fig. 38). We shall consider rays of the same type (either P or S) which issue from a given earthquake focus and are refracted without change of type through each boundary crossed. (We have seen from chapter 8 that a good part of the energy is in general carried along these rays if the changes in the properties from layer to layer are not too great.)

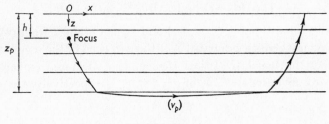

Fig. 38

We shall assume that the epicentre of the earthquake has been determined independently of the following detail, and shall take as known the distances $r_0 \Delta$ to n observing stations which record near-earthquake phases.

First, consider a particular family of rays which all have their lowest points in the same layer. We shall, on account of the smallness of the curvature of the boundaries, take as zero the depth penetrated by any ray below the lowest boundary it crosses. Then v_p and a_p are the same for all members of the family, and, by (6), T is proportional to Δ, except for the term a_p which is called the *apparent delay in starting* for the particular pulse.

From (6) we may form equations of condition to determine values of v_p and a_p for this family. A common practice has been to plot arrival-times against the Δ for all phases read on seismograms at the various stations, and to attribute to the same phase those points which appear to be associated with a particular branch of the graph.

As in § 10.4.1, we take a tentative estimate of the origin-time as zero, and let τ be the actual origin-time (referred to this zero). For a particular station, let t be the measured, and $t+\epsilon$ the actual, arrival-time for the phase in question. The actual travel-time T is $t+\epsilon-\tau$. Hence by (6)

$$(a_p+\tau)+(r_0\Delta)\,v_p^{-1}-t = \epsilon. \tag{7}$$

For the n stations, there are n equations like (7).

Since t is known, and $r_0\Delta$ is assumed known, we thus have n equations of condition to determine $(a_p+\tau)$ and v_p. The corresponding least squares solution is the solution of the pair of equations

$$n(a_p+\tau)+r_0(\Sigma\Delta)\,v_p^{-1}-\Sigma t = 0, \tag{8}$$

$$(\Sigma\Delta)\,(a_p+\tau)+r_0(\Sigma\Delta^2)\,v_p^{-1}-\Sigma(t\Delta) = 0. \tag{9}$$

Using the estimates of $(a_p+\tau)$ and v_p as obtained from (8) and (9), we may deduce estimates ϵ' of the ϵ in each of the n equations (7). By the usual statistical theory, the variances (squares of standard deviations) σ_a^2, σ_v^2 of $(a_p+\tau)$, v_p^{-1}, respectively, are given by

$$\sigma_a^2 = \frac{(\Sigma\Delta)^2}{n(\Sigma\Delta^2)-(\Sigma\Delta)^2}\frac{\Sigma\epsilon'^2}{n-2}, \tag{10}$$

$$\sigma_v^2 = \frac{n}{n(\Sigma\Delta^2)-(\Sigma\Delta)^2}\frac{\Sigma\epsilon'^2}{n-2}. \tag{11}$$

In practice, the least-squares procedure can be shortened by taking as unknown in place of v_p the small quantity y, equal to $v_p^{-1}-w_p^{-1}$, where w_p is some first approximation to v_p.

12.1.3. Error and related considerations. The equations (10) and (11) give formal measures of uncertainty in the computed $(a_p+\tau)$ and v_p. In practice there are various additional sources of uncertainty.

First, in deriving (8)–(11), the Δ have been assumed known, whereas (with a natural earthquake) the epicentre and therefore all the computed Δ are significantly uncertain. Secondly, the model conditions taken assume mathematical discontinuities between layers, constant velocity throughout any one layer, and horizontal stratification, all of which conditions may be departed from in the Earth. Thirdly, there are uncertainties in deciding on the significances of the various apparent onsets on seismograms, and in associating the onsets with specific phases. Fourthly, in deriving (8) and (9) there is the assumption that the errors ϵ are randomly distributed, whereas there is always the possibility of systematic errors contributing to the ϵ. Thus the formal uncertainties given by (10) and (11) must be regarded as *minimum* uncertainties.

At the same time, the formulae (10) and (11) are highly important, and there are strong reasons why estimates of σ_a and σ_v should accompany each near-earthquake study in which the form (6) is used. First, σ_a and σ_v give an indication of the relative quality of different sets of results. Secondly, and most important, they provide a basis through which the results from a number of single near-earthquake studies can be suitably weighted and combined by a rational procedure. The uncertainties in individual studies are commonly too high to permit significant inferences.

Failure to realise both the importance and the limitations of (10) and (11) has led to the presentation of innumerable near-earthquake studies in forms from which little use can be made.

We remark next that the model assumption of discontinuity in v is of course taken purely for mathematical convenience. It gives an adequate representation when v changes significantly over a range of depth small compared with the wave-lengths of interest; it is in this sense that the term 'discontinuity' is normally understood in seismology. Uncertainties may arise through difficulties in deciding whether a set of data is better represented in terms of a discontinuity in v at a certain depth or in terms of a continuous rapid variation of v. (The same may apply to dv/dz.)

When allowance is made for continuous variation of v with z inside a layer, this usually takes the form of a linear variation. In place of a single parameter v_p, two parameters are then required to represent the velocity in the layer. It is not difficult to extend the theory of §12.1.1 to cover this case, but the introduction of an additional parameter has the effect of increasing the formal uncertainties in the computed results.

Parameters that are introduced to deal with departures from horizontal layering likewise involve increased uncertainties. In practice when such departures are suspected, and especially in seismic prospecting (see § 18.6), there are special procedures in the gathering of data.

Finally, there is the question of the influence of the Earth's curvature, which theoretically involves deviations of the (T, Δ) relations from linearity. But by (7, (21)) the effect is only of the order of Δ^3, and at least up to $\Delta = 10°$ is quite insignificant compared with other influences.

12.1.4. Determination of layer thicknesses. We continue to consider the m-layered model crustal structure of § 12.1.2. We now let the subscript p relate to the pth layer, R_p say, from the top, and $(m + 1)$ to the region R_{m+1} just below the bottom layer R_m. Let H_p be the thickness of $R_p (p = 1, ..., m)$, and let h be the depth of the earthquake focus below the outer surface.

We shall assume that $v_p < v_{p+1}$ $(p = 1, ..., m)$. The theory of chapter 7 shows that every R_p for which $s < p \leqslant m + 1$ can then be the seat of the lowest points of some family of rays issuing from a focus inside R_s. The presence of significant reduction of velocity with depth inside the crust, which would violate this assumption, has in fact been suggested by Gutenberg though not widely supported. Such a complication would add serious difficulties to the problem of determining crustal structure.

Consider first the case of an earthquake with focus inside the top layer R_1. Then, by (3) and (6),

$$a_p = 2 \sum_{q=1}^{p-1} \alpha_{pq} H_q - \alpha_{p1} h \quad (p = 2, ..., m+1), \tag{12}$$

where

$$\alpha_{pq} = (v_q^{-2} - v_P^{-2})^{\frac{1}{2}} \quad (p = 2, ..., m+1; \; q = 1, ..., m; \; p \neq q). \tag{13}$$

Equations like (8) and (9) can be formed for m phases each corresponding to a family of rays of given type (P or S) with lowest points in $R_2, ..., R_{m+1}$, respectively. These equations yield values of v_p and $(a_p + \tau)$ for $p = 2, ..., m + 1$. The values of the v_p enable the *delay-depth coefficients* (this term is due to Lee) α_{pq} to be determined. With (12), we then have in effect $2m$ equations involving the $(2m + 2)$ quantities a_p $(p = 2, ..., m+1)$, τ, h and H_p $(p = 1, ..., m)$.

Additional information comes from observations of arrival-times associated with the family of rays which leave the focus in an

upward direction and lie entirely in R_1. For these rays (6) has to be replaced by
$$T = \{(r_0\Delta)^2 + h^2\}^{\frac{1}{2}} v_1^{-1} \tag{14}$$

which, however, reduces approximately to a particular case of (6), namely,
$$T \approx r_0\Delta/v_1 \tag{15}$$

when Δ is sufficiently large for squares of $(h/r_0\Delta)$ to be neglected. Since $T = t - \tau + \epsilon$, (15) can be written as
$$\tau + (r_0\Delta) v_1^{-1} - t = \epsilon, \tag{16}$$

corresponding to (7). Through (16), with the use of stations not too close to the epicentre, we can determine values of v_1 and τ by least squares. (All of (7)–(11) are relevant, taking $p = 1$ and $a_1 = 0$.)

The use of the approximation (15) corresponds to the adoption of a conventional origin-time analogous to that referred to in § 10.4.1.1. If there are sufficient reliable observations at small Δ, the more accurate (T, Δ) relation (14) may in theory be used to determine h as well as v_1 and τ. There are then sufficient equations to determine all the unknowns, including the thicknesses H_p. In practice, with natural earthquakes, where there is the added uncertainty of the position of the epicentre, h cannot be determined precisely in this way, and the conventional origin-time which corresponds to $h = 0$ is commonly used. The H_p are then determined taking $h = 0$ in (12).

In practice, the formal uncertainties in the estimated thicknesses H_p are often so great in a single near-earthquake investigation that no significance can be attached to the result. Numbers of studies have usually to be combined. The essential reason for this is that P and S waves pass vertically through the entire crust in not more than a few seconds, so that appreciable changes in the H_p may be accompanied by only slight changes in the a_p as given by (12).

When the focus is below the top layer, say in the layer R_s, a similar procedure determines the velocities v_p and the $(a_p + \tau)$ in all the layers below R_s and in R_{m+1}. In this case, it is again expedient to adopt provisionally a conventional origin-time corresponding to an assumed form $T \approx r_0\Delta/v_s$ in place of (15). Again, the data do not in practice enable h to be closely estimated, and the consequent uncertainties are higher because h is now greater than before and there is an unknown structure above R_s. The difficulties can be reduced in practice by bringing to bear either the results from other earthquakes with higher foci in the same geographic region, or other evidence relating to the focal depth. In practice many discordant results of near-earthquake studies have in the light of later evidence been traced to unsatisfactory assumptions about focal depth.

The foregoing discussion shows that the uncertainties attaching to determinations of thicknesses of crustal layers and focal depths within the crust by near-earthquake studies are in general much greater than those attaching to the velocities. This conclusion is well substantiated in the history of near-earthquake studies. (See subsections of § 12.2.)

12.1.5. Use of artificial explosions. Natural earthquakes can be simulated by artificial explosions which take place at or near the surface of the Earth, and send into the interior seismic waves which can be recorded in the usual way on emerging at the surface. Over the past two or three decades, elaborate techniques have been developed both in the carrying out of the explosions and in the instrumental recording of them. Many (relatively small) explosions have been carried out in the search for mineral resources, especially oil, where knowledge of rock stratification below the surface is important. But the explosion (seismic survey) method has also been increasingly applied to determine the Earth's structure down to and below the Mohorovičić discontinuity. In addition, seismic waves from nuclear explosions (see chapter 16) have been used to increase knowledge of the deeper interior.

The use of artificial explosions has several advantages over the use of natural earthquakes in unravelling the internal structure of the Earth. First, the focal depth is effectively zero, thereby removing a troublous source of uncertainty (see § 12.1.4). Secondly, the location of the epicentre is known to high precision. Thirdly, the origin-time is usually precisely known. Fourthly, advance knowledge may be available of the approximate origin-time, enabling portable instruments to be set up in strategic places and enabling recording equipment to be set running much more rapidly than would be feasible in ordinary seismograph operation; in practice, it proves possible to detect changes in the local ground displacement taking place during intervals of the order of 0·001 sec. Fifthly, artificial explosions can be used to determine structure in regions where natural earthquakes are scanty.

All the theory of the preceding subsections is relevant to the explosion method, with the simplification that, in general, τ, h and certain other parameters no longer have to be included. This makes it feasible to introduce further parameters with a view to examining complexities of structure not involved in the simple model of § 12.1.2. The following subsections will contain an indication of the importance of explosion methods in supplementing, and in many cases correcting, results from near-earthquake studies.

12.2. Early evidence on crustal structure. In this section, we refer to some of the earlier or initial investigations of crustal structure from records of bodily seismic waves in particular regions. In §§ 12.2.1–12.2.5, we consider mainly determinations of wave speeds; thicknesses of layers will be discussed in § 12.2.6.

12.2.1. Historical European near-earthquake studies. In 1909, A. Mohorovičić detected two distinct pairs of P and S phases on seismograms within 10° of the epicentre of the Kulpa Valley (Croatia) earthquake of 1909 October 8, and inferred the presence of a marked discontinuity some distance below the surface of the Earth. For phases corresponding to rays in the 'upper layer' (above the discontinuity), Mohorovičić used the notation $\bar{P}$ and $\bar{S}$. He used a form equivalent to (7, (23)) to arrive at a $\bar{P}$ speed ranging from 5·53 to 5·68 km/sec in this layer, and initially gave 54 km as the depth to the discontinuity. Similar pairs of phases were found by S. Mohorovičić and Gutenberg with two German earthquakes of 1911 and 1913. Subsequent studies in Europe, and later over the whole globe, showed that the *Mohorovičić discontinuity* (sometimes called the 'M discontinuity') is world-wide, though, as will be seen, its average depth is considerably less than 54 km.

In the Tauern (Austria) earthquake of 1923 November 28, Conrad found evidence of a third distinct P phase, which he called P^*, with speed about 6·3 km/sec. This was supported in studies of the Jersey and Hereford earthquakes of 1926 July 30 and 1926 August 14 by Jeffreys, who also identified a companion phase $S*$. Jeffreys re-named the phases $\bar{P}$ and $\bar{S}$ as Pg and Sg. The two layers associated with Pg and $P*$ have been called the *granitic* and *intermediate* layers, respectively, and the boundary between them the *Conrad discontinuity*. The notation Pn and Sn is used in near-earthquake studies for phases corresponding to rays which penetrate below the Mohorovičić discontinuity. Most early near-earthquake studies gave Pn speeds of the order of 7·8 km/sec, though Conrad had inferred 8·1 km/sec with the Schwadorf earthquake of 1927 October 8.

Sometimes provision is also made for phases P_s and S_s, corresponding to speeds of order 4·7–5·0 and 2·8–3·0 km/sec, in a thin sedimentary layer above the granitic layer. In 1931, Stoneley found in *I.S.S.* readings some evidence of a further phase P_Q, with speed about 7·0 km/sec.

In 1937, Jeffreys combined a number of European studies, and, on the formal assumption of homogeneous upper layers with horizontal boundaries, gave the following speeds:

Pg	5·57 ± 0·02 km/sec	Sg	3·36 ± 0·01 km/sec
$P*$	6·50 ± 0·03	$S*$	3·74 ± 0·03
Pn	7·76 ± 0·03	Sn	4·36 ± 0·02

This model is formally connected with the J. B. tables, but needs some corrections, especially in respect of Pn and Sn. (See the discussion in §§ 10.6.3, 13.2.)

12.2.2. Early near-earthquake studies in other regions. For near earthquakes in central Asia, Rozova in 1939 assigned P speeds of 5·46, 6·65 and 7·91 km/sec, and S speeds of 3·24, 3·74 and 4·27 km/sec. Early estimates of Pn speeds for Japan ranged from 7·5 km/sec (Matuzawa, 1929) to 7·75 km/sec (E. A. Hodgson, 1932).

In North America, Gutenberg in 1932 gave a Pn velocity of 7·94 km/sec for southern California which he later raised to 8·06 ± 0·11 km/sec, while Byerly gave 8·02 ± 0·04 km/sec for central California. At a certain stage of development, both authors gave a three-layered structure, Gutenberg's speeds being 5·58, 6·05, 6·95 and 8·06 (km/sec) for P, and 3·26, 3·65, 4·10 and 4·45 for S, while Byerly's were 5·61, 6·72, 7·24 and 8·02 for P, and 3·26 for S. The speeds near 7 km/sec in the third layer were of some interest in relation to Stoneley's phase P_Q. Subsequently, Gutenberg favoured models in which the speeds diminished with depth in part of the crust.

For New Zealand, Hayes in 1935 established the existence of upper-layer phases on seismograms, and Bullen gave, for the most probable structure on the data available by 1939, an upper layer with P speed 5·0 (km/sec), then a pair of layers with P speeds of 6·0 and 6·5 (which could, however, belong to a single layer with average speed 6·3), and a Pn speed of 7·8 for $\Delta < 4°$, but 8·1 for $\Delta > 4°$; S speeds were 3·0, 3·7 and 4·4.

In South Africa the first near-earthquake studies were made after World War II by Gane, Hales and Oliver, with the later help of Willmore. Results published in 1952 gave an upper layer with P and S speeds of 6·09 and 3·68, and Pn and Sn speeds of 8·27 and 4·83.

In South America, pioneering studies in the Andes were started by Tuve, Tatel and Lomnitz during the I.G.Y.

12.2.3. Use of major explosions. The first major explosion to be well-recorded seismically occurred at a plant at Oppau in the Palatinate when 4500 tons of chemical accidentally exploded on 1921 September 21. Assessments of the records at some ten seismological observatories gave P speeds ranging from 5·4 to 5·7 km/sec.

Other notable accidental explosions include the Burton-on-Trent explosion of 1944 November 27, from which Jeffreys inferred a Pn speed of order 8·1 km/sec, and the Port Chicago explosion (in the San Francisco Bay area) of 1946 July 17, from which Byerly inferred P speeds of 5·6–5·7 and 7·7 km/sec.

On 1947 April 18, the very large Heligoland explosion took place. As this explosion was pre-arranged, various groups were able to set up field instruments in advance. Willmore used first onsets alone to infer average P speeds of 4·4 (km/sec) for $4 < r_0\Delta < 24$ km, 5·95 for $24 < r_0\Delta < 120$ km, and 8·18 for $r_0\Delta > 120$ km. Somewhat differing results were given by other groups.

Since 1945, seismic studies of nuclear explosions (see chapter 16) have been made on an increasing scale.

12.2.4. Use of lesser explosions. Around 1924, portable instruments were being introduced to record seismic waves from quarry blasts and other relatively small explosions. Initially, records were taken at distances of order 20–30 km from the source, and later at greater distances. Wiechert and others inferred P speeds of 4·8, 6·0 and 6·7 km/sec from quarry blasts near Göttingen between 1923 and 1929. E. Rothé and others inferred a P speed of 5·5 km/sec from four explosions fired in May 1924 near a military camp at La Courtine in France.

In the United States, early velocity results from quarry blasts were: 5·0–6·0 (km/sec) for P in southern California (Wood and Richter, 1931–3); 5·4–5·6 for P in the Berkeley region (Byerly and others, 1932–5); 5·5 and 6·4 for P in the eastern Pennsylvania (Ewing and others, 1934); 6·01, 6·77 and 8·18 for P, and 3·45, 3·93 and 4·6 for S in New England (Leet, 1936).

For the Canadian Shield region, J. H. Hodgson in 1953 used rockbursts in mines to infer tentatively a P speed of 6·2 (km/sec) in the crust, and Pn speeds of 7·9 and 8·2 at nearer and more distant stations, respectively.

In Japan, between 1950 and 1954, the 'Research Group for Explosion Seismology' studied seismic records of three explosions (each with 5–8 tons of explosive) involved in a dam construction, and a fourth explosion of 30 tons in a mine. The dam explosions gave P speeds of 5·8, 6·0 and 6·1 (km/sec) in three different directions, respectively, with some indication of a further speed of 7·2. The fourth explosion gave speeds of 6·2, 7·4 and 8·2 in one direction, but 5·8 (in lieu of 6·2) in another direction.

12.2.5. Note on other regions. In Australia, a small number of near-earthquake studies had indicated the existence of a significant crustal layer as in other continental regions, but it was not till the Maralinga atom-bomb explosions of 1956 that velocities could be assigned. A group under Jaeger found P and S speeds of 6·12 and 3·56 km/sec in a single crustal layer in the region running west for ten degrees from Maralinga, and Pn and Sn speeds of 8·23 and 4·75 km/sec.

In Antarctica, values of crustal rock velocities are beginning to emerge from extensions of seismic work to determine ice-thicknesses, but the work is still in its infancy (see § 18.6.1).

12.2.6. Estimates of crustal layer thicknesses from near-earthquake studies. Mohorovičić's estimate of order 50 km for the total crustal thickness came to be much reduced in later studies. Differing assumptions on focal depth led to discrepancies sometimes approaching 20 km in estimates by different investigators in the same region. Results became more reliable when it was found that a number of investigators had assumed focal depths much too great.

Jeffreys combined various results by statistical procedures and in 1937 gave provisional estimates of $H_1 = 17$ and $H_2 = 9$ km for the thicknesses of an upper (granitic) and an intermediate layer in Europe. The standard errors were high, however, and Jeffreys decided that it was necessary to bring to bear additional sources of evidence leading to the improved values $H_1 = 15$, $H_2 = 18$ km (see § 12.5).

In other continental regions, near-earthquake studies have mostly led to total crustal thicknesses of order 30 to 40 km.

As pointed out in § 12.1.4, it is difficult to arrive at precise thicknesses of individual crustal layers from near-earthquake studies. This is reflected in the widely discordant estimates made over many years, and conclusions in very many papers have no statistical significance.

Over the period 1930 to 1935, Gutenberg (for the Alps) and Byerly (for the Sierra Nevada) produced the first seismic evidence on 'mountain roots', that is, a marked increase in the depth to the Mohorovičić discontinuity under certain mountain ranges. In some cases it appears that the depth extends to the order of an additional 30 km.

In the case of oceanic regions, on the other hand, it has been found (see § 12.6) that the Mohorovičić discontinuity rises to within less than 10 km below the ocean floor.

The question of crustal thicknesses will be further discussed in § 12.5.

12.3. More recent evidence from P and S waves. Since 1945, efforts to determine details of crustal structure have been greatly intensified, and great quantities of new data assembled. The method of seismic survey, mentioned in §§ 9.9.3, 12.1.5, has been greatly developed and has produced important evidence on crustal structure in many regions where recordings of near earthquakes are inadequate; this applies especially to oceanic regions. Notable contributors not already mentioned include: Hiller, J.-P. Rothé, Wanner, Caloi, Marcelli, Båth and Vaněk working on the European region; Riznichenko, Gamburtsev, and Savarenski, in the U.S.S.R.; Slichter, Woollard, Steinhart and Officer in the U.S.A.; and Hill, Raitt, Ewing and Oliver, working on the Atlantic and Pacific regions.

In regions where near-earthquake determinations are available, results from seismic surveys have added important supplementary evidence on many points, sometimes superceding results from near earthquakes, sometimes strengthening earlier conclusions. At the same time, many earlier discrepancies remain unresolved, and new discrepancies have arisen. An example of the latter is the detection of P speeds near $6{\cdot}0$ km/sec and failure to detect speeds near $5{\cdot}6$ in regions where the latter figure had been indicated in near-earthquake studies. It has become evident that the unravelling of even broad features of the Earth's crustal structure is a far more complicated task than was at one time thought, and that patient work will be needed over many years to come.

The seismic survey studies, along with petrological considerations, have raised questions in many regions on how far the simple model of § 12.1.2 should be departed from to allow for continuous variations of speed with depth, both across so-called discontinuities and inside the layers between discontinuities. (At the same time the model of § 12.1.2 does seem to be suitable for some regions, for example, a large part of Europe.) There also appear to be well-established variations of speed with azimuth in some regions. Sometimes there have been considerable differences in records of the one explosion taken at stations in close neighbourhood. Jeffreys attributes some apparent discrepancies to irregularities of interfaces below the surface and states that local irregularities may forbid attaching significance to velocities except as averages over some hundreds of kilometres of length.

An important positive result is that it is now well established that the crustal thickness lies between 30 and 40 km in normal continental regions, and there is no reason to deviate from the value 33 km that has been used for Earth models. The added depth to the Mohorovičić discontinuity under some (but not all) mountain ranges is well confirmed, and likewise the reduced depth under the oceans.

It is well established that the *Pn* and *Sn* speeds are of the order of 8·2 and 4·7 km/sec in many regions, though speeds down to 7·8 and 4·4 km/sec may still be relevant to others.

Work of Richter in 1950 indicated that the '*Z* phenomenon' (§ 10.6) is likely to be relatively unimportant—that in earthquakes of the type used in crustal studies the main *P* and *S* waves generally leave the focus at nearly the same time.

Certain pulses arriving at epicentral distances of 90 to 120 km have been interpreted in several countries as reflections from the Mohorovičić discontinuity, indicating that the model assumption of discontinuity may be reasonable. More evidence on such reflected waves is, however, needed. So far there has been little evidence of near-vertical reflection from the Mohorovičić discontinuity. And there have been no indications to date of any reflected waves from other boundaries between assumed crustal layers.

The intense effort spent on crustal investigations has led to the application of the full wave theory to many problems with a view to extracting information from detailed analysis of wave forms. The mathematical approach to these problems has been supplemented by recourse to 'model seismology' (see § 18.7), and attention has been given to filtering techniques (§ 9.9.4) with a view to finer identification of specific seismic phases.

12.4. Use of the phases *pP* and *sS*. Other evidence on crustal structure comes from the study of the arrival-times of the pulses *pP* and *sS* from earthquakes whose foci are below the crustal layers. The pulse *pP* is associated with a wave which ascends to the outer surface near the epicentre and is reflected there, and therefore makes two more transits of the crustal layers than the direct *P* wave. The differences between the arrival-times of *pP* and *P* at different stations will therefore be related to the thicknesses of the crustal layers. By this means, equations of condition can sometimes be derived which lead to more precise determinations of thicknesses than the usual near-earthquake studies. Similar use can be made of the phases sS and S.

12.5. Use of surface-wave studies. The theory of surface seismic waves yields equations which involve properties of the crust. Examples of equations for simple crustal models are (5, (23)) and (5, (26)), and the theory of §5.3.2 indicates one way in which the observed dispersion of surface waves can be used to derive information on crustal thicknesses. The equations involve, in addition to the thicknesses, the bodily wave velocities and elastic parameters of the layers, and relate to crustal models of the type considered in earlier sections of this chapter. The models assume that conditions approximate to spherical stratification over the considerable ranges of distance for which the thicknesses are usually estimated in this way. In practice, values for the bodily wave velocities and elastic parameters are taken from other sources, including near-earthquake studies and the procedures of §12.7.

The theory of §5.3.2 provides a single additional equation of condition on the thicknesses, and does not of itself by any means solve the whole problem of crustal structure in any region. But the single equation is sometimes much more precisely determined than any single equation emerging from near-earthquake and related studies so that the additional information can be very valuable.

In surface-wave studies, it is desirable to separate observations of Love and Rayleigh waves so far as possible. Since Rayleigh waves have no SH component, Love waves are best studied from records at stations from which the azimuth to the epicentre is due north, south, east or west (assuming N.–S. and E.–W. orientation of horizontal-component seismographs—this is sometimes deviated from). Again, since Love waves have no vertical component, Rayleigh waves are best studied from vertical-component records. Techniques are being investigated for mechanically separating Love and Rayleigh waves superposed on the same record.

In §12.2.6, mention was made of the early estimates $H_1 = 17\,\mathrm{km}$ and $H_2 = 9\,\mathrm{km}$ for the thicknesses of the upper and intermediate layers in Europe. Jeffreys sought to improve these values making use of Stoneley's studies of Love waves and his own studies of Japanese deep-focus earthquakes, and arrived at the values $H_1 = 15 \pm 3$ km, $H_2 = 18 \pm 4$ km, for the average Eurasian structure. These values are of some special interest because they were taken as standard in constructing the J. B. tables, and continue to be used for various model purposes. In 1948, Stoneley with the use of additional results on surface waves showed the whole set of data to be compatible with $H_1 = 33$ km and H_2 zero. The estimated overall average crustal thickness of 33 km for Eurasia has not been upset in later work, but there remains appreciable uncertainty on the thicknesses of individual layers.

Latterly the theory of surface waves and its application to crustal structure has been greatly extended, especially by Ewing and his collaborators. Dispersion curves for many different assumed crustal structures have now been constructed, generally with the aid of modern computing facilities. This makes it possible to eliminate many types of crustal structure from consideration in particular regions, and so narrow the possibilities in a very valuable way. Sometimes it has been possible to make inferences going considerably beyond the content of a single equation of condition. Questions of uniqueness in many crustal identifications made in this way still need examination, but the method is proving fruitful.

Press (1956) has devised a method of inferring regional crustal structures from phase-velocity measurements of Rayleigh waves. (Phase velocity is the velocity of a particular spectral or Fourier component of a wave form.) Individual crests are traced in records, taken at a network of stations in the region, of Rayleigh waves that have already been subject to considerable dispersion through having traversed a long oceanic path. When there are sufficient seismographs in the region, the method can lead to knowledge of the average crustal structure of a region whose linear dimensions are of the order to 100–200 km.

In general, the results of surface wave studies for normal continental regions are similar to those derived by Jeffreys and Stoneley for Eurasia, but there are marked differences in oceanic regions, as will be seen in § 12.6.

12.6. Oceanic and continental crustal structures. Early work of Tams, Angenheister and Gutenberg indicated that surface seismic waves over paths in the Pacific region travel faster and are differently dispersed from those in continental regions, and suggested that there are significant differences in the crustal structures.

The first reliable quantitative investigations were made in 1928 by Stoneley, taking for model purposes a crust consisting of a single layer of thickness H, with velocities, etc., as derived for the European upper layer, resting on an olivine subcrust. He found that observations of the dispersion of Love waves formally yielded $H = 19\,\mathrm{km}$ for Eurasia as against $H = 10\,\mathrm{km}$ for the Pacific region, and this showed that the crustal structures of the two regions in fact differ significantly.

A similar conclusion emerged from early Rayleigh wave investigations. Taking the above crustal model, Jeffreys, using Rayleigh wave observations of Gutenberg and Richter, obtained the formal result $H = 25\,\mathrm{km}$ for Eurasia. For this same model, the writer, using a beautiful vertical-component record traced at Wellington from the Kamchatka earthquake of 1938 November 10, derived the formal value $H = 17\,\mathrm{km}$ for the Pacific region. The differences were confirmed in further readings of the same earthquake by de Lisle.

Other assumed crustal models led to similar differences, and all pointed to the sub-Pacific crust being significantly thinner than the Eurasian. Investigations were extended by Wilson and others to the Atlantic and Indian Ocean regions, for which thinner crusts were also found.

Evidence on differences between continental structures has been supplemented by consideration of phases such as PP. Details of the downward reflection of bodily waves near the Earth's outer surface will depend on the nature of the crustal structure. Gutenberg and Richter used data on the amplitudes of waves whose places of reflection are in continental and oceanic regions to provide further evidence on the existence of significant differences in crustal structures, and sought by this means to add details on boundaries between the regions.

With the development of the seismic survey method, it became possible to investigate oceanic crustal thicknesses more directly. Work of Hill, Raitt, Ewing and collaborators yielded values ranging from 9 to 14 km for the depth of the Mohorovičić discontinuity below the ocean surface in parts of the Pacific and Atlantic regions. The corresponding P speeds in an assumed single crustal layer below the ocean sediments range from 6·5 to 6·8 km/sec, and the Pn speeds from 7·9 to 8·2 km/sec. Ewing and collaborators have constructed theoretical dispersion curves based on these results and found fairly satisfactory agreement with Love and Rayleigh wave observations in a number of cases. There remain some discrepancies, the resolving of which should add detail to knowledge of oceanic crustal structure.

Geological evidence confirms the existence of distinct oceanic and continental crustal structures. Suess, Marshall and others refer to an 'andesite line' which separates regions of different petrological and chemical composition and defines a 'Pacific basin'. The line runs east of Japan, the Marianne Islands, the Palau Islands, thence north of New Guinea and the New Hebrides towards the islands of Samoa which are on the Pacific side, and then turns southward, leaving the Kermadec Islands and New Zealand on the 'continental' side. On the American side, the boundary is close to the west coast. Turner, Verhoogen and Hess have contributed further geological detail.

Apart from major mountain systems, the main exceptions to standard continental and oceanic structures occur along the margins between continents and oceans, mid-ocean ridges, and 'arcuate structures'—island arcs with associated deep trenches.

Seismic surveys of continental margins include the work of Worzel and Shurbet (1955) near the New Jersey coast, and of Tuve and Tatel (1958) in the Andes region. Worzel found a change in the depth d of the Mohorovičić discontinuity from the order of 30 to 15 km, spread over a horizontal distance of some 200 km, with more gradual changes of depth on either side of this range of distance. Tuve and Tatel found values of d ranging from 46 to 56 km under the Andes to 10–15 km just offshore in the Pacific Ocean.

The mid-Atlantic Ridge runs roughly from north to south down the middle of the Atlantic and is about 1000 km wide south of the Azores. Ewing and Ewing (1959) found a P speed of 5·2 km/sec in a layer some 3 km thick, immediately below the sediments, and a P speed below of 7·2 km/sec in a layer at least 30 km thick; the Mohorovičić discontinuity was not reached. The presence of the Ridge contributes significantly to differences in the dispersion of surface seismic waves over different Atlantic paths.

Arcuate structures are found mainly in the Pacific Basin, for example, along the Aleutian Islands, the Marianas and the East Indies, and are associated with very high seismicity. Gutenberg and Richter have given the following sequence as characteristic of these structures, in a direction towards the centre of the arc: an ocean trough; a narrow belt of shallow earthquakes and negative gravity anomalies; strong positive gravity anomalies and earthquakes, often large, at depths near 60 km; a principal and secondary structural arc with volcanic activity, recent and older, and earthquakes of steadily increasing depths; deep-focus earthquakes.

Surface wave methods have been brought to bear by Evison and Press (and colleagues) on the crustal structure of Antarctica, using distant earthquakes. Tentative results indicate a continental type of structure over eastern Antarctica, but an average structure nearer oceanic type over western Antarctica.

Additional evidence on crustal structure comes from gravity surveys. There is in many regions a considerable correlation between gravity anomalies and changes in upper layer thicknesses as indicated in seismic surveys. On the basis of these correlations, Woollard and others have used gravity results in the attempt to fill in detailed pictures of layering where the results of seismic surveys have been limited.

12.7. Physical properties of the Earth's upper layers. By (4, (4)) and (4, (5)) the P and S velocities α, β satisfy the equations

$$k/\rho = \alpha^2 - \tfrac{4}{3}\beta^2, \tag{17}$$

$$\mu/\rho = \beta^2, \tag{18}$$

where ρ, k and μ denote the density, incompressibility and rigidity of the material. Hence if values of α and β are determined for any layer, values of k/ρ and μ/ρ are determined. By matching these values against the results of laboratory experiments at appropriate pressures and temperatures, it is possible to make some progress towards identifying materials in particular layers. As an alternative to using (17) and (18) directly, use is commonly made of the expression

$$2\sigma = (\alpha^2 - 2\beta^2)/(\alpha^2 - \beta^2) \tag{19}$$

for Poisson's ratio σ; (19) is readily deduced from (2, (40)), (4, (4)) and (4, (5)).

Much laboratory experimental data has now been assembled, starting from pioneering work by Adams, Williamson, Bridgman, Birch, Bancroft, Griggs, Ide and others. In the experiments both statical and dynamical methods have been used. Small, but for the present purpose quite negligible, differences (see § 4.6) are to be expected in results by the two methods because of the differences between isothermal and adiabatic conditions. In practice, the observed differences are not negligible, and there are also deviations in the results of experiments on different samples of the same rock. Extraneous properties such as porosity are likely to affect the laboratory results and account for various discrepancies; and attendant uncertainties have to be taken into account in matching against the seismic data. In spite of these uncertainties, which affect mainly the identification of particular materials, the results show a fairly close correlation, at pressures above $10^9\,\mathrm{dyne/cm^2}$, between the densities ρ of rocks and the values of k/ρ and μ/ρ, and therefore of α and β. With the help of these correlations, it becomes possible to estimate all three of ρ, k and μ in the outer part of the Earth with considerable reliability.

The European layer in which Pg and Sg speeds of 5·6 and 3·4 km/sec were found was early associated with granitic rock, partly on geological grounds and partly as a result of laboratory experiments. The subsequent finding near the surface of higher P speeds in continental regions forced some reconsideration of the granitic interpretation. At the same time considerable variations were found in laboratory results for granites from different sources, so that the identification of granite in the crust by this procedure became less specific; variations are in fact to be expected since, as

pointed out by Adams and Williamson, granitic rocks are com-
binations of highly compressible and less compressible mineral
grains. The granitic interpretation for continental regions therefore
rests mainly on fairly strong geological evidence to the effect that
where sediments are absent the exposed rocks are commonly
granitic, while elsewhere granitic rocks are known to underlie
sedimentary regions to a substantial degree. This interpretation
led to the adoption of a model figure of $2\cdot65\,\mathrm{g/cm^3}$ for the representative density of the upper layer in continental regions.

Laboratory experiments show that in general the silicon contents
of rocks decrease as the seismic velocities increase, so that intermediate layers may be expected to consist of rocks intermediate in
basicity between granite and the subcrustal material. An early
suggestion of a tachylyte composition for an intermediate layer led
to the adoption of a density of $2\cdot87\,\mathrm{g/cm^3}$ for that layer, though
other (but related) compositions are possible.

In view of the correlations mentioned between the densities and
seismic velocities of rocks, it is unlikely that the density values of
$2\cdot65$ and $2\cdot87\,\mathrm{g/cm^3}$ in the upper and lower parts of continental
crusts are seriously departed from, and they serve as useful representative values in Earth model calculations.

On several grounds, the higher density value of $2\cdot87\,\mathrm{g/cm^3}$ is
likely to be representative of the layer below the sediments in
oceanic regions. The grounds include the values of the velocities
inferred from seismic surveys (see §§ 12.2–12.3), and the finding that
basic rocks are specially predominant on certain Pacific islands.

Immediately below the crust, the seismic speeds are so high as
to fit laboratory data on only a small number of ordinary rocks.
Dunite, which consists largely of the mineral olivine (magnesium–
iron orthosilicate) has values of k/ρ and μ/ρ of the right order, and
has formed the basis of many model calculations for this part of
the Earth, though there are one or two other possibilities. An
olivine composition was first suggested by Adams and Williamson
in 1923, and Adams later pointed out that there are no measurements which conflict seriously with the conclusion that the material
below the crust consists of ultrabasic rock. The dunite interpretation has led to the adoption of the value $3\cdot32\,\mathrm{g/cm^3}$ for the density

ρ' just below the crust. Again, the velocity-density correlations make it fairly unlikely that this value will need serious change should the olivine interpretation be modified. Birch regards the figure of $3\cdot32\,\text{g/cm}^3$ as being close to the lower bound to ρ', and as relating to a highly magnesian olivine, and has lately suggested $3\cdot6$ as an extreme upper bound. Jeffreys considers it highly improbable that ρ' could exceed the mean density ($3\cdot34$) of the Moon.

Certain eclogites also give reasonable agreement with the Pn and Sn velocities, and Birch has considered an eclogite consisting of an assemblage of olivines, pyroxenes and garnets as being a possible constituent just below the crust. In that case ρ' would be likely to exceed $3\cdot32$, but an eclogite composition becomes somewhat improbable if it requires ρ' to exceed $3\cdot34$.

When the values of the densities at the various depths are assessed, values of the elastic parameters k and μ are simply derived using (17) and (18), the uncertainties being of the same order as with ρ. By (19), σ is determined from knowledge of α and β alone.

12.8. The Mohole. The foregoing discussions make it clear that, notwithstanding the enormous effort put into seismic investigations of the Earth's crustal structure, many uncertainties will remain for a long time. Over the past few years the prospect has arisen of gaining additional knowledge by direct observation. At its 1957 meeting in Toronto, the International Association of Seismology and the Physics of the Interior of the Earth sponsored the idea of drilling a hole to just below the Mohorovičić discontinuity, and providing samples all the way down for direct laboratory examination. Subsequent work on this idea has come to be called the 'Mohole project'.

In the search for oil, holes have already been successfully driven into the Earth to depths approaching the order of $10\,\text{km}$ in land regions. The Mohole Project could not, however, be carried out in land regions since the depth to the Mohorovičić discontinuity there exceeds $30\,\text{km}$. But the Project is feasible in an oceanic region if the technical problems of boring down through the floor under a deep ocean can be solved. This involves such questions as controlling operations from a ship necessarily a long way above the ocean floor.

There is fair likelihood that the technical problems will be solved in the foreseeable future. In that event, a great deal of precise information can be expected, including knowledge of the density, elastic properties and composition at all levels in the vicinity of the hole. In particular, definite knowledge of the nature of the material just below the Mohorovičić discontinuity, and confirmation or modification of the density value of $3 \cdot 32 \, \text{g/cm}^3$ would be of the utmost importance to problems on the whole of the Earth's upper mantle. Information on such matters as temperature gradients, heat conductivities and distributions of radioactive matter would also be of great importance.

CHAPTER 13

SEISMOLOGY AND THE EARTH'S DEEP INTERIOR

We now concern ourselves with conditions in the Earth below the crustal layers. Seismology is in a unique position to give information on these conditions, since earthquake waves penetrate to all parts of the Earth's interior and emerge at the outer surface bearing evidence of the regions they have traversed. Thus nearly all quantitative work on certain aspects of the Earth's deep interior is based directly or indirectly on seismological results.

13.1. Discontinuities within the Earth. We have already referred to the Mohorovičić discontinuity separating the Earth's crust from the material below. We saw in chapter 12 that conditions as indicated by travel-time studies of near earthquakes are fairly heterogeneous above the level of this discontinuity. In striking contrast, the travel-times for P and S seismic waves both indicate that the Earth is much more uniform in its properties for some considerable distance below this level.

13.1.1. Existence of a central core. The existence of a central core within the Earth appreciably different from the outer shell had been suggested by Wiechert in 1897. Seismological evidence for the existence of such a core was put forward by Oldham in 1906, and Gutenberg in 1913 estimated the depth of the boundary of this core as 2900 km below the Earth's outer surface. Later precise work of Jeffreys gave the depth as 2898 ± 4 km (this figure applies to the model Earth defined in § 10.6.3).

Direct evidence of the existence of a central core is the occurrence of a 'shadow zone' for P waves emerging between epicentral distances of about 105° and 142°; in this shadow zone the amplitudes of P waves are much reduced, while there are strong amplitudes setting in near $\Delta = 142°$. Such a shadow zone would correspond to the presence of a discontinuity surface in which the P velocity sharply diminishes from above to below; the waves setting in at

$\Delta = 142°$ correspond to the phase PKP. The main observed results correspond to the case described in § 7.3.8 (see Fig. 28), and show very clearly two branches in the travel-time curve of PKP for $\Delta > 142°$.

The precise depth determination of Jeffreys was made using observations of Gutenberg and Richter, Scrase, Stechschulte and Tillotson on travel-times of ScS and PcP. The prominence of the phase ScS on many earthquake records not very distant from the epicentres is evidence of the sharpness of the discontinuity. This discontinuity is, in fact, more sharply defined than all others within the Earth.

The region of the Earth outside the central core is called the *mantle*. Both P and S waves are transmitted throughout the mantle, but only P waves have been detected in the central core.

13.1.2. Discontinuities in the mantle. Let α and β denote the P and S velocities at distance r from the Earth's centre, or depth z below the surface. Let R be the radius of the Earth stripped of its crust. Below the Mohorovičić discontinuity, the mantle is characterised on the whole by much smoother variation of α and β with z than in the crust above. But there are some significant abnormalities, especially in the outermost 1000 km, or 'upper mantle'.

Early work of Byerly on the Montana earthquake of 1925 June 28, and of Lehmann on the Iceland and Azores earthquakes of 1929 July 13 and 1931 May 20 indicated a sharp change of gradient in the P travel-time (T, Δ) curve at an epicentral distance near 20°. Examination by Jeffreys and Bullen of some further eighty well-recorded earthquakes confirmed this result for both P and S waves, and the phenomenon came to be called the '20° discontinuity'. On data available up to 1939, Jeffreys derived P and S velocity distributions in which α and β increase steadily and normally as r decreases from $1 \cdot 00R$ to $0 \cdot 94R$ (where $z = 413$ km), while the gradients $d\alpha/dz$ and $d\beta/dz$ increase discontinuously at $r = 0 \cdot 94R$ and then steadily diminish until at $r = 0 \cdot 85R$ (where $z \approx 1000$ km) the gradients resume normal values; α and β are continuous in the solution throughout this whole range of depth.

The circumstances correspond to features described in § 7.3.3, including triplication of the (T, Δ) curves over a range of values of the epicentral distance Δ. In order to derive any velocity distribution precisely, full details are required of the corresponding (T, Δ) curve, including details of any upper branches and cusps. In practice, when triplication occurs, it is difficult to detect, and measure to suitable precision on seismographs, all the needed arrival-times of onsets after the first. As Jeffreys has stressed, this makes for appreciable uncertainty in inferred velocity values corresponding to the 20° discontinuity. In his 1939 calculations, he found, for example, that the evidence only slightly favoured continuity in α and β at $r = 0.94R$. There also continues to be appreciable uncertainty in the depth at which the discontinuities in $d\alpha/dz$ and $d\beta/dz$ occur, so that the term '20° discontinuity' is more suitable as a general description of the phenomenon than a description in terms of specific velocity changes at a specific depth.

In 1938, the writer drew attention to the parallel phenomenon of marked changes in electrical conductivity a few hundred km below the Earth's surface, as indicated in work of Price and Lahiri.

Over a period of years starting from 1939, Gutenberg brought seismic amplitude data to bear to infer negative P and S velocity gradients at depths of order 100–150 km. If these negative velocity gradients do exist and are such as to violate the condition $dv/dr < v/r$ (see §7.2.3), the problem of estimating values of α and β in the upper mantle becomes seriously complicated.

More recent work of Jeffreys (1953, 1958) gave a smooth P time curve (for the Earth stripped of its crust) from 0° to about 15°, with marked changes in $dT/d\Delta$ between 15° and 16° and milder changes beyond 16°. Calculations of Lehmann, Jeffreys, and Bullen based on such evidence suggests that the main increase in $d\alpha/dz$ may take place nearer $z = 200\,\text{km}$ than 400 km, with some likelihood of additional but milder abnormalities between 200 and 1000 km. Jeffreys has since reported (1962) that the existence of the 20° discontinuity in the Pacific region seems clear.

Other evidence on the structure of the upper mantle comes from analyses of seismic waves of periods 3 min and more. Work of Dorman and others has suggested compatibility with Gutenberg's negative velocity gradient (see §14.4). But some points of consistency and uniqueness need to be critically examined before definite conclusions can be drawn.

Nuclear explosions are supplying additional valuable evidence. In seismic records of the 'Gnome' explosion of 1961 (see § 16.1), Romney and others found remarkable variations of travel-times with azimuth. To the north-east, observations were consistent with a practically linear (T, Δ) curve for P, and a velocity of 8·4 km/sec. To the north-west, the times were longer by amounts reaching 10 sec or more near $\Delta = 15°$ and then diminishing. The 20° discontinuity may therefore be relevant to some regions but not all.

The final resolution of the P and S velocity distributions in the upper mantle continues in fact to be one of the outstanding problems of the interior of the Earth. Birch has pointed out that when the nature of the upper mantle is understood 'we may be well on the way to a grasp of the dynamics of the Earth's interior'.

In the lower mantle, i.e. where $1000 \, \text{km} < z < 2900 \, \text{km}$, the variation of the P and S velocities appears to be less complicated. Most travel-time studies yield fairly uniform and normal P and S velocity gradients down to at least 2700 km depth, but there is evidence of a continuous reduction to zero gradients taking place between 2700 and 2900 km.

13.1.3. Discontinuities within the central core. The shadow zone already referred to for the range $105° < \Delta < 142°$ is not devoid of observations of P and PKP phases. For a number of years these observations had all been attributed to diffraction associated with the boundary of the central core and the 142° cusp, an explanation which remains relevant to many of the observed waves. But in respect of certain observations extending back from $\Delta = 142°$, Lehmann in 1936 pointed out that the amplitudes were sufficiently great to suggest the existence of an *inner core* in which the P velocity is significantly higher than that in the surrounding part of the central core. In 1938 Gutenberg and Richter, using more extensive data, found strong support for Lehmann's hypothesis, and supplied quantitative details. Jeffreys later applied Airy's theory of diffraction near a caustic to show explicitly that diffraction was an inadequate explanation of observed features of the PKP pulse for $\Delta < 142°$. More recently, Burke-Gaffney and Bullen, in a study of seismic records of certain nuclear explosions of 1954, detected Lehmann's waves, and waves which could correspond to the diffracted waves, separately on the same seismograms. The existence of the inner core is now well established.

For want of a better name, the part of the 'central core' outside the inner core has been called the 'outer core'.

Evidence from the Solomon Islands and Celebes Sea earthquakes of 1932 January 9 and 1934 June 29 led Jeffreys to infer the existence of a transition region, about 150 km thick, occupying the region $0 \cdot 36R_1 < r < 0 \cdot 40R_1$, between the inner and outer core, where R_1 is the radius of the central core. The value $0 \cdot 36R_1$ corresponds to an inner core radius of 1250 km, which Jeffreys states may need to be reduced by the order of 50 km. The evidence also led Jeffreys to infer that $d\alpha/dz$ is negative in the transition region. He postulated that α is here proportional to r (this corresponds to $d\alpha/dr = \alpha/r$; cf. §7.2.3), and showed that this postulate is compatible with the J. B. tables but not uniquely required by them. In his formal solution, α jumps discontinuously by 20 % across the boundary (at $r = 0 \cdot 36R_1$) between the transition region and the inner core proper. An independent analysis by Bolt of 24 further earthquakes gave support to these conclusions. (But see also §13.8.3.)

In contrast, Gutenberg's velocity determinations gave a transition region in which there is first a sharp increase in $d\alpha/dz$ at the bottom of the outer core proper, $d\alpha/dz$ diminishing steadily and fairly rapidly with increasing depth until the inner core proper is reached, the net effect being an increase of about 10% in α inside the transition region.

More recently, Caloi (1961) has stated that he has found evidence on seismograms of a phase $PKiKP$, recorded within epicentral distances of 20°, which would correspond to reflection upwards from the boundary of the inner core. Caloi regards this as crucial evidence favouring a velocity distribution of the Jeffreys type against the Gutenberg type.

A feature common to all velocity distributions, including Lehmann's original results, is that α increases fairly sharply with increasing depth at or near the inner core boundary. This is a key feature of this part of the Earth.

Throughout the outer core proper, $d\alpha/dz$ is fairly steady and normal, while inside the inner core it is steady but abnormally small (but positive).

13.1.4. Division of the Earth's interior into regions. In 1940–2, in work on the Earth's density variation (see §§ 13.4.2–13.5), the writer found it convenient to divide the Earth into regions according to depth, and used the nomenclature A, B, …, G for this purpose. The division, which is based on the velocity distributions entailed by the J. B. travel-time tables, is shown in the table below. For convenience of computation, the depths in the third column are given to the nearest km but, as the preceding discussions have indicated, are mostly not determined to this order of accuracy. The gradients mentioned in the last column are with respect to increase of depth.

Region	Level	Depth (km)	Features of region
....	Outer surface	—	....
A			Crustal layers
....	Base of crustal layers (distant R from the Earth's centre)	33	....
B			Steady positive P and S velocity gradients
....	$0.94R$	413	....
C			Transition region
....	$0.85R$	984	....
D			Steady positive P and S velocity gradients
....	$0.548R = R_1$	2898	....
E			Steady positive P velocity gradient
....	$0.40R_1$	4982	....
F			Negative P velocity gradient
....	$0.36R_1$	5121	....
G			Small positive P velocity gradient
....	Earth's centre	6371	....

In 1950, the writer subdivided the region D into D′ and D″, extending from 984 to 2700 km, and 2700 to 2900 km, respectively, following evidence (see § 13.6.1 and 13.8.2) that the diminution in velocity gradients inside D″ is physically significant.

The nomenclature in the table has been widely followed, and in spite of various uncertainties continues to serve as a useful basis in discussing regions of the Earth's interior. It is possible that the specification of the regions B and C will require significant modification in due course; but it still seems appropriate to reserve the two letters B and C for this part of the Earth, introducing primed symbols, as was found necessary for D, should this be required at a later stage. The region F is another part of the Earth where the specification may need some small modification (see § 13.8.3).

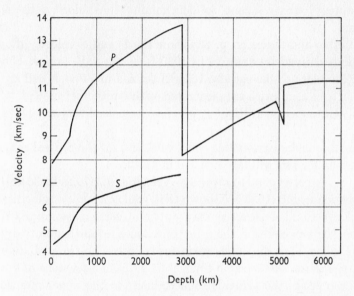

Fig. 39. P and S velocity distributions in the Earth's interior.

Region	Depth (km)	P velocity (km/sec)	S velocity (km/sec)	Region	Depth (km)	P velocity (km/sec)
....	33	7·76	4·36	....	2898	8·10
	100	7·95	4·45		3000	8·22
B	200	8·26	4·60		3200	8·47
	300	8·58	4·76		3400	8·76
....	413	8·97	4·96		3600	9·04
C	600	10·25	5·66	E	3800	9·28
	800	11·00	6·13		4000	9·51
(——)	1000	11·42	6·36		4200	9·70
	1200	11·71	6·50		4400	9·88
	1400	11·99	6·62		4600	10·06
	1600	12·26	6·73		4800	10·25
	1800	12·53	6·83	....	4982	10·44
D	2000	12·79	6·93	F	5121	(9·40)
	2200	13·03	7·02	....	5121	11·16
	2400	13·27	7·12	G	5700	11·26
	2600	13·50	7·21	....	6371	11·31
	2800	13·64	7·30			
....	2898	13·64	7·30			

13.2. The P and S velocity distributions. As pointed out in §10.4.4, the travel-time data show the Earth to be remarkably close to a state of spherical symmetry. Except where stated, departures from spherical symmetry will be ignored, so that the methods in chapter 7 are relevant to determining the velocity distributions.

The table and figure on p. 223 show the P and S velocity distributions derived by Jeffreys in 1939 from the J.B. tables. The velocities relate to the standard Earth defined in §10.6.3, and are in broad agreement with values derived by those other seismologists, notably Gutenberg and Richter, who have also used very extensive data.

The table includes no values of S velocities for the central core. The reason for this will be discussed in §13.3.

The tables correspond to Pn and Sn velocities of 7·76 and 4·36 km/sec. Evidence since 1939 has shown that, while Pn and Sn velocities of order 7·8 and 4·4 km/sec may apply in certain geographical regions, the values reach the order of 8·2 and 4·7 km/sec in many other regions. Thus the tables are in need of correction immediately below the crust. At the same time, starting from a few tens of km below the crust, the principal uncertainties in the upper mantle are in the velocity gradients rather than in the velocities themselves. There are other appreciable uncertainties, notably in the region F.

In spite of these various uncertainties, and the accumulation of much important data since 1939, there are advantages in continuing to use the tables for many model purposes. First, the tables have the advantage of being consistent with a large quantity of travel-time data analysed according to explicit statistical procedures, and also with a large body of subsequent computations relating to the physical structure of the Earth's interior. Secondly, evidence on the needed corrections is still self-conflicting in a number of respects, and for general purposes it is not desirable to apply corrections some of which would need to be altered by the same order at a later stage. But, as with all mathematical models, it is important to bear in mind the velocity uncertainties when applications are being made to other problems. For a more detailed discussion of the uncertainties, see Jeffreys, *The Earth* (4th ed.), pp. 121–2.

It may be remarked that, for the region B of an Earth stripped of its crustal layers, the J. B. travel-times fit the formulae

$$T = 490 \cdot 5 \sin (5\Delta/3), \quad T = 933 \cdot 7 \sin (1 \cdot 56\Delta) \tag{1}$$

for P and S rays, respectively, within the order of $0 \cdot 1$ sec. By $(7, (22))$, the corresponding velocities satisfy the relations

$$v = ar^{-\frac{7}{3}}, \quad v = br^{-2 \cdot 12}, \tag{2}$$

respectively, where a and b are constants.

13.3. The states of the Earth's mantle and central core.

The fact that S as well as P waves are transmitted through all parts of the Earth's mantle shows that, in respect of its response to stresses whose time duration is of the order of that in seismic wave transmission, the Earth is solid, i.e. has marked rigidity (μ), down to a depth of approximately 2900 km.

This result is in contrast to the evidence from seismograms that only P and not S waves have been observed to be transmitted through the central core. It indicates, see equation $(4, (5))$, that rigidity in the central core is on the whole inappreciable, i.e. that the greater part of the central core, and in particular at least the region E, must be essentially in a fluid state. (There are, however, reasons for believing that the *inner* core may be solid; see § 13.8.5.)

Support of this conclusion comes from studies of the amplitudes of the phase SKS. These amplitudes are much greater than would be expected to be the case if the rigidity μ in the region E of the central core were comparable with its incompressibility k.

It is well to appreciate, however, that the evidence that the rigidity in the greater part of the central core is small or zero does not come entirely from seismology. Astronomical observations yielding data on the movements of the Earth's poles, together with observations of the Earth's tidal movements, give information on the rigidity of the Earth as a whole. The rigidity throughout the Earth's mantle is known to good accuracy (see § 13.5) from observations of S seismic waves and knowledge of the density distribution. These data are theoretically sufficient to yield an estimate of the mean rigidity of the central core. Calculations made by Takeuchi in 1951 and Molodenski in 1955 show directly in this way that the rigidity in the outer core is at most a small fraction of the incompressibility. (This applies strictly to behaviour under stresses with periods up to the order of 12 h.)

13.4. The Earth's density variation. Since the famous experiment of Cavendish in 1799, who used a modified form of apparatus devised by Michell, it has been known that the mean density of the Earth is of the order of $5 \cdot 5 \, \text{g/cm}^3$. This figure implies the existence in the Earth's deep interior of material considerably denser than the typical surface rocks. A recent estimate of the Earth's mean density is $5 \cdot 517 \, \text{g/cm}^3$, given by Jeffreys using the value of $6 \cdot 670 \times 10^{-8}$ c.g.s. units given by Boys and Heyl for the constant of gravitation G. The corresponding value of the mass of the Earth is $5 \cdot 977 \times 10^{27} \, \text{g}$. The uncertainty in each of these figures is about 1 part in 1300.

A second observational result which must be fitted by any representation of density in the Earth is that the moment of inertia I about the polar axis is $0 \cdot 3335 M a^2$, where M and a are the mass and mean radius of the Earth. This value, which is accurate to one part in 300, has been derived by Jeffreys from studies of the figure of the Earth and related data on the motion of the Moon.

13.4.1. Early models of density variation. Let ρ, p, k and μ denote the density, pressure, adiabatic incompressibility and rigidity at depth z below the Earth's surface (or distance r from the centre).

Early representations of density variation in the Earth were formal mathematical relations, plausible but very arbitrary, set down to assist in studies of large-scale terrestrial and planetary phenomena. Laplace, for example, took a chemically homogeneous Earth model in which dk/dp is set equal to 2. This equation of state yields the density law

$$\rho = A r^{-1} \sin Br. \tag{3}$$

Roche took the still simpler density law

$$\rho = A - Br^2. \tag{4}$$

Knowledge of M and I enables A and B in either (3) or (4) to be determined, and thence ρ as a numerical function of r. Laplace's law gives 2·6 and 11·2 g/cm³ for the densities at the surface and centre of the model; Roche's law, 2·4 and 10·3 g/cm³.

Wiechert allowed for a central core, but had to take the densities ρ_0, ρ_1 in the mantle and core as constants in order to get a determinate result. He obtained $\rho_0, \rho_1 = 3\cdot4$, $8\cdot4$ g/cm³, amended by Jeffreys in 1929 to 4·27, 12·04 g/cm³, respectively.

13.4.2. Equations for density gradient. An outstanding importance of the P and S velocity distributions is that through (4, (4)) and (4, (5)) they lead to well-determined values of k/ρ and μ/ρ throughout much of the Earth's interior. If additional numerical information were available on some third explicit function of any of ρ, k and μ, the values of all three of these quantities could be immediately computed. In practice, the procedure is more involved, and rests on a variety of evidence.

By (4, (4)) and (4, (5)), we can write

$$k/\rho = \alpha^2 - 4\beta^2/3 = \phi, \quad \text{say}, \tag{5}$$

and
$$\mu/\rho = \beta^2, \tag{6}$$

where α and β denote the P and S velocities. It is sufficiently accurate in the following discussion to take μ as zero in the outer core (see § 13.3), so that k/ρ, μ/ρ and the rather important quantity ϕ can be regarded as observationally determined within fairly close limits all the way from the Mohorovičić discontinuity to the base of the region E.

For present purposes it is sufficient to represent the stress at a point of the interior in terms of the mean $(-p)$ of the principal stresses (see § 4.7). Strictly, ρ should then be regarded as a function of the pressure p, the temperature T, and an indefinite number of parameters specifying the chemical composition. It is convenient temporarily to take the entropy S as an argument instead of T. For the variation of ρ with z in a chemically homogeneous region of the Earth, we can then write

$$\frac{d\rho}{dz} = \left(\frac{\partial\rho}{\partial p}\right)_S \frac{dp}{dz} + \left(\frac{\partial\rho}{\partial S}\right)_p \frac{dS}{dz}. \tag{7}$$

By (2, (36)), we have for adiabatic changes of a chemically homogeneous material

$$k \, d\rho = \rho \, dp. \tag{8}$$

Let g denote the gravitational force per unit mass at distance r from the centre, and m the mass inside the sphere of radius r. By ordinary hydrostatic theory and the theory of attraction,

$$dp = g\rho \, dz, \tag{9}$$

where

$$g = Gm/r^2. \tag{10}$$

By (5), (9) and (10), the first term on the right-hand side of (7) is equal to $Gm\rho/r^2\phi$.

Next, let α_p denote the coefficient of thermal expansion at constant pressure, and τ the excess of the temperature gradient over the adiabatic gradient, at depth z. By standard thermodynamical theory,

$$\alpha_p = -\rho^{-1}(\partial\rho/\partial T)_p, \tag{11}$$

and

$$\tau = \frac{dT}{dz} - \left(\frac{\partial T}{\partial p}\right)_S \frac{dp}{dz}$$

$$= \left(\frac{\partial T}{\partial S}\right)_p \frac{dS}{dz}.$$

Thus

$$\tau = -\frac{1}{\rho\alpha_p}\left(\frac{\partial\rho}{\partial S}\right)_p \frac{dS}{dz}. \tag{12}$$

By (12), the second term on the right-hand side of (7) is equal to $-\alpha_p\tau\rho$.

Hence (7) becomes

$$\frac{d\rho}{dz} = \frac{Gm\rho}{r^2\phi} - \alpha_p\tau\rho. \tag{13}$$

The form (13), neglecting the term in τ, was used in 1923 by Adams and Williamson. In 1936, the writer applied it in an effort to determine the Earth's complete density distribution. The term in τ in (13) is due to Birch, though derived by him in another way.

Birch, in a combined theoretical-experimental study, has estimated that a departure of 1 deg./km from an adiabatic temperature gradient could affect the right-hand side of (13) by the order of 10 %. Work of Uffen (1952) and Verhoogen (1954) on temperature variation makes it likely that the actual departure is appreciably less than 1 deg./km at most depths. The writer showed in 1956 that when the density distribution is derived by the method to be outlined in § 13.4.3, a 10 % error arising from neglect of the term in τ in (13) would lead to errors in the computed mantle densities nowhere exceeding $0 \cdot 07 \, \text{g/cm}^3$. It follows that, on the procedure to be given, the simplified form

$$\frac{d\rho}{dz} = \frac{g\rho}{\phi} = \frac{Gm\rho}{r^2\phi}, \tag{14}$$

is a satisfactory approximation in parts of the Earth that are chemically homogeneous and devoid of phase changes.

13.4.3. Procedure for determining the detailed density distribution. With the use of (14) and the relation

$$dm = 4\pi r^2 \rho \, dr, \tag{15}$$

it is formally possible to derive a density distribution for any range of values of r for which ϕ is known, provided starting values of m and ρ are available at some point.

Let m' and ρ' be the values of m and ρ just below the Mohorovičić discontinuity. There is evidence that ρ' is of the order of $3 \cdot 3 \, \text{g/cm}^3$. The evidence (see § 12.7) includes: (i) data on the general increase (with depth) of the basicity of rocks in the outer part of the Earth, and on the broad correlation between basicity, density and seismic velocities; (ii) results of laboratory experiments on rocks at pressures up to 2×10^4 atmospheres; (iii) the likelihood that the mean density, $3 \cdot 34 \, \text{g/cm}^3$, of the Moon provides an upper bound to ρ'.

In 1936, the writer used (14) and (15) to derive a trial density distribution for the mantle between 33 and 2900 km depth, taking ρ' equal to $3 \cdot 32 \, \text{g/cm}^3$ and m' equal to the mass of the Earth minus a conventional allowance for the crust. No subsequent evidence has required amendment of the value $3 \cdot 32 \, \text{g/cm}^3$, and an error of $0 \cdot 1 \, \text{g/cm}^3$ in this value of ρ' would affect the estimated mass below 400 km depth by only 1 part in 200. Any error due to uncertainty in m' is likewise slight.

With a view to testing the trial distribution, the corresponding moment of inertia of the mantle was computed and subtracted from the known I for the Earth, with the result $I_1 = yM_1R_1^2$, where $y = 0.57$ and I_1, M_1 and R_1 are the moment of inertia, mass and radius of the central core. This value of y exceeds the value 0.40 for a uniform sphere and would entail a substantial decrease of density with depth inside the central core—a conclusion that must be rejected for stability reasons and so demands scrutiny of the assumptions underlying the trial distribution.

The essential assumptions are: (a) the assumed value for ρ'; (b) neglect of the term in τ; (c) neglect of possible changes of chemical composition and phase. In regard to (a), the calculations showed that ρ' would need to be at least $3.7 \, \text{g/cm}^3$ to reduce y from 0.57 to 0.40, while all available evidence is against so high a value of ρ'. In regard to (b), it can be shown that any significant temperature effect could only increase y. It therefore follows, with strong probability, that the faulty assumption is (c) and hence that there are marked changes in chemical composition (or phase changes) in the mantle between crust and core. Further examination indicated that at least a large part of the changes must occur high up in the mantle, most probably in the upper mantle.

It follows also that the simplified equation (14) is inapplicable throughout all of the regions B, C and D. The trial procedure was then modified by abandoning the use of (14) in C where, because of the abnormal velocity gradients, it was natural to assume that the main mantle inhomogeneities occur. Indeterminacy immediately arose through lack of an equation for $d\rho/dz$ in C, and consequently also of starting values to take for ρ and m at some point of D. However, the simple dependence of α and β on ρ, according to (4, (4)) and (4, (5)), indicates that discontinuities in α, β, $d\alpha/dz$ and $d\beta/dz$ must, virtually certainly, be accompanied by corresponding discontinuities in ρ and $d\rho/dz$. Thus, on the velocity distributions of §13.2, it is permissible to assume continuous variation of ρ from B through C to D, a discontinuous change in $d\rho/dz$ at the boundary between B and C, and continuity in $d\rho/dz$ through C to D. By assuming in C a quadratic law of density variation with depth, with constants chosen to fit the requirements just

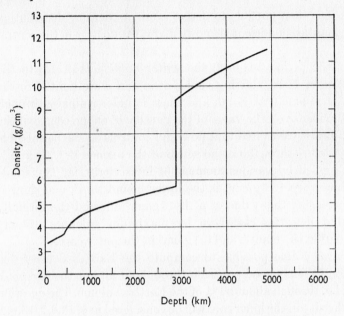

Fig. 40. Variation of density in the Earth Model A.

Region	Depth (km)	Density (g/cm³)	
....	33	3·32	
	100	3·38	
	200	3·47	
B	300	3·55	
	413	3·64	
....		Hypothesis (i)	Hypothesis (ii)
	500	3·88	3·90
C	600	4·11	4·14
	800	4·46	4·52
(------)	1000	4·65	4·71
	1400	4·88	4·95
	1800	5·10	5·17
D	2200	5·31	5·37
	2600	5·51	5·57
....	2898	5·66	5·72
	2898	9·7	9·1
	3000	9·9	9·2
E	3500	10·5	9·8
	4000	11·1	10·3
	4500	11·6	10·8
....	4982	11·9	11·1
F			
....	5121	12·0	
G			
....	6371	12·3	22·3

stated, it is then possible to derive a unique density distribution for the mantle if sufficient is known about the density in the central core.

Over the period 1936–42, the writer applied (14) also to the central core. Here, starting values of m and ρ are limited to the datum that $m = 0$ at $r = 0$, and there is indeterminacy through lack of evidence on the value of the density ρ'' at the centre of the Earth. But it transpired that powerful controls on the permissible density values throughout the whole of the regions B, C, D and E were supplied by various moment of inertia criteria. The whole procedure gave $12 \cdot 3 \, \mathrm{g/cm^3}$ as the lower bound to ρ'', and showed that increasing this value of ρ'' by $5 \, \mathrm{g/cm^3}$ affected the formally computed densities elsewhere by maximum amounts of only $0 \cdot 03 \, \mathrm{g/cm^3}$ in the mantle and $0 \cdot 4 \, \mathrm{g/cm^3}$ in the outer core.

It thus became possible to compute the Earth's density distribution to fairly good precision throughout all but the regions F and G, i.e. through about 99 % of the Earth's volume. The question of the density in the inner core will be considered in §§ 13.6.2, 13.8.4.

13.5. Earth Model A. In 1940–2, the calculations outlined in § 13.4.3 were used with the velocities of § 13.2 to derive density distributions on two fairly extreme hypotheses: (i) $\rho'' = 12 \cdot 3$; (ii) $\rho'' = 22 \cdot 3 \, \mathrm{g/cm^3}$ (the latter value being taken quite arbitrarily). The distributions are shown on p. 231.

A model with density values midway between those of the hypotheses (i) and (ii) has been called Model A. Strictly, the non-linearity innate in (14) and (15) forbids the taking of simple means and this point was actually raised in connection with Model A; Bolt has verified that the effect of non-linearity is quite trivial in the present numerical context. Fig. 40 shows the density values for Model A from the crust to the base of the region E.

By (4, (4)) and (4, (5)), the density determination carries with it the determination of the elastic parameters k and μ, and hence also, by (2, (35), (39) and (40)), of the Lamé parameter λ, Young's modulus E and Poisson's ratio σ. The table on p. 233 and Fig. 41 show the Model A values of these parameters in units of $10^{12} \, \mathrm{dynes/cm^2}$ (or 10^6 bars).

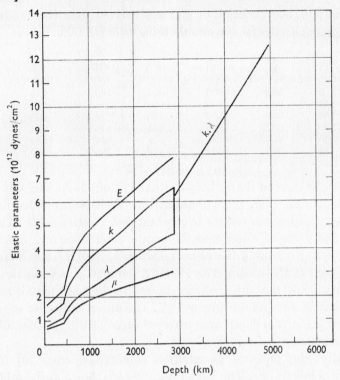

Fig. 41. Variation of elastic parameters in the Earth.

Region	Depth (km)	λ	μ	k	E	σ
....	33	0·74	0·63	1·16	1·60	0·269
	100	0·80	0·67	1·24	1·70	0·272
B	200	0·90	0·74	1·38	1·89	0·275
	300	1·01	0·81	1·54	2·07	0·277
....	413	1·14	0·90	1·73	2·30	0·280
	500	1·42	1·10	2·15	2·82	0·283
C	600	1·69	1·32	2·57	3·38	0·281
	800	2·06	1·69	3·19	4·31	0·275
(.........)	1000	2·33	1·89	3·59	4·82	0·276
	1400	2·76	2·15	4·20	5·51	0·281
	1800	3·27	2·39	4·87	6·16	0·288
D	2200	3·81	2·63	5·57	6·81	0·295
	2600	4·32	2·88	6·23	7·49	0·300
	2898	4·49	3·03	6·51	7·87	0·300
....	2898	6·2		6·2		0·5
	3000	6·5		6·5		0·5
E	3500	8·1		8·1		0·5
	4000	9·7		9·7		0·5
	4500	11·1		11·1		0·5
....	4982	12·6		12·6		0·5

From (10), the variation of g is also derived from the density distribution, results for the mantle being as in the table below.

Depth (km)	g (cm/sec²)	Depth (km)	g (cm/sec²)	Depth (km)	g (cm/sec²)
0	982	600	1001	1800	985
33	985	800	999	2000	986
100	989	1000	995	2200	990
200	992	1200	991	2400	998
300	995	1400	988	2600	1009
413	998	1600	986	2898	1037

It will be noticed that g keeps within 1 % of 990 cm/sec² down to a depth of 2400 km. It is a useful and fairly reliable simplification for many purposes to treat g as constant down to this depth. The maximum value of g occurs at the mantle-core boundary. Inside the whole central core, g diminishes monotonely from this maximum and is zero at the centre. The Model A value of g at a depth of 4000 km below the outer surface is 800 cm/sec², and may differ from that in the actual Earth by 4 %. The uncertainties for some distance below this depth are greater because of the considerable uncertainty of ρ''.

Finally, the pressure distribution is obtained from (9) by numerical integration. The Model A values are shown in the table on p. 235 and in Fig. 42. The actual values in the Earth are not likely to deviate from these by more than 8 % in the regions F and G, nor 3 % elsewhere.

Other Earth models have been contructed by various authors, for example Bolt and Bullard. These are usually based on Model A, or contain artificial assumptions designed to assess the effects of specific departures from Model A. In § 13.6, a second model of the writer, fairly closely related to Model A, is discussed.

Båth (1954) explored the possibility of estimating the density change $\Delta\rho$ at the mantle-core boundary through its connection with energy partitioning of waves reflected at the boundary, and also with changes of phase in the waves. Båth concluded that observations of PcP waves positively establish that $\Delta\rho > 0$.

A model corresponding to the hypothesis (i) on p. 231 is called Model A'.

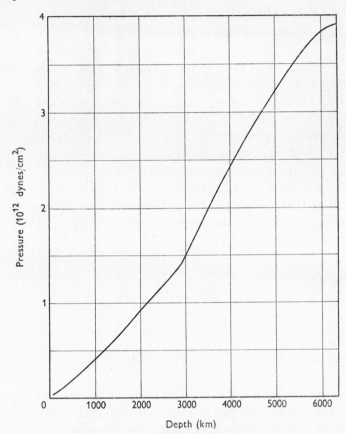

Fig. 42. Pressure distribution in the Earth.

Region	Depth (km)	Pressure ($\times 10^{12}$ dynes/cm^2)	Region	Depth (km)	Pressure ($\times 10^{12}$ dynes/cm^2)
....	33	0·009	....	2898	1·37
	100	0·031		3000	1·47
B	200	0·065		3200	1·67
	300	0·100		3400	1·85
....	413	0·141		3600	2·04
C	600	0·213	E	3800	2·22
	800	0·300		4000	2·40
(........)	1000	0·392		4200	2·57
	1400	0·58		4400	2·73
	1800	0·78		4600	2·88
D	2200	0·99		4800	3·03
	2600	1·20	....	4982	3·17
	2800	1·32	F	5121	3·27
....	2898	1·37	G	5700	3·71
			....	6371	3·89

13.6. Earth Model B

13.6.1. Compressibility-pressure hypothesis. The incompressibility k, the density ρ and the rigidity μ are three parameters whose values indicate the primary physical characteristics of the material at any point of the Earth's interior. A striking feature of the Model A results is that, whereas the changes in ρ and μ at the mantle-core boundary are very large, the formally indicated change in k is merely (a reduction of) 5 %. The uncertainties in certain of the postulates underlying Model A would, moreover, permit the change in k to be zero.

A second striking feature emerged following an examination by the writer (1949) of dk/dp. For a chemically homogeneous region in which the term in τ is neglected, we have by (5), (8) and (9)

$$dp/d\rho = \phi,$$

and hence
$$\frac{dk}{dp} = \frac{d(\phi\rho)}{\phi\,d\rho}$$

$$= 1 + \frac{\rho\,d\phi}{\phi\,d\rho}$$

$$= 1 + g^{-1}\frac{d\phi}{dz}. \tag{16}$$

Values of $d\phi/dz$ are yielded directly from the seismic velocity data, and are $2\cdot2 \times 10^3$ cm/sec^2 between 2500 and 2700 km depth (i.e. in the lowest 200 km of D'), and $2\cdot1 \times 10^3$ cm/sec^2 in the outermost 200 km of E. Also g is approximately 1000 cm/sec^2 at these depths. On evidence of Birch, D' and E are likely to be nearly uniform in chemical composition, so that it is permissible to use (16) and hence derive $dk/dp = 3\cdot2$, $3\cdot1$ near the base of D' and top of E, respectively. Thus the suggestion arises that dk/dp, in addition to k, is nearly continuous between mantle and core.

It is necessary to note that $d\phi/dz$ falls continuously to zero inside D'', so that formal application of (16) would give values of dk/dp falling to unity inside D''. However, this fall, being continuous, implies a marked continuous variation of composition and so invalidates the use of (16) inside D''. Thus the present method fails to determine a value for dk/dp in D'', and provides no evidence against the near-continuity of dk/dp between mantle and core. The question of the heterogeneity of D″ will be further considered in § 13.8.2.

The contrast near the mantle-core boundary between the apparently slight changes in k and dk/dp on the one hand, and the very large changes in ρ and μ on the other, led the writer to set up a hypothesis on the variation of compressibility with pressure. The initial (1946) form of the hypothesis was that, at pressures of the order of a million atmospheres, the value of k for ordinary materials is determined predominantly by pressure rather than by composition. Following calculations of Feynman and others indicating a relatively small but significant degree of dependence of k on the representative atomic number Z, the writer in 1949 re-stated the hypothesis in the form that, to good approximation, k is a smoothly varying function of p for the materials present in the Earth below a depth of 1000 km.

Related work by the writer in 1952 provided evidence that the representative atomic number for the region E does not exceed 28 (the value for nickel) and might well be as low as 23. In subsequent studies, Knopoff and MacDonald (1960) gave reasons for preferring the value of 23, while more recently still Birch (1961) has expressed a preference for 25.

13.6.2. Construction of Model B. In 1950, the writer set up a second Earth Model, B, in which a central postulate is that k and dk/dp vary smoothly with p at all depths below 1000 km.

In deriving the density distribution for Model B, the simplified equation (14), with the use of the numerical values of α and β, was applied in D′ and E, for which alone there is now good evidence of approximate chemical homogeneity. In D″, F and G, the numerical values of α and β were also used, but only in conjunction with the k–p hypothesis. The values of α and β were not used above D′ because of the degree of uncertainty in them in the upper mantle.

In conjunction with the known values of the mass and moment of inertia of the Earth, the procedure of the last paragraph was found to entail severe restrictions on density values in the upper mantle. In particular, between depths of about 200 and 1000 km below the outer surface, the procedure precluded the marked reduction in ρ, with decreasing depth, that occurs in Model A. For this reason, it was postulated that the density for a considerable distance above D′ is given by smoothly extrapolating upward from D′ to a level $z = b$, say. It was further postulated that the Model A density distribution applies above $z = b$. With the additional postulates, the procedure gave a discontinuity in ρ of $0.5\,g/cm^3$ at $z = b$, and $b = 80\,km$. The additional postulates were introduced solely to secure a definite self-consistent model compatible with the earlier postulates, and are somewhat arbitrary in relation to the density in the outermost $200\,km$ or so; and no special significance attaches to the formally indicated density jump near $z = 80\,km$ in Model B.

Properties of Model B

Region	Depth	ρ	p	k	μ	g
-------	33	3·32	0·009	1·16	0·63	985
	80	3·36	0·025	1·22	0·66	986
	80	3·87	0·025	(1·40)	(0·76)	986
(B, C)	200	3·94	0·071	(1·58)	(0·83)	985
	400	4·06	0·150	(1·92)	(0·99)	983
	600	4·18	0·231	(2·61)	(1·34)	980
-------	1000	4·41	0·400	3·37	1·78	976
	1400	4·63	0·58	3·96	2·03	976
D′	1800	4·84	0·76	4·58	2·25	982
	2200	5·03	0·96	5·26	2·48	997
	2600	5·22	1·16	5·89	2·71	1010
-------	2700	5·27	1·22	6·13	2·81	1042
D″	2898	5·57	1·33	6·40	2·97	1069
	2898	9·74	1·33	6·4	0·0	1069
E	3500	10·60	1·95	8·2	0·0	937
	4000	11·16	2·42	10·1	0·0	815
	4500	11·63	2·85	11·6	0·0	647
F	4982	12·00	3·22	12·1	0·0	607
G	5121	15·4	3·33	13·6	(3·2)	573
-------	6371	18·1	3·95	16·4	(5·0)	0

Subsections of § 13.8 contain a broad indication of the method of determination of the Model B density values in regions of abnormal density variation.

From the Model B values of ρ as thus derived, values of p, k, μ, E, σ and g can be deduced by the procedures used for Model A.

The table on p. 238 shows various Model B results, the units being as with the Model A tables. In deducing values of the elastic parameters, the values of α and β need to be used. In respect of the upper mantle, however, this involves the difficulty that the variations of α and β as given in § 13.2 do not match the variation of ρ in Model B (as they do in Model A). Hence the values of k and μ between 80 and 1000 km are included in brackets and are for broad reference purposes only. The values for μ in the inner core are also included in brackets; they have been formally derived by (5) and (6) from the values given for α, ρ and k and may need to be substantially reduced. Some of the entries in the table incorporate small corrections, not yet published, from previous work.

13.7. Ellipticities of surfaces of equal density within the Earth. Knowledge of the density distribution also enables values of the ellipticity ϵ involved in § 10.9.2 to be computed. If the moment of inertia (about a diameter) of the material enclosed within a sphere of radius r of the model Earth is equal to zmr^2, where m as previously denotes the mass of this material, the coefficient z is readily calculated from knowledge of the density distribution. The value of η, as defined by (10, (31)), for the corresponding level surface within the actual Earth is then found by using the approximate equation

$$1 - \tfrac{3}{2}z = \tfrac{2}{5}(1+\eta)^{\frac{1}{2}} \tag{17}$$

obtained by Radau and Darwin in investigations of the theory of the figure of the Earth. The validity of this equation depends on the form of the Earth's density variation, and has been substantiated for Model A.

The fact that the values of η and ϵ given in § 10.9.2 have of necessity to be calculated in the first instance from density values determined using P and S velocity values deduced from travel-time tables set up prior to the use of ellipticity corrections is of small consequence, since the ellipticity corrections are (see § 10.9.2) so small. It will in fact be appreciated from the discussion given in chapter 10 that the quantitative study of features of the Earth's deep interior rests very much on methods of successive approximations. It is only after a fair number of successive approximations that we are able to set down numerical results to the degree of precision indicated in the results of chapter 10 and the present chapter.

13.8. Further implications of the k–p hypothesis

13.8.1. Relation between gradients of ρ and φ.

Consider a region of the Earth, not necessarily homogeneous, in which k and ρ vary continuously with z. We shall here neglect temperature effects which can be allowed for as in § 13.4.2. Since $k = \phi\rho$, we have

$$\frac{dk}{dp}\frac{dp}{dz} = \rho\frac{d\phi}{dz} + \phi\frac{d\rho}{dz},$$

and hence by (9)

$$\frac{d\rho}{dz} = \frac{g\rho}{\phi}\frac{dk}{dp} - \frac{\rho}{\phi}\frac{d\phi}{dz}$$

$$= \frac{\eta g\rho}{\phi}, \tag{18}$$

where

$$\eta = \frac{dk}{dp} - g^{-1}\frac{d\phi}{dz}. \tag{19}$$

Comparison of (14) and (18) shows that the coefficient η is an index of the departure of a region from chemical homogeneity, being equal to unity in a chemically homogeneous region and greater than unity elsewhere. The expression (19) for η is an important generalisation of (16).

By (9) and (18), η also gives the ratio of k to $\rho\,dp/d\rho$, which was used by Bolt in another context on Earth models.

13.8.2. Density gradient in the region D″.

The discussion in § 13.6.1 showed that (16) is inapplicable in D″. In its place, we can use the generalisation (19) in conjunction with the k–p hypothesis to determine $d\rho/dz$. The hypothesis requires that inside D″, $dk/dp \approx 3$, the value which applies immediately above and below D″. Since on the data of § 13.2, $d\phi/dz \approx 0$ inside D″, we therefore obtain $\eta \approx 3$ in D″. Thus D″ is characterised by a density gradient about three times the value that would apply if the region were chemically homogeneous. Hence the important conclusion emerges that there is either an accumulation of some denser matter inside the lowest 200 km of the mantle, or possibly a continuous phase transition.

Since g is adequately determined for the present purpose, (19) shows that this conclusion depends essentially on the assumed values of dk/dp and $d\phi/dz$. Even should the k–p hypothesis require some modification, the physical evidence still indicates that dk/dp must be appreciably in excess of unity in this part of the Earth. Hence the conclusion of significant inhomogeneity inside D″ is likely to be disturbed only if it should become necessary to increase the assumed velocity gradients in D″ to approximately the values in the lower part of D′.

13.8.3. Density gradient in the region F. The Model B results in § 13.6.2 include the very large density increase of $3\cdot4\,\text{g/cm}^3$ through the short range of depth (140 km) occupied by the region F. Equations (18) and (19) show immediately how this abnormally steep density gradient is entailed on the k–p hypothesis and the Jeffreys velocity values. The velocity values give

$$d\phi/dz \approx -15 \times 10^3 \,\text{cm/sec}^2$$

in F. Taking $g \approx 600\,\text{cm/sec}^2$ and $dk/dp \approx 5$, (19) then gives $\eta \approx 30$ for F. The density gradient which corresponds to this value of η is much greater than that indicated for D″, and in fact exceeds that in any other part of the Earth (apart from where actual discontinuities occur).

The abnormally high value of η indicated for F depends very much on the assumed P velocity gradient, and so is uncertain mainly to the extent that $d\phi/dz$ is uncertain (cf. § 13.8.2). One of the outstanding problems in the seismology of the Earth's deep interior is to reduce the latter uncertainty, or at least set feasible upper and lower bounds to the mean value of $d\alpha/dz$ in F.

Bolt has recently (1962) produced a new set of P velocity values between a depth of 4560 km and the Earth's centre. His tentative results are: $d\alpha/dz$ falling to zero for $4560 < z < 4710$ km; α suddenly increasing from $10\cdot03$ to $10\cdot31$ km/sec at $z = 4710$ km; $d\alpha/dz$ close to zero for $4710 < z < 5160$ km; α suddenly increasing again at $z = 5160$ km, from $10\cdot31$ to $11\cdot23$ km/sec; and $d\alpha/dz$ again close to zero for $5160 < z < 6370$ km. This model is compatible with the data used by Jeffreys in inferring a negative velocity gradient for the region F. The steeply negative gradient set down by Jeffreys for F is replaced by gradients close to zero extending over a range of depth much greater than that of F. But the model is not merely an alternative to the Jeffreys model. The presence of two discontinuous jumps in α inside the central core requires the (T, Δ) curve for core waves to have two distinct branches of the type $B''C''D''$ of Fig. 25 (c) (§ 7.3.3); and Bolt has been able to choose the velocity distribution so that the second branch fits early P arrivals (preceding the phase $PKIKP$) for $\Delta < 142°$ found by Gutenberg (1958) and also by Burke–Gaffney and the writer.

This new model like the old is not unique, but is the simplest compatible with the whole set of data used and provides an improved basis for discussing the character of the transition between the outer and inner core. By (19), with the removal of negative values of $d\phi/dz$, it gives results compatible with an appreciably reduced central density.

13.8.4. Density in the inner core G. On both the Jeffreys and Gutenberg velocity distributions, $d\phi/dz$ though positive is abnormally small inside the inner core. On the k–p hypothesis, use of (19) as in §§ 13.8.2, 13.8.3 yields a value of order 4 for η in the inner core, indicating a degree of inhomogeneity in the inner core comparable with that in D''. On the Model B postulates, the density increases by $2\cdot7\,\mathrm{g/cm^3}$ inside G and reaches $18\cdot1\,\mathrm{g/cm^3}$ at the centre. The writer has shown that with Bolt's velocities the central density can be as low as $15\,\mathrm{g/cm^3}$ (though a higher value is not precluded).

13.8.5. Solidity of the inner core. A key observational result for the core is the existence (§ 13.1.3) of a sharp increase in α from outer to inner core. Writing (4, (4)) as

$$k + 4\mu/3 = \rho\alpha^2 \tag{20}$$

shows that this increase in α must be due to a sharp increase in k or μ (or both), since ρ is an increasing function of depth. If the inner core were fluid, there would be no increase in μ, in which case the increase in k would have to be so large as to violate the k–p hypothesis seriously. For this reason, the writer inferred in 1946 that the inner core is solid (in respect of its response to stresses of seismic wave periods). From physical data on the variation of k with atomic number, he has estimated that any increase in k near the inner core boundary is unlikely to exceed one-fifth of the increase needed to keep the inner core fluid, and that the rigidity of the inner core probably lies between 2 and 5×10^{12} dyne/cm^2.

A solid inner core would transmit S seismic waves, so that there is the possibility of confirming its solidity by detecting $PKJKP$ readings on seismograms, where J corresponds to an S wave passage through the inner core. Theoretical travel-times of the phase $PKJKP$ have been prepared, but energy calculations show that the phase is, on the most favourable assumptions on the nature of the discontinuity at the inner core boundary, only on the border of observability for $205° < \Delta < 230°$, and below the border for other Δ. Several investigators consider that they have identified $PKJKP$ on occasions, but statistical scrutiny indicates that much more evidence is required before a positive conclusion can be drawn. At the same time, failure to detect $PKJKP$ does not disprove the solidity of the inner core, since the actual nature of its boundary could be incompatible with the excitation of detectable S waves.

Another possibility is connected with the phase $PKiKP$. Caloi regards his evidence (§ 13.1.3) on this phase as supporting strongly the inference that the inner core is solid.

The notion of a solid inner core has also been examined from other aspects. Birch's experimental work on materials at high pressure led him to suggest in 1940 that the inner core might possess rigidity. In 1953, Simon inferred that a transition from liquid to solid iron at the inner core boundary would correspond to a temperature of 3600 °C at the pressures involved, a temperature that is well in agreement with other evidence. Jacobs in 1954 showed that an Earth previously wholly molten could well have started solidifying from the centre upward, a solid inner core growing until the curve representing the adiabatic temperature distribution in the Earth intersected the melting-point curve at two points which would correspond, respectively, to the inner-outer-core boundary and the outer-core-mantle boundary, leaving a molten outer core trapped between. Lubimova (1956) carried out temperature calculations which led her to infer that the inner core is below melting point. Chandrasekhar has calculated that a boundary like that which a solid inner core would provide is necessary to sustain convection currents in the outer core of the type needed on the Elsasser–Bullard theory of the Earth's magnetism.

13.8.6. An equation of state for the deeper interior. The Model B values of k and p fit the simple quadratic relation

$$k = 2 \cdot 25 + 2 \cdot 86 p + 0 \cdot 16 p^2, \tag{21}$$

where the units are 10^{12} dyne/cm^2, within 2 % for

$$0 \cdot 4 \times 10^{12} < p < 3 \cdot 2 \times 10^{12} \, \text{dyne/cm}^2,$$

i.e. between the top of the region D and the base of E. This equation of state embodies the seismic evidence and the compressibility-pressure hypothesis, and serves for model purposes in comparison with equations of state evolved by Birch, Shimazu and others, independently of seismic data. (One of Birch's simpler cases is (2, (86)).) The gradient dk/dp, equal to $2 \cdot 86 + 0 \cdot 32 p$, increases with p, a property which is not likely to be indefinitely sustained at pressures beyond those in the Earth.

13.9. Questions of the Earth's internal composition. The contribution of seismology to knowledge of the Earth's internal composition rests on numerical detail of the type already given. Endeavours to identify the actual materials present involve further matters such as the results of high-pressure experiments on rocks and metals, and thermodynamical and geochemical considerations. A brief account will here be given of some questions that are fairly closely related to the seismological observations.

The question of the composition of the crustal layers and of the material immediately below the crust has been discussed in chapter 12.

13.9.1. The regions B and C. In § 12.7, evidence was given on the likelihood of olivine $((\text{Mg}, \text{Fe})_2 \text{SiO}_4)$ being the principal constituent of rocks just below the crust. The density and velocity gradients associated with Model A (see §§ 13.4.3, 13.5) were considered to indicate chemical homogeneity in the region B but not in C, and to be compatible with a fairly uniform olivine composition throughout B.

In 1936, Jeffreys suggested that the changes setting in at the top of C might be associated with the transformation of ordinary olivine to a high-pressure modification. Bernal, recalling Gold-schmidt's assertion (1931) that magnesium germanate (Mg_2GeO_4) is transformed under pressure to a denser modification, indicated that the same could probably apply to forsterite (Mg_2SiO_4) which is a principal constituent of olivine rocks such as dunite. The density jump at the transition would be about 9 % for forsterite.

In 1952, Birch compared values of dk/dp as given by (16) with his experimental results on rocks, and confirmed that the velocity data of § 13.2 were reasonably compatible with chemical homo-geneity in B. He attributed the variations in the region C prin-cipally to polymorphic changes in the minerals present, leading to more closely packed structures, but suggested that some change of chemical composition might also be needed to account for the large range of depth of the transition region C.

Over the period 1958–60, Ringwood concluded from investiga-tions of a solid solution of Mg_2SiO_4 in the spinel Ni_2GeO_4 that forsterite would transform into a spinel structure at pressure and temperature of $1\cdot3 \times 10^{11}\,(\pm 10\,\%)\,dyne/cm^2$ and 600 °C, or at $1\cdot75 \times 10^{11}\,(\pm 30\,\%)\,dyne/cm^2$ and 1500 °C, the density jump being $11\,(\pm 3)\,\%$. He demonstrated the transformation of fayalite (Fe_2SiO_4) to a spinel structure at $0\cdot38 \times 10^{11}\,dyne/cm^2$ and 600 °C, with a density jump of 12 %. The stated pressures occur at depths 400, 500 and 120 km, respectively, below the Earth's surface.

These results support in some further detail the view that the Model A results are compatible with the presence of ordinary olivine in B and the spinel form in C. After allowing for ordinary com-pression inside C, the further density jump connected with the phase transitions is, however, found to be rather greater than the 10 % or so expected for forsterite. This suggests again that there is some change of chemical composition in C. An obvious possibility is that the iron-magnesium ratio in the olivine increases with depth inside C. Ringwood states that Model A can be fitted precisely in the regions B and C by assuming a composition of dunite and peridotite (which is closely related to dunite but consists less exclusively of olivine), with up to 10 % of garnet in the form $Mg_3Al_2(SiO_4)_3$.

With Model B, the more marked density changes in the upper

mantle occur at shallower depths. It is likely that these changes could be accommodated in similar ways, since many minerals are now known to undergo polymorphic transitions at the pressures involved. Until the numerical differences between Models A and B are more fully resolved, there must remain considerable uncertainty on the detailed variation of composition in the upper mantle.

In 1961, Birch set down a simple empirical relation between α, ρ and the mean atomic weight w, derived from experiments on silicates and oxides in the density range from 2·6 to 5 g/cm³. With α in km/sec and ρ in g/cm³, the relation is

$$\alpha \approx 3\cdot31\rho - f(w), \qquad (22)$$

where $f(w) = 2\cdot55$, $5\cdot7$ units for $w = 21$, 25, respectively; for $w = 21$, the standard error of α as given by (22) is stated to be 0·28 km/sec. For a selection of rocks including granites, igneous rocks, dunites, peridotites and eclogites, Birch gives values of w ranging from 20·9 to 22·1. For the average dunite w is 21·5, and with $\rho = 3\cdot32$ g/cm³, (22) then gives $\alpha = 8\cdot05 \pm 0\cdot28$ km/sec, verifying the compatibility of the density 3·32 with the observed Pn velocities.

Birch states that the form of the crystal structure has little influence on (22), so that relations between α and ρ for particular regions of the Earth may be matched against (22) with a view both to testing for departures (over and above phase changes) from chemical homogeneity, and estimating the mean atomic weight. If α is taken as 8·0 km/sec just below the crust, $\partial\alpha/\partial\rho$ is found to be close to 3·3 units for the region B of Model A, agreeing with chemical homogeneity. For the region C, $\partial\alpha/\partial\rho$ is about 2·4 units, suggesting a small degree of chemical change, while the indicated w ranges from 21·5 to 22·5. Birch states that the most serious uncertainty in applying (22) is the effect of temperature.

13.9.2. The region D. The application by Birch of (16) to the region D′ gave results compatible with chemical homogeneity, while (22) suggested a slightly increasing iron content with increase of depth, the indicated mean atomic weight ranging from 22·5 to 23 for Model A. The values of k/ρ and μ/ρ in D′ do not fit simple extrapolations from data on any silicate rock occurring at the

Earth's surface, but are compatible with the inferred properties of a spinel modification of olivine. Birch has suggested that D′ may possibly consist rather of closely packed oxides of magnesium, silicon and iron, which would be chemically equivalent to olivine; Ringwood has suggested a 'homogeneous spinel phase consisting of a disordered solid solution'.

Birch supports the conclusion in § 13.8.2 of an increased density gradient in D″, and suggests an increasing iron content with depth in this region. Ringwood estimates that D″ contains about 5–10 % of metallic iron mingled with silicates.

Birch states further that when temperature effects are allowed for, it may be possible to 'reconcile all the data with a mantle of nearly uniform mean atomic weight close to that of the average chondritic meteorite'.

13.9.3. The core. Prior to 1948, it was widely held that the central core consists largely of iron or nickel-iron, the evidence used being the high core density and early findings on meteorite compositions. In 1937, Jeffreys and the writer had independently shown that if the mantles of terrestrial planets have the same chemical composition, and if the cores likewise have the same composition but distinct from that of the mantles, then the overall compositions would be widely different, the mantle-core mass ratios being 2·1, 3·6 and 5·4 for the Earth, Venus and Mars, respectively.

In 1948 Ramsey, and in 1949 the writer, made the radically different suggestion that the Earth's core is not chemically distinct from the mantle but consists of a high-density modification (which would be metallic in form) of the mantle material. (Ramsey regarded this as applying to the whole core, the writer to the outer core only.) On this theory, the density ρ would be largely a function of the pressure p alone from the top of the region B to at least the lower part of E. The theory proved to be closely compatible with uniform overall compositions of the three planets, in the light of observational data on the planetary masses, mean densities and moments of inertia. (For Mercury, a composition of higher mean atomic weight was indicated; this was attributed to Mercury's proximity to the Sun.) On the writer's calculations, the agreement is best if the Earth's inner core is chemically distinct from both the mantle and outer core. The theory meets difficulty in so far as it requires a phase change at the mantle-core boundary involving a density jump in the ratio 1·6 to 1·7, which geochemists consider improbably high. Decisive tests on the point have not, however, yet been carried out.

Ramsey showed that a side-product of the theory is that in certain conditions planets with small cores could be gravitationally unstable. The writer and Datta have calculated that by this mechanism sufficient gravitational energy could have been suddenly released from a primitive Earth–Moon body to form the Moon.

As pointed out in § 13.6.1, the available evidence indicates for the region E an atomic number rather less than that of iron (26) and nickel (28). In 1952, Birch estimated that the density in E exceeds that of iron at the same pressures by 10–20 %, and suggested that the outer core may consist of iron alloyed with lighter elements, conceivably including metallic hydrogen. (At pressures of order $0·7 \times 10^{12}$ dyne/cm² —the pressure at a depth of 1600 km below the Earth's surface—it has been calculated that hydrogen changes to a metallic form and jumps in density from 0·4 to 0·8 g/cm³.) MacDonald and Knopoff, and Ringwood, in 1958–9 independently suggested that silicon is a major component of the Earth's core; Ringwood, taking account of chondritic meteorite composition, has proposed a core containing 20 % silicon and 7 % nickel.

On such proposals, the mantle and core are not in chemical equilibrium. Ringwood suggests that silicon and nickel diffuse from the core into the mantle and precipitate metallic iron in the region just above the core. The effect would be a mechanically unstable contact zone with consequent small regional differences in iron content, and could account for vagaries in observations of the P phase at distances beyond 105°, to which Lehmann has drawn attention.

The argument in § 13.8.4 shows that the P velocity gradient inside the inner core entails a mild degree of chemical inhomogeneity in the inner core, which must also be somewhat different in composition from the outer core. Other calculations of the writer imply that the representative atomic number for the inner core is greater than that for the outer core, but does not exceed the value for nickel–iron. It appears fairly certain that whatever deviations there may be from a nickel–iron composition in the region E, these deviations are not markedly present in G.

It is likely that the region F is some form of transition region, but until the P velocity distribution becomes more certainly determined in this part of the Earth, there is little point in speculating on the composition of F.

Lyttleton recently (1963) put forward a new theory of mountain building which makes use of pressure-compressibility-density values in the deeper interior. The theory envisages a primitive Earth, cold and wholly solid. Contraction is considered to take place with rise in temperature through the formation of a molten core of higher density than the primitive solid material. The theory is of some interest in the present context in that it revives interest in the view that the outer core is a high-density modification of the material of the mantle.

Birch (1963) has assembled evidence, including evidence from shock-wave experiments at pressures of the order of 10^6 atm, suggesting that the central density of the Earth does not exceed 13 g/cm³. Bullen (1964), using the relations (18) and (19) (which he has since subjected to critical examination), has shown that, on the currently available seismic data, a central density less than 14·7 g/cm³ would require $d\mu/dz$ to have a significantly negative value in the lower core. Since the presence of a rigidity gradient entails the presence of rigidity, new evidence is thus incidentally provided that the inner core is solid. On this line of evidence, the Earth's core consists of a fluid outer part (or parts), at the bottom of which there is a fairly sudden jump in rigidity (to the order of 10^{12} dyne/cm²), followed by a trend back toward fluidity. The analysis also gives, on the basis of Bolt's P velocity data for the core, a slight balance of probability favouring the presence of a second solid region immediately outside the inner core proper.

CHAPTER 14

LONG-PERIOD OSCILLATIONS
OF THE EARTH

Recently there has been a remarkable extension in the range of periods of ground movements that can be recorded, enabling the whole spectral interval to be filled in from ordinary surface-wave periods of a minute or so to periods of the order of hours such as occur in earth tidal movements. In particular, it has become possible to measure fundamental free vibrations of the whole Earth and to provide important additional evidence on the Earth's interior.

In the theory of seismic waves considered in earlier chapters, the source energy has been usually looked upon as being transmitted outward from the focus in the form of P and S and ordinary surface waves. The emphasis has been on the wave motions of travelling disturbances which affect only a relatively small part of the Earth at any one time, rather than on what is happening to the vastly larger Earth as a whole. All such wave motions can, however, be looked at from a more general standpoint as belonging to some mode of vibration of the whole Earth, although for periods of a few minutes or less the modes would be of high order. Mention has already been made in § 3.2.5 of some cases where the more general approach has been usefully brought to bear. For Earth oscillations with periods exceeding a few minutes, the more general theory is necessary.

It transpires that natural free oscillations of the Earth have periods up to the order of an hour. The mathematical theory of these oscillations is heavy and lengthy. In this chapter only a broad indication of the theory will be given, together with the details of its application to the structure of the interior of the Earth in the light of observations so far gathered.

14.1. General theoretical background. The vibrations of a perfectly elastic solid sphere were first considered by Poisson in 1829. Kelvin and G. H. Darwin later developed important theory on the straining of an elastic sphere, with applications to Earth tidal problems.

In 1882, Lamb discussed in some detail the simpler modes of vibration of a uniform sphere and showed that two distinct classes of vibration are possible. In a valuable review paper, Stoneley (1961) refers to these two classes as C_1 and C_2. With the C_1 class, the dilatation and the radial component of displacement vanish everywhere, while with C_2 the radial component of the curl of the displacement vanishes everywhere. This classification continues to be relevant for more complicated spheres such as the commonly used Earth models.

In his notable work of 1911, Love investigated the statical deformation and small oscillations of a uniform gravitating compressible sphere. In *The Earth* (1959), Jeffreys presents the statical case succinctly and draws attention to the defect that a uniform compressible Earth model would have lighter materials at greater depths. Love obtained a period of 60 min for the slowest mode of C_2 type in his model.

Following the Kamchatka earthquake of 1952 November 4, Benioff recorded a ground motion of 57 min period on his strain seismograph (§ 9.9.2), and this stimulated renewed activity on the theory of long-period Earth oscillations.

Pekeris, Jarosch and Alterman (1956, 1959) simplified Love's analysis by working entirely in spherical polar coordinates. They reproduced a number of Love's results, and extended them to various non-homogeneous spherical Earth models. The more difficult cases required at least six differential equations of the first order to be solved subject to heavy boundary conditions, and the degree to which electronic computers are needed makes it clear that the calculations would have been mostly impossible in Love's day. In the course of the computations, Pekeris used both direct numerical integration procedures and variational methods. The extension to heterogeneous models made possible close comparisons between theory and observation.

Other important calculations of the fundamental periods of realistic Earth models have been carried out since 1954 by Matumoto and Satô, Jobert, Takeuchi, and Gilbert and MacDonald.

14.1.1. The basic equations. Let r, θ, ϕ be spherical polar co-ordinates referred to the centre of a spherically symmetrical Earth model of radius a. During an oscillation, let u, v, w be the components of the displacement from the undisturbed configuration in the directions of r, θ, ϕ increasing, respectively. Let λ and μ denote the Lamé parameters and ρ and k the density and incompressibility. Zero suffixes will relate to the undisturbed configuration. Allowance needs to be made for the presence of initial stress which is taken, as usual, to be a hydrostatic pressure p_0 such that $dp_0/dr = -g_0\rho_0$. Let p_{rr}, $p_{r\theta}$, etc., and e_{rr}, $e_{r\theta}$, etc., denote the spherical polar components of additional stress and strain.

The strain components and the dilatation Δ are found to be connected with u, v, w by

$$\left.\begin{aligned}
e_{rr} &= \frac{\partial u}{\partial r}, \quad e_{\theta\theta} = \frac{1}{r}\frac{\partial v}{\partial \theta} + \frac{u}{r}, \quad e_{\phi\phi} = \frac{1}{r\sin\theta}\frac{\partial w}{\partial \phi} + \frac{v}{r}\cot\theta + \frac{u}{r}, \\
2e_{r\theta} &= \frac{\partial v}{\partial r} - \frac{v}{r} + \frac{1}{r}\frac{\partial u}{\partial \theta}, \quad 2e_{r\phi} = \frac{1}{r\sin\theta}\frac{\partial u}{\partial \phi} + \frac{\partial w}{\partial r} - \frac{w}{r}, \\
2e_{\theta\phi} &= \frac{1}{r}\frac{\partial w}{\partial \theta} - \frac{w}{r}\cot\theta + \frac{1}{r\sin\theta}\frac{\partial v}{\partial \phi},
\end{aligned}\right\} \quad (1)$$

$$\Delta = \frac{\partial u}{\partial r} + \frac{2u}{r} + \frac{1}{r\sin\theta}\frac{\partial}{\partial \theta}(v\sin\theta) + \frac{1}{r\sin\theta}\frac{\partial w}{\partial \phi}. \quad (2)$$

The stress-strain relations take the form

$$\left.\begin{aligned}
p_{rr} &= p_1 + 2\mu e_{rr}, \quad p_{\theta\theta} = p_1 + 2\mu e_{\theta\theta}, \quad p_{\phi\phi} = p_1 + 2\mu e_{\phi\phi}, \\
p_{r\theta} &= 2\mu e_{r\theta}, \quad p_{r\phi} = 2\mu e_{r\phi}, \quad p_{\theta\phi} = 2\mu e_{\theta\phi},
\end{aligned}\right\} \quad (3)$$

where $\qquad\qquad p_1 = -(p_0 + ug_0\rho_0) + \lambda\Delta.$

We shall consider only free oscillations, so that gravity will be the only external force entering the equations. During an oscillation let ψ be the gravitational potential associated with the excess density distribution $\rho - \rho_0$ and the accompanying surface displacements. The components of body force per unit mass are then expressible as

$$g_0 - \partial\psi/\partial r, \quad -r^{-1}\partial\psi/\partial\theta, \quad -(r\sin\theta)^{-1}\partial\psi/\partial\phi.$$

The equations of motion (2, (9)) are found (putting $f_i = \partial^2 u_i/\partial t^2$ —see § 2.3.2) to take the form

$$
\left.
\begin{aligned}
\rho \frac{\partial^2 u}{\partial t^2} &= \rho g_0 - \rho \frac{\partial \psi}{\partial r} + \frac{\partial p_{rr}}{\partial r} + \frac{1}{r} \frac{\partial p_{r\theta}}{\partial \theta} + \frac{1}{r \sin \theta} \frac{\partial p_{r\phi}}{\partial \phi} \\
&\qquad + r^{-1}(2p_{rr} - p_{\theta\theta} - p_{\phi\phi} + p_{r\theta} \cot \phi), \\
\rho \frac{\partial^2 v}{\partial t^2} &= -\frac{\rho}{r} \frac{\partial \psi}{\partial \theta} + \frac{\partial p_{r\theta}}{\partial r} + \frac{1}{r} \frac{\partial p_{\theta\theta}}{\partial \theta} + \frac{1}{r \sin \theta} \frac{\partial p_{\theta\phi}}{\partial \phi} \\
&\qquad + r^{-1}\{(p_{\theta\theta} - p_{\phi\phi}) \cot \theta + 3p_{r\theta}\}, \\
\rho \frac{\partial^2 w}{\partial t^2} &= -\frac{\rho}{r \sin \theta} \frac{\partial \psi}{\partial \phi} + \frac{\partial p_{r\phi}}{\partial r} + \frac{1}{r} \frac{\partial p_{\theta\phi}}{\partial \theta} + \frac{1}{r \sin \theta} \frac{\partial p_{\phi\phi}}{\partial \phi} \\
&\qquad + r^{-1}(3p_{r\phi} + 2p_{\theta\phi} \cot \theta).
\end{aligned}
\right\}
\tag{4}
$$

The equation of continuity is found to yield

$$
\rho - \rho_0 = -(\rho_0 \Delta + u \, d\rho_0/dr)
\tag{5}
$$

(cf. (4, (13))), and (4, (12)) gives

$$
\nabla^2 \psi = -4\pi G(\rho_0 \Delta + u \, d\rho_0/dr).
\tag{6}
$$

On substituting from (1), (2) and (3) into (4) and (6), a set of complicated second-order differential equations between the variables u, v, w and ψ is derived. These equations can in principle be solved when λ, μ and ρ_0 are given as functions of r, and when suitable boundary conditions are prescribed.

The boundary conditions include regularity at the origin, and, at the deformed surface at all times, vanishing of the stress-components and equality of the internal and external gravitational potentials and their gradients. Other boundary conditions may have to be set down to allow for discontinuities in λ, μ and ρ_0 as functions of r in the models considered.

In the next section, an indication will be given of particular modes that have been studied.

14.2. Particular modes of vibration

14.2.1. Radial oscillations of a homogeneous Earth. We consider here an Earth model in which ρ_0, k and μ are constant through-

out. Let α and β denote the P and S velocities. Radial oscillations will be represented by the form

$$u = U(r)\exp(i\gamma t), \quad v = w = 0. \tag{7}$$

On substituting into equations in §14.1.1, and simplifying, the equation

$$\frac{d^2U}{dr^2} + \frac{2}{r}\frac{dU}{dr} - \frac{2U}{r^2} + h^2U = 0, \tag{8}$$

where

$$3h^2\alpha^2 = 3\gamma^2 + 16\pi G\rho_0, \tag{9}$$

can be derived for U. An appropriate solution of (8) is found to be

$$U = (hr)^{-2}\sin(hr) - (hr)^{-1}\cos(hr). \tag{10}$$

The requirement that p_{rr} must vanish at the boundary $r = a + u$ gives

$$2\lambda U r^{-1} + (\lambda + 2\mu)\,dU/dr = 0 \quad \text{at} \quad r = a. \tag{11}$$

From (10) and (11), the eigen-value equation

$$(ha)^{-1}\tan ha = (1 - h^2a^2\alpha^2/4\beta^2)^{-1} \tag{12}$$

can be derived.

For an assigned value of α/β, (12) yields roots for ha, from which the corresponding periods $2\pi/\gamma$ can be deduced from (9) when α and ρ_0 are also assigned.

The results in this section correspond to those derived by Pekeris, and apart from a correction incorporated in (9) are essentially equivalent to earlier results of Love. Pekeris points out that the presence of the term in G in (9) exhibits a de-stabilising effect of gravity.

14.2.2. Radial oscillations of a spherically symmetrical Earth.
When ρ_0, λ and μ are variable functions of r, (8) has to be replaced by the more general equation

$$\frac{d}{dr}\left(\rho_0\alpha^2\frac{dU}{dr}\right) + \frac{2\rho_0\alpha^2}{r}\frac{dU}{dr} + \left(\frac{2}{r}\frac{d\lambda}{dr} - \frac{2\rho_0\alpha^2}{r^2}\right)U + \rho_0\left(\gamma^2 + \frac{4g_0}{r}\right)U = 0. \tag{13}$$

From (11) and (13), the periods for an assigned Earth model can be derived by heavy numerical integration, with the help of electronic computers.

14.2.3. Spheroidal oscillations. A more general class of oscillations is given by the form

$$u = U(r) S_n \exp(i\gamma t), \quad v = V(r) (\partial S_n/\partial\theta) \exp(i\gamma t),$$
$$w = (\sin\theta)^{-1} V(r) (\partial S_n/\partial\phi) \exp(i\gamma t), \tag{14}$$

where $S_n(\theta, \phi)$ is a spherical harmonic of order n. These have been called spheroidal oscillations, and the radial oscillations (7) correspond to the particular case $n = 0$. The radial component of the curl of the displacement given by (14) is found to vanish, so that spheroidal oscillations are of the C_2 class.

Apart from the case $n = 1$ (which would involve the presence of a constraining force to keep the centre at rest) there are in general solutions for all integral n. For each n, there exist a fundamental oscillation and higher mode oscillations.

The procedure for finding the oscillation periods is again to substitute into equations in § 14.1.1, this time from (14), but the resulting equations are too complicated to be set down here. The reader is referred to Alterman, Jarosch and Pekeris (1959).

14.2.4. Torsional (toroidal) oscillations. Another class of oscillations is given by

$$u = 0, \quad v = (\sin\theta)^{-1} V(r) (\partial S_n/\partial\phi) \exp(i\gamma t),$$
$$w = -V(r) (\partial S_n/\partial\theta) \exp(i\gamma t). \tag{15}$$

It can be verified that with (15) the dilatation Δ and the radial component u vanish everywhere. Thus (15) is of the C_1 class. These oscillations have been referred to sometimes as toroidal because they involve particle motions over spherical surfaces concentric with the model, and sometimes as torsional because Δ vanishes for them.

Since Δ vanishes, the density at any point of the medium is undisturbed during the oscillations, so that there is no perturbation in the gravitation field. This property is important in practice since instruments designed to record fluctuations in gravity, while they may record the oscillations (14), will not record (15).

Oscillations of the type (15) were first considered by Matumoto and Satô and by Jobert.

Since the density is undisturbed in torsional oscillations, it follows that the oscillations are controlled entirely by elastic forces. For an Earth model which has a solid mantle and fluid core, the torsional property ensures that the motion will be confined to the mantle.

14.2.5. Core oscillations. In contrast to the case of § 14.2.4, it is possible to have spheroidal oscillations which are largely confined to the fluid core. The calculations of Pekeris indicate that when the ratio of the core and mantle densities exceeds a certain minimum (between 3 and 4), the periods of these core oscillations can exceed the periods of all regular free oscillations. (Numerical results are shown in § 14.3.) In order to estimate the extent of the mantle motion in core oscillations, Pekeris considered vibrations excited by compressional point-sources at depths of zero and 200 km, respectively, below the outer surface of an Earth model of the type in which the long-period core oscillations can occur. He found that at the surface of the mantle, the amplitudes of the core oscillations for $n = 2$ would be 10^{-4} to 10^{-3} of those with the corresponding regular spheroidal oscillations; for $n > 2$ the amplitudes of the core oscillations would be smaller still.

14.2.6. Forced oscillations. Pekeris has extended the theory of earlier sections to cover forced oscillations induced by periodic tidal potentials. The interest of this in relation to seismology is that it shows how recent developments have been closing the spectral gap between ordinary earthquake periods and the much longer periods of tidal motion.

14.3. Some numerical results. An Earth model is defined for present requirements when ρ, α and β, or ρ, k and μ, are given as functions of r. Models for which calculations have been carried out include (among others) Model A (§ 13.5), Model B (§ 13.6), models in which density values of Models A and B are combined with various sets of values of α and β, and models with mass-average properties corresponding to these models or to their mantles and cores separately. In some cases, values of ρ have been combined with values of α and β which do not have matching discontinuities (see the sixth paragraph of § 13.4.3); this inconsistency has usually been in respect of the upper mantle, and caution is needed in interpreting the results for such cases.

A model with uniform solid mantle and uniform fluid core, each having the same mass-average properties as in Model B and having the same mass-ratio between mantle and core, will be called Model B′; and an entirely uniform solid model having the Model B mass-average properties, Model B″. Inner cores are disregarded in all cases.

For torsional oscillations Pekeris obtained the following periods for Model B, F denoting a fundamental oscillation, and (i), (ii), ... the first, second, ... overtones:

	$n = 2$ (min)	$n = 3$ (min)	$n = 4$ (min)
F	44·1	28·6	21·9
(i)	12·7	11·6	10·5
(ii)	7·3	7·1	6·9

Adapting results of Matumoto, Satô and Jobert, Pekeris computed periods for Model B″ corresponding to seven of the nine results in the table, and obtained results which agreed with those in the table within 0·5 min. The smallness of the differences for two such widely different models indicates that torsional oscillations can be of only limited help in discriminating between plausible Earth models.

For spheroidal oscillations, Pekeris obtained:

	Regular oscillations			Core oscillations
Mode	Model B (min)	Model B′ (min)	Model B″ (min)	Model B (min)
$n = 0$, F	20·65	—	26·7	—
(i)	10·2	—	10·6	—
$n = 2$, F	53·7	56·0	44·3	100·9
(i)	24·7	25·2	—	—
(ii)	15·5	16·3	—	—
(iii)	9·8	10·4	—	—
(iv)	8·0	7·9	—	—
$n = 3$, F	35·5	—	—	85·5
(i)	17·9	—	—	—
(ii)	13·6	—	—	—
$n = 4$, F	25·7	—	—	76·9
(i)	14·4	—	—	—

Although only a small number of calculations were carried out for Models B′ and B″, the differences from Model B were sufficient to show that spheroidal oscillations are capable of discriminating fairly finely between some Earth models.

The initial calculations of Pekeris also included results for two Earth models with densities computed by Bullard, one of which is essentially Model A of § 13.5. The results indicate that the periods (both fundamental and overtones) for Model A agree within about 0·5 % with those for Model B for $n = 2$. Pekeris later included a model incorporating certain P and S velocity values of Gutenberg, and extended the calculations for fundamental spheroidal and torsional modes for this model and Model B to $n = 60$. Other calculations have been made by Gilbert and MacDonald, and by Bolt and Dorman, who derived periods for spheroidal oscillations with n up to and beyond 140.

14.4. Earth oscillations and surface waves.

The numerical results exhibited in § 14.3 relate to fairly small values of n. As n increases, the associated oscillation periods steadily decrease. For an Earth model based on Model A and the Jeffreys P and S velocity values, Bolt and Dorman gave the following fundamental periods for spheroidal oscillations: $n = 20$, 5·8 min; $n = 30$, 4·3 min; $n = 40$, 3·5 min; $n = 50$, 2·9 min; $n = 75$, 123 sec; $n = 100$, 95 sec; $n = 140$, 70 sec.

The values of the periods for higher n thus merge with the values for ordinary surface waves, and the theories of Earth oscillations of higher mode and of surface-wave propagation are in fact closely linked. The connection is illustrated by the equivalence of a progression of simple Rayleigh waves round the surface of a homogeneous Earth to two superposed standing waves of equal amplitudes and periods. Much of Love's original work on surface waves was, moreover, closely tied to the theory of fundamental Earth oscillations, and a study of his work shows the connection intimately.

It follows that the free oscillations of the Earth are influenced increasingly, as n increases, by the structure of the Earth at higher levels. Spheroidal oscillations for which n is less than about 10 depend essentially on the characteristics of the Earth as a whole. For n between 10 and 100 (approximately), i.e. for periods between about 10 min and 100 sec, the oscillations depend markedly on the structure of the mantle. For periods less than about 100 sec, the oscillations are determined mainly by the structure in the outer-most 50 km of the Earth.

In 1937, Stoneley showed how long-period surface wave observations might be applied to problems of the structure of the Earth below the crust, and since 1950 a great body of theory has been developed by Ewing, Press, Jardetzky, Oliver and others.

Ewing and Press (1958) observed Rayleigh waves of order up to R_{18} from the Mongolian earthquake of 1957 December 14 and found periods up to 10 min. (The notation R_1, R_2, R_3, ... refers to long-period Rayleigh waves which have travelled distances Δ, $2\pi - \Delta$, $2\pi + \Delta$, $4\pi - \Delta$, $4\pi + \Delta$, ... from the epicentre, where $\Delta \leqslant \pi$. With Love waves, a corresponding notation G_1, G_2, G_3, ... is used.) Followed by others, they have brought such observations to bear on the structure of the mantle by an extension of the methods described in chapter 5.

Dorman, Ewing and Oliver (1960) worked out dispersion curves, for eleven model representations of the outermost 600 km of the Earth, for Rayleigh waves with periods up to 250 sec. They concluded that both the 20° discontinuity and a prominent low-velocity channel (for S waves) are essential to a good Rayleigh wave solution for periods greater than 75 sec. They gave the depth of the lower boundary of the low-velocity layer as of the order of 200 km; and the depth of the upper boundary as of the order of 100 km under continental areas, but only 60 km under oceans. Their findings are closely compatible with data of Gutenberg and Lehmann. Alterman, Jarosch and Pekeris also find evidence from Rayleigh waves to support the existence of a low-velocity layer in the upper mantle. Landisman and Satô have found evidence from Love wave dispersion of a low-velocity layer, but rather less marked than in the Rayleigh wave results. Knopoff (1961) has drawn attention, however, to the considerable difficulty in securing uniqueness in applications of surface-wave data to the detailed structure of the Earth.

Pekeris has drawn attention to a further important connection between spheroidal oscillations and Rayleigh waves, which comes from work of Jeans. This is that the Rayleigh wave-length λ and the value of n for the corresponding fundamental spheroidal oscillation are connected approximately by

$$2\pi R \approx (n + \tfrac{1}{2})\lambda, \tag{16}$$

where $2\pi R$ is the circumference of the Earth. Brune, Nafe and Alsop have verified (16) in observations for $n > 20$. Brune, Ewing and Kuo have also verified that analyses of seismograms of surface waves in terms of standing waves and progressive waves give comparable results.

The power of the surface-wave approach to problems of the Earth's mantle and its intimate connection with higher modes of oscillation of the Earth indicate that observations of the latter are also likely to throw important light on the structure of the mantle. Further detail is given in §§ 14.5.3, 14.6.

14.5. Observations of Earth oscillations

14.5.1. Historical. Following the Kamchatka earthquake of 1952 November 4, Benioff found indications on his strain seismograph (§ 9.9.2) of two unexpected long wave periods of about 57 and 100 min. He suggested that these periods related to fundamental oscillations of the Earth excited by the Kamchatka earthquake, and he stimulated others to carry out the theoretical calculations already mentioned.

During the following 7 years, there were no reports of similar long-period waves from earthquakes, and many seismologists attributed Benioff's readings to some purely instrumental effect. Then in 1960 at the Helsinki meeting of the I.A.S.P.I.E., there occurred one of the most dramatic scientific sessions this author has witnessed.

Press announced that Benioff had once again observed long-period waves, this time from the Chilean earthquakes of 1960 May 22. Thereupon Slichter announced that his group had observed similar long-period waves, not on a seismograph, but on a LaCoste–Romberg tidal gravity meter. Comparison showed that a number of periods of the two groups were in good agreement, notably periods of about 54, 35·5, 25·8, 20, 13·5, 11·8 and 8·4 min, but that certain of Benioff's periods were missing in Slichter's results. Pekeris, who was also present at the session, studied the missing periods and announced that these periods corresponded to his calculations for torsional oscillations, and further that torsional oscillations (see § 14.2.4) would not be recorded on a gravity meter. The two sets of results were thus shown to be in remarkable accord, and all doubt as to the genuine recording of free long-period oscillations of the Earth was removed.

That was not quite the end of the drama. Before the meeting closed, it was announced that the long-period oscillations had also been recorded by Bogert on a Lamont long-period seismograph in the Bell Telephone Laboratories, by a group under Ewing on both strain and pendulum seismographs, and by Press on a Lamont seismograph. Each group had independently and hastily prepared tentative reports for the Helsinki meeting, and all the results were found to be in good accord. Subsequently (1961) detailed accounts were published.

14.5.2. Periods exceeding 13 min. In the table on p. 262, a list of all the observational periods greater than 13 min is shown, apart from four periods (61·2, 59·8, 41·3 and 29·9 min) attributed by the observers concerned to atmospheric oscillations. The results in the table are designated as: (a) Benioff–Press group; (b) Slichter group; (c) Ewing group; (d) Bogert. The entries for (c) are averages of authors' stated results for different instruments and different components of the ground motion.

The identifications of the observed periods are those assigned by the observers, except for six periods listed as 'unidentified'; these six periods (two for group (a) and four for (d)) have been entered in the table where they fit best. For all entries, the units are minutes.

Theoretical results for Model B are shown in the table for comparison.

Scrutiny of the table shows that the observational results are in good accord both with one another and with the theoretical Model B results. The agreement for the range of values of n shown is found to be almost as good with Model A, but is less satisfactory for models which deviate markedly from these two.

Slichter (1961) has further observed a spectral peak with period 86 min on his gravity-meter records of the Chilean earthquakes. The 100 min period found by Benioff in 1952 does not, however, appear to have been repeated in the Chilean earthquake observations.

Mode		Theoretical (Model B)	Observational			
			(a)	(b)	(c)	(d)
		Torsional				
$n = 2$,	F	44·1	42·3(?)	—	44·7	—
$n = 3$,	F	28·6	28·6	—	28·5	28·8
$n = 4$,	F	21·9	21·8	—	21·8	$\begin{cases}22\cdot5\\21\cdot5\end{cases}$
$n = 5$,	F	18·1	17·9	—	17·8	—
$n = 6$,	F	15·5	15·5	—	15·1	—
$n = 7$,	F	13·7	13·5	—	13·5	—
		Spheroidal				
$n = 0$,	F	20·65	—	20·5	—	20·4
$n = 2$,	F	53·7	$\begin{cases}54\cdot5\\53\cdot1\end{cases}$	$\begin{cases}55\cdot0\\52\cdot8\end{cases}$	53·4	54·4
	(i)	24·75	24·5	24·65	24·7	—
	(ii)	15·5	15·1	15·0	15·5	15·0
$n = 3$,	F	35·5	$\begin{cases}35\cdot9\\35\cdot2\end{cases}$	$\begin{cases}35\cdot9\\35\cdot2\end{cases}$	36·0	35·4
	(i)	17·9	17·6	$\begin{cases}17\cdot9\\17\cdot7\end{cases}$	18·0	17·7
	(ii)	13·6	—	13·5	—	—
$n = 4$,	F	25·7	25·8	25·85	25·8	25·5
	(i)	14·4	—	14·3	—	14·2
$n = 5$,	F	19·85	19·8	19·8	19·7	19·6
$n = 6$,	F	16·1	16·0	16·1	16·1	15·9
$n = 7$,	F	13·6	13·5	13·4	—	13·4

It will be noticed from the table that, in several cases, the observations include two periods close together where the calculations have given only one. Such observations have been tentatively attributed to departures from spherical symmetry and to the Earth's rotation. Pekeris, and Backus and Gilbert, have shown that the Earth's rotation can produce period separations of the right order. The existence of separated periods adds, however, to the complexity of the interpretation of the observational results.

Long-period oscillations from the Chilean earthquakes were also recorded outside the American continent. For example, Bolt and

Marussi (1962) reported observations of fundamental torsional observations for $2 \leqslant n \leqslant 24$ on a sensitive tiltmeter at Trieste, with some indication of the four lowest fundamental spheroidal modes.

14.5.3. Periods from 3 to 13 min. In addition to the periods in the table of § 14.5.2, all four groups of observers reported periods of spheroidal oscillations with values of n from 8 to at least 38 (to 42 in the case of group (c)). Group (a) reported torsional oscillations with values of n up to 11, and group (c) to 9. The shortest of these reported periods (spheroidal, $n = 42$) is 3·4 min.

Below 13 min, the intervals between consecutive fundamental periods of spheroidal oscillations range from 75 sec $(n = 8, 9)$, through 15 sec $(n = 20, 21)$ to 4 sec $(n = 40, 41)$. Thus for the larger n there are possible difficulties in identifying particular modes. The identifications are also complicated by the presence of overtones and torsional oscillations (though with the use of the gravity meter the latter can be eliminated). In attempts to separate the various periods, use was made by the various observing groups of power-spectrum techniques in statistical communication theory, and in particular of procedures of Blackman and Tukey (1958). In spite of the smallness of the period intervals for larger n, the periods obtained by the four groups agree sufficiently closely to suggest that reliable identifications were in fact made over the whole range of values of n. But confirmation from further earthquake data is desirable.

For $7 \leqslant n \leqslant 23$ and $35 \leqslant n \leqslant 38$, the periods fit best, among models so far tried, a combination of Model A with Gutenberg's velocities; for $24 \leqslant n \leqslant 32$ and $40 \leqslant n \leqslant 42$, the fit is slightly better with Model B. The maximum discrepancy (15 sec) between the observed results and calculated results for Model B occurs at $n = 12$, where the observed period is 8·36 min.

14.6. Application to the internal structure of the Earth. The numerical results show the capacity of observations of long-period oscillations of the Earth to discriminate fairly finely between different Earth models. In applying the observations to gaining improved knowledge of the internal structure of the Earth, it is in theory desirable to set up an indefinite number of Earth models, compute all the periods of their free oscillations down to the order of 3 min, and check against the observations. Models could then be steadily eliminated until only a small range survives. In practice, one works from existing models, seeking to amend them by successive approximation until full compatibility with the observations is achieved within the uncertainties of the observations. Questions of uniqueness of course still remain.

The compatibility of Model B with the observations of periods exceeding 13 min indicates that no amendments to the density distribution, at least in the outer core of Model B, can be expected from the Chilean observations for larger n. There is a faint indication that Model B fits better than Model A in respect of the core.

The observed periods between 5 and 13 min indicate, however, that Model B does need some amendment, more probably in respect of the outer mantle. As pointed out in § 13.6, there were certain arbitrary features in the construction of Model B in the outermost few hundred km. However, it looks as if the adjustment of these arbitrary features will not be sufficient, and that further adjustments will be needed. The two main sources of uncertainty in the construction of Model B are (i) the uncertainty over region F, (ii) the assumption that k is continuous between mantle and core. (The further assumption that dk/dp is also continuous is not likely to affect the mantle density very much.) The assumption (ii) is mainly responsible for Model B having an appreciably higher density in the regions B and C than Model A, and a slightly lower density in the region D'. The observed periods in the range $7 \leqslant n \leqslant 23$ make it likely that Model B will need to be altered somewhat towards Model A in the mantle. This would mean further that the incompressibility is suddenly slightly diminished at the mantle-core boundary, but not necessarily by as much as the decrease of 0.3×10^{12} dyne/cm^2 which occurs in Model A.

Other points of interest relate to Benioff's 1952 observations of periods of 57 and 100 min, which agree within the observational uncertainties with the calculated periods (§ 14.3) for spheroidal and core oscillations of Model B for $n = 2$. There is of course the possibility that the 57 min period arose from atmospheric oscillations excited by the Kamchatka earthquake. A feature of the 100 min period is that, of the various models used by Pekeris, only Model B gave core oscillations with a period of order 100 min; Pekeris attributed this to the core density being higher in Model B than in the other models. There remains, however, the difficulty that the amplitudes of core oscillations would normally be expected to be extremely small, so that the genuineness of the observed 100 min period oscillations is still in question. If, however, they should perchance come to be confirmed, most important evidence would be provided on the density near the Earth's centre.

It is already known that Model A requires some amendments in the values of k/ρ and μ/ρ in the region B, arising from needed increases in the velocity values of § 13.2. It is likely that uncertainties in the P and S velocity distributions in the whole outer mantle are responsible for the main discrepancies for $n > 7$. Thus by successive approximations from Model A and B, it may be possible to use the long-period oscillations to arrive at an improved model. If the conclusions of Dorman and others mentioned on p. 259 on long surface waves are substantiated, allowance will have to be made for decreases in μ/ρ, and possibly k/ρ, with depth in the outermost 200 km of the region B. There is the further possibility that departures from spherical symmetry are an important influence down to this order of depth.

The 86 min period reported by Slichter (§ 14.5.2) may prove to be of interest in respect of the core. It agrees with the expected period for core oscillations of Model B for $n = 3$, but there is again the question of the very low amplitude of this mode, according to the theory. Slichter suggests rather that a mode of this period could reasonably be produced by oscillations of the inner core as a rigid body in the surrounding fluid core. There is thus the possibility that long-period oscillations may provide crucial evidence on the solidity of the inner core.

Stoneley and others have also drawn attention to the possibility of using long-period information from both earthquakes and large explosions to throw light on focal mechanisms.

All these considerations make it evident that observations of long-period oscillations of the Earth are providing a valuable new tool in investigating the Earth's interior.

266

CHAPTER 15

EARTHQUAKE OCCURRENCE

The data in seismology consist in large part of measurements of the effects of and records produced at the Earth's outer surface by seismic waves. In the preceding three chapters, we have shown that from these data we can make inferences concerning features of the Earth's interior through which the waves have passed. Working back still further we can offer some comments on circumstances connected with the occurrence of earthquakes, and in particular with circumstances near the foci of earthquakes.

15.1. Energy released in earthquakes. It is evident that an earthquake is associated with the fairly sudden release of energy somewhere inside the Earth, and we first of all consider the quantity of this released energy.

If, following a particular earthquake, it were possible to estimate the earth movements at a sufficient number of points of the Earth's outer surface, it would then be possible, using formulae based on (8, (19)) and (8, (20)) (the constants of proportionality being inferred using formulae such as (8, (10)), to estimate with high precision the total energy released in the earthquake.

But there are in practice several difficulties in the way of making precise estimates of this energy. There is, for instance, the difficulty of estimating the appropriate transmission factor for each refraction of a wave through an internal discontinuity surface (see § 8.5.2). Further, we have seen in chapter 9 that the computation of precise details of the local earth movement from the seismograms traced at an observatory is by no means an easy task. Hence, in practice, approximate methods are used which yield estimates of the energy released, uncertain to the extent of a factor of order about 10.

We may mention here a simplification which is of fairly wide applicability. In general, it is to be expected that at least a moderate fraction of the total energy in an earthquake will leave the focus in waves of *SH* type. Now we have seen that (on the theory of chapter 6) *SH* waves are reflected and refracted only into *SH* waves, and conversely that reflected and refracted SH waves arise only from incident SH waves. Jeffreys has pointed out accordingly that it is reasonable to estimate the order of the total energy in many earthquakes from observations only of the horizontal earth movements during the passage of S waves.

We now discuss representative formulae that have been used to estimate the energies of various types of earthquakes.

15.1.1. Case of near earthquakes. In the case of the Jersey earthquake of 1926 July 30, Jeffreys observed that the records traced at observatories within 500 km of the epicentre showed relatively large Sg waves, and that most of the observed horizontal movement in these waves was at right angles to the line joining an observatory to the epicentre. The energy calculations were therefore made from these waves alone. Jeffreys assumed that the energy travelled out symmetrically with a cylindrical wave front in a granitic layer, of density ρ g/cm³ and thickness H cm, say. Let Δ degrees be the epicentral distance of a particular observatory (within 500 km of the epicentre). Assuming the waves to constitute a simple harmonic group, it would then follow from (8, 10)) that the energy in the Sg waves would be

$$(2\pi H r_0 \sin \Delta)\,(2\pi^2 \rho L C^2 \tau^{-2}), \tag{1}$$

where r_0 is the radius of the Earth, L is the length of the wave train, C is the amplitude of the earth movement, and τ is the period. This expression is readily reduced to

$$\pi \rho H L v_m^2 r_0 \sin \Delta, \tag{2}$$

where v_m is the maximum velocity of the earth movement in the particular train of waves.

A formula equivalent to (2) was used by Jeffreys to estimate the energy in the Jersey earthquake from observations at a number of single stations; values of ρ and H were assigned, and Δ was known to good accuracy. The estimates made independently from the data from the different stations were in fair agreement. The total energy released in the earthquake (including that sent out in P and SV waves) would of course be possibly a few times greater than the value (about 10^{19} ergs) given by the calculations.

It is evident that a similar method may be applied to near earthquakes in general.

It should be noted that the bodily waves in earthquakes do not normally constitute a simple harmonic group, and a more accurate formula than (1) would be

$$4\pi^3 \rho r_0 \sin \Delta \int HcC^2 \tau^{-2} dt, \tag{3}$$

where c is the wave velocity, and the integration is taken over the interval of time occupied by the passage past the particular observatory of the group of waves considered. (In (3), H is being taken constant, but is put after the integral sign in order to facilitate a comparison made in § 15.1.3.) In practice, the formula (1) or (2), with $\sin \Delta$ replaced by Δ, indicates the order of the required energy sufficiently accurately for ordinary purposes.

15.1.2. Use of assumption of spherical symmetry about the focus. Galitzin obtained a formula for estimating the order of the released energy from observations at a single station on the assumption that the disturbance would spread out symmetrically in all directions from the focus. This formula, as later modified by Jeffreys, is equivalent to

$$4\pi^3 \rho (2r_0 \sin \tfrac{1}{2}\Delta)^2 \int cC^2 \tau^{-2} dt. \tag{4}$$

(Sometimes a factor of the form $e^{k\Delta}$ is included in formulae such as (4) to allow for possible absorption of energy during transmission—cf. § 4.5.1.) In the derivation of (4), focal depth is neglected, and it is assumed that the (assumed spherical) spreading out of the disturbance is essentially confined to the lower side of the focus. Also in (4) C denotes the amplitude in the incident waves, but it is assumed that this amplitude is of the same order as that of the observed earth movement; it may be noted that in the case of SH waves the amplitude of the incident waves is one-half that of the surface earth movement; with other incident waves the corresponding amplitude ratio varies with the angle of emergence and therefore with Δ (see § 8.3). The assumption of spherical symmetry about the focus is of course not realised with actual earthquakes; but the use of (4) is likely to yield useful rough estimates of the energy in P or S bodily waves as recorded at stations for which Δ

does not exceed about $90°$. In practice the factor $e^{k\Delta}$ is frequently ignored on account of the smallness of the observed absorption of seismic waves. The derivation of (4) is easily carried out within the assumptions just stated, and is left as an exercise for the reader.

For an earthquake of appreciable focal depth h, it would be necessary to replace (4) by

$$8\pi^3\rho\{h^2+4r_0(r_0-h)\sin^2\tfrac{1}{2}\Delta\}\int cC^2\tau^{-2}dt; \qquad (5)$$

the coefficient 4 in (4) is replaced by 8 in (5) in order to allow for energy which would spread upwards as well as downwards from the focus; the factor in curled brackets corresponds to the square of the length FP (where F is the focus and P a point of the Earth's surface) as indicated in Fig. 43.

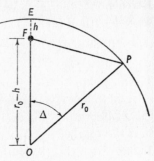

If P is at the epicentre E, (5) degenerates to the formula

$$8\pi^3\rho h^2\int cC^2\tau^{-2}dt. \qquad (6)$$

Fig. 43

A formula equivalent to (6) was made the basis of a method of Gutenberg and Richter for assessing energy in earthquakes. Observations of C and τ are, of course, not normally available at the epicentre of an earthquake, and Gutenberg and Richter set up empirical formulae whereby the order of the integral in (6) could be estimated from observations at stations some distance from the epicentre; these formulae in effect indicate the variations of C and τ with the focal distance FP in particular regions.

15.1.3. Use of observations of surfaces waves. With earthquakes in which the greater part of the released energy goes into forming surface waves, and therefore with many shallow-focus earthquakes, use of the formula (4) will not lead to satisfactory estimates of the total energy released. For such earthquakes, Jeffreys used the Rayleigh wave formulae (5, (18)). The conditions attending the simpler Rayleigh wave theory of §5.2 are not realised in the actual Earth (see chapter 12), but the assumption that these conditions hold is nevertheless likely to lead to a result of the correct order.

By $(5, (18))$ the components of the velocity of the earth movement during the passage of a group of Rayleigh waves are given by

$$\dot{u}_1 = a\kappa c\{-\exp(0\cdot85\kappa x_3) + 0\cdot58\exp(0\cdot39\kappa x_3)\}\cos\{\kappa(x_1 - ct)\},$$

$$\dot{u}_3 = a\kappa c\{-0\cdot85\exp(0\cdot85\kappa x_3) + 1\cdot47\exp(0\cdot39\kappa x_3)\}\sin\{\kappa(x_1 - ct)\},$$

where the suffixes 1, 3 indicate components parallel to the direction of propagation of the waves, and vertically upwards, respectively; a is a constant determining the amplitude, $2\pi/\kappa$ is the wave-length, c is the wave velocity, and $x_3 = 0$ is taken as the equation of the Earth's outer surface. We deduce that the mean value over one wave-length of $(\dot{u}_1^2 + \dot{u}_3^2)$ is

$$a^2\kappa^2 c^2\{0\cdot86\exp(1\cdot70\kappa x_3) - 1\cdot82\exp(1\cdot24\kappa x_3) + 1\cdot24\exp(0\cdot78\kappa x_3)\}. \tag{7}$$

The mean kinetic energy per unit volume is $\frac{1}{2}\rho$ times the expression (7), and the total mean energy per unit volume is (by § 3.3.6) double this. Integrating this result over the range $0 \geqslant x_3 \geqslant -\infty$, we find that the total energy per unit earth surface area is $0\cdot63\rho a^2\kappa c^2$, i.e. $1\cdot26\pi\rho a^2\lambda\tau^{-2}$, by $(3, (40))$, where τ is the period and $\lambda = 2\pi/\kappa$ is the wave-length. It follows that the order of the energy in the Rayleigh waves will be given from observations at an observatory whose epicentral distance is Δ by

$$2\cdot5\pi^2\rho r_0\sin\Delta\int ca^2\lambda\tau^{-2}\,dt. \tag{8}$$

Now the amplitude of the horizontal component of the surface motion in Rayleigh waves is seen by $(5, (19))$ to be $0\cdot42a$, $= C$ say. The formulae (3) and (8) then become formally identical if we put $2\cdot5 \times (0\cdot42)^{-2}\lambda = 4\pi H$, i.e. $H = 1\cdot1\lambda$. Thus the energy in the Rayleigh waves may be estimated from observations of the horizontal component of the surface movements at any single observatory, by using the formula (3) and interpreting H as corresponding to an 'equivalent layer' of thickness roughly equal to the wave-length of the passing Rayleigh waves. The formula (3) was first used in this way by Jeffreys in estimating the energy of the Pamir earthquake of 1911 February 18.

15.2. Earthquake magnitude. In 1935, Richter set up a 'magnitude scale' of earthquakes, in which the magnitude of an earthquake is defined as the logarithm (to base 10) of the maximum amplitude (measured in microns; $1\mu = 10^{-4}$ cm) traced on a seismogram by a standard short-period seismograph (free period 0·8 sec; statical magnification 2800; damping coefficient λ (§ 9.4) = 0·8), distant 100 km from the epicentre. Reduction of observed amplitudes at various distances to the expected amplitudes at the standard distance of 100 km is made by empirical tables set up on the assumption that the ratio of the maximum amplitudes at two given distances is the same for all earthquakes considered, and independent of the azimuth. These assumptions lead to results of practical value since the range of energy released in different earthquakes is very great. The scale is applied directly only to earthquakes of normal focal depth.

Richter first applied the magnitude scale to earthquakes recorded in the Californian region within 600 km of the epicentre. Later, Gutenberg and he set up further empirical tables whereby observations made at distant stations and on seismographs of other than the standard type could be reduced to correspond to the standard conditions in Richter's definition. The empirical tables were extended to cover earthquakes of significant focal depth and to enable independent magnitude estimates to be made from bodily and surface wave observations.

The various extensions introduced some arbitrariness into the definition of a comprehensive magnitude, and several scales came to be used. Steps are being taken towards selecting a scale for international adoption. Here, the symbol M will relate to Richter's preferred scale (1958) in which $M = 8·9$ for the greatest known earthquakes. For various theoretical purposes, Gutenberg and Richter have also used a 'unified magnitude' m, connected with M by the relation $m = 2·5 + 0·63M$. (For $M = 8·9$, 6·75, 0·0, $m = 8·1$, 6·75, 2·5, respectively.)

15.2.1. Magnitude, energy and frequency. Gutenberg and Richter sought to connect the magnitude M with the energy E of an earthquake by the form

$$aM = \log_{10}(E/E_0), \tag{9}$$

and after several revisions arrived in 1956 at the result $a = 1·5$,

$E_0 = 2.5 \times 10^{11}$ ergs. Båth, working on independent material, obtained a closely similar result. Shebalin and Buné have sought to modify (9) by including explicitly a term depending on the focal depth, and have used large explosions of known energies to serve as a check.

The Gutenberg–Richter formula gives $E = 2.5 \times 10^{11}$ and 5.6×10^{24} ergs for earthquakes of magnitude zero and 8·9, respectively. A unit increase in M thus corresponds to a 30-fold increase in energy. Zero magnitude corresponds to the smallest instrumentally recorded earthquakes, 1·5 to the smallest felt earthquakes, 3 to those felt at distances up to 20 km; those of 4·5 cause slight damage near the epicentre; those of 6 are destructive over a restricted area; those of 7·5 are at the lower limit of *major earthquakes* (i.e. earthquakes well recorded at distances up to 80°).

For the period 1904–57, Richter gives the magnitudes of the eight greatest earthquakes as follows: Kansu, 1905 July 23 (8·7); Colombia-Ecuador, 1906 January 31 (8·9); Tien-Shan, 1911 January 3 (8·7); Samoa, 1917 June 26 (8·7); Sanriku (Japan), 1933 March 2 (8·9); Kamchatka, 1938 November 10 (8·7); Andaman Islands, 1941 June 26 (8·7); Assam, 1950 August 15 (8·7). Eight other earthquakes are assigned a magnitude of 8·6 for this period.

Gutenberg and Richter have also given empirical relations for the frequencies of earthquakes of various magnitudes. Let N be the average number of shocks per year for which the magnitude lies between M and $M + 0.1$. They find that, over sizable ranges of M, formulae of the form

$$\log_{10} N = A - BM$$

fit the data well both for the world at large and for particular regions. For example, for the whole world, they give for shallow earthquakes: $A = 8.2$, $B = 1.1$ when $M > 7.3$; $A = 4.6$, $B = 0.6$ when $5.8 < M \leqslant 7.3$. The frequency for these earthquakes thus increases by a factor ranging from about 12 down to 4 when the magnitude is diminished by one unit. The increase in frequency with reduction in M falls short, however, of matching the decrease in the energy E. Thus larger earthquakes are overwhelmingly responsible for most of the total seismic energy release. For $M < 5.8$, there are no reliable data available on N, but Gutenberg and Richter have estimated that the number of earthquakes per year strong enough to be felt is of the order of 10^5, and that the total number per year that could be recorded may reach 10^6.

Gutenberg and Richter have estimated that the total annual energy released in all earthquakes is about 10^{25} ergs, corresponding to a rate of work between 10 and 100 million kW. This is of the order of 0·001 of the annual amount of heat escaping from the Earth's interior. Eighty per cent. of the total earthquake energy comes from shocks of magnitude 7·9 and more, i.e. whose energy is of the order of 10^{23} ergs or more.

15.3. Causes of earthquakes.

We have already pointed out that earthquakes arise through the fairly sudden release of energy within some confined region of the Earth. This energy is liable to be gravitational potential energy, kinetic energy, chemical energy, or elastic strain energy. The release of such energy may be regarded as the immediate cause of an earthquake. The prior question as to the processes which give rise to the accumulation of this energy is far more difficult to answer.

15.3.1. Tectonic earthquakes.

A variety of evidence indicates that, of the four types of energy listed above, only elastic strain energy could be released in sufficient quantity to cause the Earth's major earthquakes. Earthquakes caused by the release of elastic strain energy are called *tectonic earthquakes*.

Direct evidence of the slow accumulation and subsequent release of such energy comes from field studies of earthquake phenomena. Reid's notable study of the San Francisco earthquake of 1906 April 18 led him to put forward in 1911 his 'elastic rebound theory', which drew attention to the significance of elastic strain energy in connection with earthquakes. A tectonic earthquake occurs when the stresses in some region inside the Earth have accumulated to the point of exceeding the strength of the material, leading rapidly to fracture. With some earthquakes there is a series of fractures produced with the ensuing oscillations, all tending in the same direction and extending over great distances; in the case of the 1906

San Francisco earthquake there was slipping along a fault plane (the San Andreas fault) detectable for a distance exceeding 400 km.

15.3.2. Volcanic earthquakes. Earthquakes are observed to be associated with volcanic activity in every volcanic region of the Earth. In this case the released energy may be of chemical origin, or may be kinetic energy as when motion of a mass of magma below a volcano is suddenly stopped; in other cases the immediate cause may be an excessive accumulation of gas pressure.

Volcanic activity can also be a secondary cause of earthquakes by producing stress and strain in adjacent regions, leading to the occurrence of tectonic earthquakes.

All earthquakes which arise essentially from volcanic activity are small, being recorded only on seismographs that are very close to the epicentre. Actually major earthquakes have been known to originate near volcanoes, but careful field investigations (for example that of Wood) indicate that these earthquakes are not immediately connected with the local volcano. (See also § 15.6.3.)

15.3.3. Other types of earthquakes. Other natural earthquakes (all of relatively small energy) include those caused by the release of gravitational potential energy, for example, those due to the collapse of caverns near the Earth's surface, and those due to landslides. In addition, chemical and nuclear explosions produce seismic waves (see chapters 12 and 16).

15.4. Dimensions of the focal region. The disruption of the Earth's outer surface which accompanies some earthquakes sometimes extends over large distances. In § 15.3.1, we referred to the extent of slipping in the 1906 San Francisco earthquake. The Assam earthquake of 1897 June 12 caused complete destruction of buildings over an area of 20 000 km².

But in spite of the frequently great size of the disrupted region, instrumental records make it clear that, in general, the major part of the energy in an earthquake issues from within a confined region of much smaller dimensions. This region is called the *focal region*, and estimates of the order of its size for any particular earthquake can be made using the theory set down in § 4.2. The formulae (4, (9)) and (4, (10)) indicate that if the linear dimensions of the focal region of a particular earthquake are of the order $2a$, then the times occupied by the ensuing first P and S half-oscillations, recorded at a station not too close to the epicentre, are of the order of $4a/v$, where v is the relevant wave velocity. Now observations of earthquakes at stations within a few hundred kilometres of the epicentre show that in general these times are less than a second. This indicates that the linear dimensions of the focal region are in general of an order somewhat less than the distance travelled in $\frac{1}{2}$ sec by P or S waves near the Earth's outer surface, i.e. are of the order of a few kilometres or less. (In the case of minor earthquakes the dimensions will of course be much less.)

In view, however, of the degree of uncertainty attending the interpretation of data from seismographs, it would be premature to lay down at present a convention whereby the focal region of an earthquake would be precisely defined. There is likewise some inherent vagueness in the definition of the point called the *focus*, but ordinarily this vagueness will be unimportant in relation to the formal uncertainties of focal determinations in practice.

We may note that Byerly and Bridgman have suggested that the 'focus' for the initial P waves may possibly be sometimes at some distance away from that for the initial S waves in an earthquake (cf. the Z phenomenon, § 10.6). There is, however, no strong evidence to indicate that the distance between such a pair of 'foci' is ever appreciable.

15.5. Focal depth. Reference to the focal depths of earthquakes has already been made in chapter 10 in connection with the setting up of travel-time tables for various earthquake phases. We have pointed out (§ 10.4.1.1) that the great majority of earthquakes originate within 50 km of the Earth's outer surface; these are the normal earthquakes. We now discuss the question of the existence of deeper-seated earthquakes. It transpires that such earthquakes do exist, and further that they are of special importance in a number of geophysical problems.

15.5.1. Evidence of abnormal focal depth. Early attempts to measure focal depth were made by Galitzin and Walker, using observations of the apparent angles of emergence (see § 8.3) of earthquake waves at various epicentral distances. But the results were subject to wide uncertainty because of the dependence of the angles of emergence on the properties of the Earth's crustal layers.

In 1922, Turner observed that in the case of some earthquakes, P waves appeared to arrive at stations near an earthquake's anti-centre (see § 10.9.1) significantly earlier than would be the case with a normal earthquake. This led Turner to put forward the hypothesis that the earthquakes in question had foci at depths appreciably greater than the normal. The calculations of Turner were, however, based on the Zöppritz–Turner tables (see § 10.6.3), and the extent of uncertainty in values in these tables made it desirable that Turner's hypothesis should be independently tested if possible.

In 1928, Wadati found that, with Japanese earthquakes, the difference between the arrival-times of P and S waves near an epicentre was sometimes abnormally great. This observation also suggested an abnormal depth of focus. Further, it happened that both Turner and Wadati independently found about the same focal depth for some of these earthquakes.

In 1928, Jeffreys pointed out that a crucial test of the hypothesis of the existence of deep-focus earthquakes could be made by examining whether the surface waves from earthquakes suspected to be of deep focus were abnormally small (see § 3.2.5). In 1931, Stoneley discovered that phases that had earlier been recorded as 'L' and 'M' for earthquakes suspected to be of deep focus mostly arrived much earlier than the L and M phases in normal earthquakes, the difference reaching as much as 10 min in some cases. Stoneley in fact showed that these 'L' and 'M' phases were really associated with bodily waves whose amplitudes exceeded those of the actual surface waves. With this discovery, the existence of genuine deep-focus earthquakes was placed beyond doubt.

Another crucial test was provided in the studies of Scrase in 1931 and of Stechschulte in 1932 of phases such as pP, sP, etc. Scrase and Stechschulte estimated focal depths from observations of the differences between the arrival-times of the phases P and pP, P and sP, and S and sS.

We may note that the apparently late reading of phases such as PKP near the anticentre with some earthquakes was once regarded as evidence of an abnormally 'high focus' with these earthquakes. But it was shown by Tillotson and others that such readings had arisen from misidentification of phases, particularly with earthquakes in which the main release of energy at the focus had been spread over a longer time interval than usual. It is now known, moreover, that the great majority of continental earthquakes have their foci in the granitic layer, the average focal depth being less than 20 km.

15.5.2. Calculation of focal depth. When the travel-time tables became sufficiently accurate, it was possible to estimate the focal depth of an earthquake from a set of observations at different stations of the P phase alone. For instance, at an epicentral distance $\Delta = 50°$, the J. B. tables (see § 10.9.1) indicate that the P travel-time for an earthquake with focus at the base of the crustal layers would exceed that for the case $h = 0·01$ by 7 sec; for the case $h = 0·02$, by 13 sec; for the case $h = 0·06$, by 37 sec; for the case $h = 0·10$ (i.e. at a depth of about 630 km below the crustal layers) by 55 sec. At $\Delta = 10°$, the corresponding differences would be 2, 4, 5, 4 sec, respectively. It is evident that this gives a means of estimating the focal depth of a well-observed earthquake with some precision.

For precise calculations, the use of statistical theory is necessary as in other seismological calculations. Improved accuracy is frequently attainable by taking into account readings of other phases, notably PKP and pP, sP, etc.

The uncertainty in the determination of the focal depth of a deep-focus earthquake is usually a little greater than the uncertainty in the determination of the epicentre of an equally well-observed normal earthquake, but it is sometimes possible to estimate such focal depths within less than 10 km. As a rule the $I.S.S.$ gives estimates of focal depth to the nearest two-hundredth of the Earth's radius, i.e. to the nearest 30 km, approximately.

We shall include numerical results for deep-focus earthquakes in the next section.

15.6. Distribution of the world's earthquakes

15.6.1. Geographical distribution of normal major earthquakes. The epicentres of the Earth's major earthquakes have long been known to lie mainly in two belts. This is indicated in early catalogues such as those of Montessus de Ballore, and was clearly shown in precise work of Turner and Miss Bellamy based on *I.S.S.* data. Subsequently, Gutenberg and Richer made a very full study of the Earth's present seismicity.

One belt passes round the Pacific Ocean and affects countries with coastlines bordering on this ocean, for instance New Zealand, New Guinea, Japan, the Aleutian Islands, Alaska, and the western regions of North and South America; Gutenberg and Richter estimate that 80 % of the energy at present released in earthquakes comes from earthquakes whose epicentres are in this belt. The seismic activity is by no means uniform throughout the belt, and there are in places a number of branches from the main belt.

The second belt passes through the Mediterranean region eastward through Asia and joins the first belt in the East Indies. The energy released in earthquakes from this belt is 15 % of the total.

There are a number of lesser belts of seismic activity, including ones in the Arctic Ocean, the Atlantic Ocean, the western Indian Ocean, and East Africa. Most other parts of the world experience at least occasional normal earthquakes.

The geographical distribution of the many lesser earthquakes is less precisely determined because of the dependence of the relevant data on the geographical distribution of observatories. But it is to be expected, and all evidence supports this, that the frequency distributions of the lesser earthquakes are closely related to the belts mentioned above.

15.6.2. Distribution of deep-focus earthquakes. The table of Gutenberg and Richter on p. 279 shows the distribution, for a thirty-year period, of earthquakes whose focal depths were 80 km or more. The depths given in the table are in kilometres below the outer surface, a range of depth of $\pm$ 25 km being involved in each case.

Gutenberg and Richter distinguish between 'intermediate' focal depths ranging from about 70 to 300 km and greater focal depths. Of the total energy released in earthquakes, 12 % comes from 'intermediate' earthquakes and 3 % from deeper earthquakes.

The table shows that: (i) the frequency falls off rapidly with increasing focal depth in the intermediate range, while below this range the distribution in depth is fairly uniform until the greatest focal depths are approached; (ii) the greatest focal depth is not more than about 700 km; (iii) there are suggestions of characteristic focal depths in some particular geographical regions; (iv) the deeper earthquakes are almost entirely confined to the circum-Pacific belt. (The sole known exceptions to (iv) are an earthquake of focal depth 650 km and magnitude $7\frac{1}{4}$ under Spain on 1954 March 29, and one off Italy of focal depth 450 km and magnitude $5\frac{1}{4}$ on 1955 February 17.)

Region \ Depth	100	150	200	250	300	350	400	450	500	550	600	650	700
Mexico, Central America	20	4	2	—	1	—	—	—	—	—	—	—	—
South America	46	22	18	7	2	—	—	—	—	1	5	11	—
New Zealand, Tonga, Samoa	11	3	3	1	2	1	4	—	6	9	10	5	1
New Hebrides to New Guinea	22	16	9	1	2	3	3	1	—	—	—	—	—
Sunda Islands	21	12	9	1	—	1	3	—	1	—	10	1	5
Celebes to Mindanao	3	6	10	2	4	—	1	—	2	1	3	1	1
Luzon to Kiushiu	10	7	4	3	—	—	—	—	—	—	—	—	—
Japanese Islands	33	26	12	5	12	27	25	12	14	14	6	1	—
Hindu Kush	1	—	14	25	—	—	—	—	—	—	—	—	—
Others	11	13	1	1	—	—	—	—	—	—	—	—	—
Total	178	109	82	46	23	32	36	13	23	25	34	19	7

15.6.3. Distribution of earthquakes in relation to other geophysical phenomena. There is a marked correspondence between the geographical distributions of major earthquakes and of volcanic activity, particularly in circum-Pacific countries. Gutenberg and Richter find, however, that volcanic vents are generally some hundreds of kilometres distant from the majority of the epicentres of major normal earthquakes. They state also that earthquakes of 'intermediate' focal depth frequently occur directly below structures marked by volcanic vents, but that there is probably no immediate causal connection between these earthquakes and the volcanic activity, both being 'very likely due to the same remote orogenic processes'. These conclusions are consistent with those stated in § 15.3.2. Reference has previously been made (§ 12.6) to the association of earthquakes with arcuate structures.

15.7. Conditions near the focus

15.7.1. Strain energy before an earthquake. There is a connection between the energy released in an earthquake and the strength of the materials near the focus.

Suppose that P_{ij} and E_{ij} are the deviatoric stress and strain tensors (as defined in §2.5) at any point P of a region in which there is an appreciable strain leading to subsequent fracture causing an earthquake. Then by (2, (70)), the corresponding distortional strain energy, U say, is given by

$$U = \iiint \mu E_{ij}^2 d\tau, \tag{10}$$

where the integral is taken through the volume of the region in question. We shall write

$$P_{ij}^2 = (\alpha S)^2, \tag{11}$$

where S^2 is the value which the function P_{ij}^2 would take if the material at P were on the point of fracturing; thus $0 \leqslant \alpha \leqslant 1$, and S may be taken as an index of the strength (see §2.5.5). Then since $P_{ij} = 2\mu E_{ij}$ (equation (2, (68))), we have, neglecting variation in μ and S through the region,

$$4\mu U = S^2 \iiint \alpha^2 d\tau = S^2 Q, \quad \text{say}, \tag{12}$$

where Q would be the volume of the strained region if α were equal to unity throughout.

In addition to the distortional strain energy U, there will in general be some dilatational strain energy, V say, corresponding to the first term on the right-hand side of (2, (70)); this may be expected to be of the order of U. In general, because of the occurrence of aftershocks (see §15.8.1), the energy E released in seismic waves in a major earthquake will be appreciably less than $U + V$. Thus the order of U/E is at least $\frac{1}{2}$, and may be appreciably greater. Hence (12), with U replaced by yE, where $0.5 < y < 5$ (say), may be expected to give a useful connection between the orders of the released energy, the strength of the material concerned, and the extent of the strained region prior to the earthquake.

The data in chapters 12 and 13 show that between the upper crustal layer and a depth of 700 km the rigidity μ ranges from about

0.4×10^{12} to 1.5×10^{12} dyne/cm². Hence for the greatest earth-quakes, taking the released energy E as 5×10^{24} ergs, S^2Q is between 10^{37} and 10^{38} dyne²/cm. It follows that with these earthquakes the strength of the material in the vicinity of the focus and also the extent of the strained region must be considerable. Laboratory experiments indicate a strength of order 10^9 dyne/cm² for granite and other rocks which predominate in the Earth's crustal layers. Taking $S = 10^9$ dyne/cm² would then give Q approaching 10^{20} cm³, i.e. 10^5 km³, in the case of one of the greatest earthquakes.

On this calculation, the minimum volume of the strained region just prior to the earthquake would be of the order of that of a sphere of diameter 50 km, and if the strain were confined to this sphere the material would have to be at breaking point throughout the whole volume. In practice, the main fractures are confined to a focal region of much smaller volume, and outside the focal region the prior state would be mostly short of breaking point. Hence the actual volume inside which substantial prior strain existed would be appreciably greater than 10^5 km³.

Since Q could hardly exceed so large a value by much more than a factor of 10, the calculation sets both a severe lower limit to the strength of the Earth's materials where the largest earthquakes originate, and also a severe upper limit to the energy E that can be released in an earthquake. The strength cannot be very much less than 10^9 dyne/cm² and E cannot be much greater than 10^{25} ergs. This calculation when first made by the writer (1953) was one factor leading to a large reduction in an estimate, current at the time, of 10^{27} ergs for the energy of the largest earthquakes. Similar conclusions were reached by Tsuboi (1956), who brought to bear Japanese data on aftershocks of large earthquakes in assessing the volume of the strained region.

Gutenberg and Richter find that earthquakes with nearly the greatest energy include ones with focal depths up to 150 km, and that the deepest earthquakes can have energies approaching one-tenth of the greatest value. It follows that the strength of materials in the Earth up to a depth of 600–700 km is comparable with the strength in the crust, refuting an earlier view that the material below the crust is much weaker than the crust.

The strength S involved here is not necessarily equal to the 'fundamental strength' as defined in § 2.5.5, since the fracture that accompanies an earthquake may be immediately preceded by some plastic flow. (For example, in Japan, tiltmeters have provided some evidence of progressive tilting of land blocks just prior to the occurrence of certain earthquakes.) Jeffreys has, however, developed arguments based on detail in § 2.5 to show that the fundamental strength and S are likely to be of the same order in the outer part of the Earth.

15.7.2. Faults and fracture. In 1776, Coulomb postulated that a brittle material under stress fractures along a plane of greatest tangential stress. Let p_1, p_2, p_3, where $p_1 > p_2 > p_3$, be the principal stresses just before a fracture. In 1849, Hopkins showed that on the Coulomb postulate the plane of fracture, which is also the plane of greatest shear stress, passes through the direction of p_2 and bisects the angle between the directions of p_1 and p_2, thus making an angle of $\pm\frac{1}{4}\pi$ with p_1; the magnitude of the greatest shear stress is $\frac{1}{2}(p_1 - p_3)$.

In 1905, Anderson suggested that the fracture starts when the stress-difference $p_1 - p_3$ exceeds $S + \mu p_n$, where S is a measure of the strength, p_n is the normal stress at the plane of fracture, and μ is a friction coefficient. Let θ be the angle between the plane of fracture and the direction of p_1. Then $\mu = 0$ gives the Hopkins result $\theta = \pm\frac{1}{4}\pi$, while $\mu = 1$ gives $\theta = \frac{1}{8}\pi$ or $\frac{3}{8}\pi$. (For proof, see Jeffreys, *The Earth*, 1959, Appendix A.)

Laboratory experiments show that for a bar of brittle material under longitudinal thrust (the behaviour is very different under tension) θ is about 45°, agreeing with the Hopkins result. In geological conditions, where there is a superimposed heavy load on the material under thrust, there is evidence that θ may be reduced to 30° or less, and Anderson's theory becomes relevant. Jeffreys suggests that the Coulomb–Hopkins theory may apply to good approximation at the initiation of fracture, and the Anderson theory after slip has begun.

Tectonic earthquakes are associated with fractures below the Earth's surface, and the above theories are relevant to the production of new faults. When the accumulated strain energy becomes excessive near an already existing fault, however, slipping is likely to take place along that fault, irrespective of the preceding theory, since the strength near such a fault is likely to be lower than that elsewhere. On the theory of § 15.7.1, it is probable that the largest earthquakes are accompanied by much new faulting, since the presence of substantial older faulting in the focal region would, through the consequent lowering of S, prevent S^2Q from approaching the order of 10^{38} dyne^2/cm. Observed faults are commonly assumed to be the seat of one or more past earthquakes, although movements along visible faults are often secondary effects. The actual faulting during an earthquake may be very complex, and it is a matter for investigation (see § 15.7.3) whether in a particular earthquake the main energy issues from a single fault plane.

Observed faults sometimes show relative displacements of the order of a kilometre, whereas the amplitudes of earthquake movements reach at most the order of several centimetres. Jeffreys has estimated that a fault of throw 100 m would be possible at a single stage only if the displacement along the fault occurred at such a rate as to form a layer some 15 cm thick of a crush-rock such as pseudotachylyte made amorphous by the heat generated. If no pseudotachylyte is formed the indicated maximum throw is about 4 cm in a first single movement, possibly somewhat greater in the subsequent throws since the strength at the fault is then diminished. Since most faults show little or no pseudotachylyte, Jeffreys concludes that a large succession of movements is required to produce the larger known faults.

15.7.3. Focal mechanisms and patterns of initial surface earth movement. Attempts have been made to infer the character of faulting in the focal region of an earthquake from observed distributions of the directions of the first onsets in waves arriving at the Earth's surface. Onsets have been called *anaseismic* or *kataseismic* according as the direction is away from or towards the focus, respectively.

With some earthquakes, more particularly deep-focus earthquakes, a pattern becomes recognisable when the directions of the P onsets are plotted on a map: there are broad areas in which the first onsets are predominantly anaseismic, separated from predominantly kataseismic areas by nodal curves near which the surface earth movements are abnormally small. The existence of such patterns was shown by Omori, Shida and Ishimoto. Kawasumi (1937) has given an interesting account of the early Japanese work.

In 1923, Nakano theoretically examined the patterns of first movements that would occur at the surface of a homogeneous Earth model, taking various model representations of the forces at the earthquake focus. The two representations that have since been most considered are: (a) a pair of forces constituting a couple; (b) a set of four equal coplanar forces constituting a pair of couples of equal and opposite moments, the forces of one couple being at right angles to the forces of the other. The type (a) envisages the development of a simple 'fault plane' at the focus, the forces of the couple being parallel to and on opposite sides of the plane. The type (b) is equivalent to a set of four equal forces in two perpendicular lines intersecting at a focal point O, the pair in one line acting towards O on opposite sides, and the other pair acting away from O.

In 1926, Byerly, assuming a focal mechanism of type (a), sought to use patterns of P onsets over the whole globe to infer the orientation of the fault-plane in a large earthquake. The mechanism (a) yields two P nodal curves at the Earth's surface. For a homogeneous Earth, one curve is in the plane containing the assumed fault, and the other is in the plane (called the 'auxiliary plane') which passes through the focus and is perpendicular to the forces of the couple. For the actual Earth, the nodal curves are displaced from these locations because of curvature of the rays between focus and surface, but knowledge of shapes of seismic rays enables allowance to be readily made for this.

On the assumption of the mechanism (a), and given an adequately well determined pattern of first P movements, it thus becomes possible to locate two planes, one of which is the plane containing the fault. Given which is which, the direction of motion on the fault is also indicated. Unfortunately the P observations do not enable any discrimination to be made between the two planes. In theory, the discrimination can be made from observations of S

onsets, for which, on the mechanism (a), the amplitudes are a maximum in the auxiliary plane and a minimum in the fault plane. In practice, however, it is a difficult problem to assess the S amplitudes to the needed precision.

With the mechanism (b), the theory again gives two nodal curves for P, while the S amplitudes are a maximum on both these curves. In principle, it should therefore be possible to discriminate between the two types of mechanism (a) and (b), assuming that one of these types is sufficiently representative of the focal conditions and that sufficiently reliable S observations are available.

J. H. Hodgson, Ritsema and Keilis-Borok have extended the techniques developed by Byerly for deriving fault-plane solutions on the model assumption (a), and consider that the observations in general favour this model. On the other hand, Honda finds (b) to be more compatible with observations of Japanese earthquakes.

Various writers have stressed the need for caution in interpreting ostensible patterns of first movements. First, it needs to be realised that the whole of this approach to conditions at the focus is one of model representation, and that modifications of the models used may be later required. The special difficulties attaching to S are emphasised in model experiments carried out by Press. Keilis-Borok and Ritsema have devoted some attention to the problem of using S observations to best advantage. Dix and Knopoff stress the need for an adequate statistical approach in seeking to define P as well as S patterns. Benioff considers that fault-plane solutions are reliable only for the largest earthquakes in which the extent of faulting is large enough to eliminate local effects; with smaller earthquakes there may be serious complications caused by the presence of older faults. Keilis-Borok and colleagues find that diffraction effects near an assumed fault-plane can be significant.

Hodgson has pointed out that all studies seem to point to the predominance of strike-slip (nearly vertical—transcurrent) faulting in most regions. Exceptions appear to be the predominance of normal faults at great depths in the East Indies, and the occurrence of dip-slip faults profusely in the Hindu Kush and the Pamir Knot area and occasionally in the Bonins and off the coast of British Columbia.

Scheidegger made a statistical analysis of all fault-plane determinations (some 200) available up to 1959, and inferred a connection between the focal motions and tectonic stress directions which he considers agrees fairly well with geological evidence.

Båth and Benioff used studies of aftershocks of the Kamchatka earthquake of 1952 November 4 as a basis for discriminating between the two possible fault-plane solutions given by Hodgson for the main shock. Benioff subsequently derived a generalisation for the circum-Pacific region, and describes the tectonic activity now in progress in that region as a tangential clockwise rotation of the continental margins relative to the oceanic basin, together with a radial movement of the margins towards the basin. Assuming a constant rate of movement based on data for the San Andreas fault (§15.3.1), he estimates the time of a complete revolution as about 3×10^9 years. Honda suggests that in his region there is a tendency for the Pacific side to be relatively forced downward and toward the Asiatic continental side, though other interpretations are possible. Honda (1962) has contributed a valuable review paper on the whole subject.

15.8. Foreshocks, aftershocks, and related phenomena. Inspection of the *International Seismological Summary* for any year shows that there are frequently series of earthquakes occurring within a time interval of the order of a few days or weeks (sometimes longer), all having approximately the same epicentre.

15.8.1. Aftershocks of major earthquakes. The usual circumstance in such series is the occurrence of a major earthquake followed by a host of lesser earthquakes. This is to be expected since the disruption attending a major earthquake will not be expected to relieve all of the accumulated strain energy at once; further, this disruption is liable to cause an increase in the stress and strain at a number of places in the vicinity of the focal region, bringing the material at some points close to the stress at which fracture occurs. These lesser earthquakes which follow a major earthquake are called *aftershocks*, and in some cases their frequency may be for a time of the order of a hundred a day or more.

It sometimes happens that a major earthquake is succeeded by another major earthquake at approximately the same focus within a few hours or days. The extreme case is that of multiple earthquakes (see § 4.3). But in the great majority of cases the first major earthquake of a series is much more intense than all the aftershocks.

In general, the number of aftershocks per day decreases on the whole with increasing time. Work of Omori at the beginning of this century indicated that the aftershock frequency is roughly inversely proportional to the time t since the occurrence of the major earthquake of the series. Later investigators have found that formulae of the form $a/(t+b)$, where a, b are constants, fit the frequency data well with particular series of earthquake aftershocks.

Benioff has suggested a parallel between movements near the focus in aftershocks, and the elastic afterworking of rocks in laboratory conditions.

15.8.2. Foreshocks of major earthquakes. As a rule, major earthquakes occur without detectable warning in the nature of less intense foreshocks; this is why there is often great loss of life attending the greater earthquakes.

There is, however, evidence that some major earthquakes are preceded by foreshocks. Kunitomi states that in the North-Idu earthquake of 1930, there were foreshocks during the preceding 3 weeks, increasing steadily in frequency to 70 felt shocks on the day prior to the occurrence of the main earthquake. Imamura found that the tendency for foreshocks to occur is limited to particular seismic zones, and stated that in Japan not more than 20% of major earthquakes are preceded by foreshocks.

Other work of Imamura suggests that in some regions, destructive earthquakes are 'heralded some tens of years in advance' by an increase in the frequency of lesser earthquakes in a particular region. But this again applies only to particular zones.

15.8.3. Earthquake swarms. It sometimes happens that large numbers of lesser earthquakes occur in a particular region over an interval of time which may extend to some months, without a major earthquake occurring. In the Taupo region of New Zealand, for instance, there occurred between May and December of 1922 a series of many hundreds of earthquakes some sufficiently strong to overthrow a few chimneys, but none approaching the intensity of a major earthquake. Such series of earthquakes are called earth-quake swarms. Earthquake swarms have occurred in other regions, including Germany, Japan, California and South America.

15.9. Periodicities, correlations, and prediction

15.9.1. Frequencies of aftershocks.
The most marked systematic phenomenon in earthquake frequency is the occurrence of series of aftershocks following major earthquakes. The most common frequency law is that given in § 15.8.1. Suggestions of periodicities in aftershocks have been made from time to time, but a statistical study by Jeffreys of a number of aftershocks series gave no significant periodicities.

15.9.2. Other suggested periodicities and correlations.
Other suggestions of periodicities have been made, for example, greater earthquake frequency in winter than in summer, or at night than in the day, but the periodicities have not been substantiated.

It has been suggested that the instants of occurrence of earth-quakes are liable to be determined by discernible *trigger forces*, which are relatively small forces independent of the main forces producing the elastic strain which leads to the earthquake; that these forces—which may include tidal effects, temperature effects, abnormal changes in barometric pressure, and other effects—act as 'last straw' phenomena when the stress difference is already very close to the strength at some point in the focal region. This suggestion has led to investigations of correlations between earth-quake occurrence and such influences, and to the search for related periodicities, but again nothing significant has emerged. Detailed evidence on suspected earthquake periodicities has been presented by Davison.

A completely different suggestion is that of Benioff who has put forward evidence that earthquakes of magnitude exceeding 8 may not be entirely independent events, but may be related in some form of global stress-system.

15.9.3. Long-range fluctuation in earthquake occurrence.
Another question sometimes raised is whether there have been significant fluctuations in earthquake occurrence over the span of

historical time. Gutenberg and Richter gave a list of cases in which there has been unusual seismic activity over relatively short intervals of time, for example, an unusual number of very destructive shocks in Palestine and Syria during the eleventh and twelfth centuries; a long series of strong earthquakes in the Indian Ocean between 1925 and 1933; brief series of large earthquakes as in the Mississippi Valley in 1811 and 1812; and apparently isolated earthquakes such as the Baffin Bay earthquake of 1933 November 20. In the main regions of present seismic activity there is, however, no evidence whatever of any significant fluctuations during historical time.

The most comprehensive account of earthquake occurrence over a long period of time is the *Chronological Tabulation of Chinese Earthquake Records* prepared under the direction of S. P. Lee by the historical and seismological divisions of the Academia Sinica in Peking. Lee refers to 1180 major Chinese earthquakes between 1189 B.C. and A.D. 1955.

The observations of geologists make it probable that there have been marked fluctuations in earthquake occurrence over geological time. It is likely, however, that some seismic regions, in particular the circum-Pacific belt, have been active over long eras, although there may have been changes in details.

15.9.4. Prediction of earthquakes. Prediction is concerned with applying empirical formulae and principles gleaned from past observations to anticipated happenings in the future; and is governed by probability considerations.

In the case of earthquakes, predictions can be made from the features of past earthquake occurrence set down in the preceding sections. It is extremely probable, for instance, that the epicentres of major earthquakes will for some considerable time be largely confined to the belts referred to in § 15.6.1. It is possible to predict (with high degrees of probability, assignable from present knowledge) that during the next century Great Britain will be less seriously affected by earthquakes than Italy or Japan; that in the New Zealand region, Auckland city will be less affected than Wellington; and so on.

It may be predicted from § 15.8.1 that whenever a major earthquake occurs in a given region, it is very probable that there will be a number of aftershocks for some time in that region all less intense than the original earthquake; at the same time it is evident that the probability that there will be another equally intense earthquake within some days or weeks is not negligible.

It needs to be emphasised that in the present state of knowledge of earthquake phenomena, it is not possible to attach other than extremely low probability to predictions that go beyond the indications of the above remarks. In due course, this knowledge may include a much fuller understanding of conditions below the Earth's outer surface and of the forces at work which build up elastic strain energy. The advent of tiltmeters and strain seismographs, and the very great effort being put into the investigation of the Earth's crust by explosion methods, are all steps in this direction. But it will be a long time before predictions can be made with sufficient precision and sufficient reliability to mitigate the disastrous effects of great earthquakes.

E. A. Hodgson quotes Mark Twain in his answer to a question concerning the time of occurrence of the next major earthquake in a certain region: 'I was gratified to be able to answer promptly, and I did. I said that I did not know.'

CHAPTER 16

SEISMOLOGY AND NUCLEAR EXPLOSIONS

The use of explosion seismology in unravelling crustal structure in various parts of the world has already been referred to in chapter 12. The methods have brought a new degree of control into seismic investigations (see § 12.1.5) since origin-times and locations of explosions, unlike those of natural earthquakes, are usually known within negligible errors. Explosion experiments can be planned in advance, so that a suitable disposition of recording stations can be contrived and also seismograms with much finer detail obtained. In crustal seismic exploration, the source energy comes usually from chemical explosions (mechanical sources of energy are sometimes used for minor experiments). With the advent of nuclear explosions, there has arisen the possibility of extending the seismic explosion method, and all the experimental controls that go with it, to problems of the Earth's deeper interior.

Although, so far, seismic applications of nuclear explosions have been mainly secondary to other purposes, a quantity of valuable information has already been derived, and developments are taking place rapidly. This chapter will outline some of the results achieved, and refer to further problems such as the identification of nuclear explosions on seismic records.

16.1. Historical survey. The first atom bomb was exploded in New Mexico on 1945 July 16d. 12h. 29m. 21s. (G.C.T.) at latitude 33° 40′ 31″ N. and longitude 106° 28′ 29″ W. from a tower 100 ft. above the ground. The origin-time at source was uncertain by 15 sec, the time here given being that estimated by Gutenberg from seismic data; this time is considered to be reliable within 2 sec. It has become customary to express the energy yielded in a nuclear explosion in terms of equivalent kilotons or megatons of TNT explosive ($1 \, \text{kt} = 10^3 \, \text{tons}$; $1 \, \text{Mt} = 10^6 \, \text{tons}$). The yield for this explosion was 19·3 kt. The explosion gave a Pn speed com-

patible with earlier seismic results, but was of only limited seismological value because of the uncertain origin-time. A paper on
seismic aspects was published by Leet.

On 1946 July 24, the first underwater atomic explosion took
place 90 ft. below the ocean surface near Bikini Atoll. This was the
first, and for a considerable time the sole, nuclear explosion for
which source data were made generally available. It was remarkable
in being recorded at eight seismic stations at distances between
69°·0 and 78°·6. Gutenberg and Richter (1946) gave P readings
for those stations, from which the writer (1948) determined a mean
residual of $-1·8 \pm 0·8$ sec against the J. B. tables for a surface focus.
The negative residuals were attributed to crustal differences
between the Bikini and the average continental region. The explosion, meagrely recorded as it was, gave a glimpse of what might
be achieved for seismology through nuclear explosions.

No further open publication on nuclear-explosion seismology
appeared until 1952, when Gutenberg gave the results of his seismic
analysis of the first five atomic explosions in Nevada; these explosions took place, each at an altitude a little over 1000 ft.,
between January 27 and February 6, 1951. Gutenberg inferred a
Pn speed of 8·2 km/sec for the region and a crustal thickness
35–40 km.

In 1953, Gutenberg, in a further paper bearing the enigmatic
title 'Travel times of longitudinal waves from surface foci' gave P
residuals against the travel-time tables for 33 observations of
'waves originating at known surface sources in the Pacific area'.
Again the residuals were negative, of order -2 sec.

The first hydrogen-bomb explosion (14 Mt) was exploded on
1952 October 31 at Eniwetok Atoll at 20 ft. above sea level. Seismic
readings were published by Rothé in 1960.

In the middle of March 1954, it was announced that a hydrogen
bomb had been exploded near Bikini, and reports by Japanese
fishermen indicated that the explosion had occurred shortly before
dawn on March 1, local time. This information was sufficient for
Burke-Gaffney to identify provisionally a corresponding P wave
onset at Riverview Observatory, the identification being confirmed when routine readings arrived from Brisbane. From this

start he ultimately traced readings of seismic waves from four such explosions in routine station bulletins from twelve countries. The readings enabled him and the writer to compute origin-times which, when the source data were later released, proved to be accurate within 0·0, 0·4, 0·6 and 0·1 sec, respectively, for the four explosions. The first, that of 1954 February 28 (G.C.T.), was stated to be a surface explosion of 15 Mt.

From the seismic readings of these explosions, Burke-Gaffney and the writer found, once again, negative P residuals, and also found that the P travel-times from Bikini to the United States and Australia agreed within less than a second. An unexpected result of some significance was the evidence on waves preceding the phase $PKIKP$ for $\Delta < 142°$, already referred to in § 13.1.3. A point of some interest on the matter of detecting nuclear explosions (§ 16.4) was that it transpired that observers at most of the overseas stations whose bulletins were used had been unaware that they had read phases of other than a minor earthquake. (In one or two cases, on being written to for supplementary information, they supplied detail relating to natural earthquakes which had been recorded near the same time.)

In 1955, a group of seismologists put forward the idea that nations might co-operate to carry out four atomic (not hydrogen-bomb) explosions at seismically useful locations, with a view to applying nuclear energy to winning knowledge of the Earth's interior. The proposal proved to be premature, but had the effect of arousing considerable interest in possible seismological applications.

In 1956, a series of atomic explosions took place at Maralinga in central Australia (see § 12.2.5), and led to the first reliable crustal knowledge in a region where it had not proved possible to make useful inferences from records of natural earthquakes.

Following the reading of an address on seismological aspects of nuclear explosions at the September 1957 meeting in Toronto of the I.A.S.P.I.E., a release was made, in advance for the first occasion, of source details of a coming nuclear explosion in Nevada. This was the Rainier explosion of 1957 September 19, which took place 790 ft. below the surface and was the first underground nuclear explosion. Intense efforts were made by the seismologists to record seismic waves from it, and many left the Toronto meeting to set up special field instruments. The immediate seismic rewards were not great, the yield being only 1·7 kt and only a small proportion of the energy going into seismic waves. Bailey and Romney state that useful records of P waves were obtained at distances to 9°, the travel-times fitting the formula $8·0 + r_0\Delta/8·0$ sec for $r_0\Delta > 180$ km, while less definite P waves were detected up to 17°·7 in the United States and at 33°·4 in Alaska. The Rainier explosion came to be much discussed through being the first explosion of direct relevance to the problem of detecting underground explosions.

Shortly after this time, Carder and Bailey published (1958) the most comprehensive study then made of seismic records of nuclear explosions, covering more than a thousand records. Their analysis supplied residuals against the J. B. tables over a wide range of distance, and gave some new information on crustal layering, som important evidence on the 20° discontinuity, and some interesting observations of the phase PcP. At College (Alaska), the latter phase while nearly as large as P on records of Bikini explosions (for which $\Delta = 62°·16$) was barely recognisable from Eniwetok explosions $(\Delta = 63°·23)$, and similarly at Matsushira $(\Delta = 34°·82, 32°·87)$; these observations could be of importance to mantle-core boundary problems.

From 1958 onward, increasing quantities of source data on nuclear explosions were released to seismologists and subsequently to others, and increasing efforts were put into studies of seismological aspects.

On 1958 August 20, a new type of problem was emphasised when a Geneva Committee of representatives from several countries produced a report on the detection of nuclear explosions, making considerable reference to seismology. This problem will be discussed in § 16.4.

Among further recent investigations on seismic aspects of nuclear explosions may be mentioned the work of Oliver, Ewing and colleagues on surface waves from high-altitude explosions; of J. T. Wilson and Willis on the general wave spectrum; and of Johnson and others on conditions close to the source. Of considerable potential importance to seismology is the 'Gnome'

3 kt explosion in New Mexico on 1961 December 10 at a depth underground of 1200 ft. (see § 13.1.2).

In 1960, Kogan published details of Soviet analyses of seismic records of various Marshall Islands explosions, and gave average P residuals of $-1\cdot8 \pm 0\cdot6$ sec against the J. B. tables, but S residuals of the order of $+4$ to $+5$ sec. Kogan refers to the possible use of PcP readings to estimate the density ratio on the two sides of the mantle-core boundary.

Brune, Nafe and Oliver (1960) have analysed seismic surface waves from explosions near Novaya Zemlya.

According to information provided by Johnson for the 1960 meeting at Helsinki of the I.A.S.P.I.E., nearly 300 known nuclear explosions had been carried out by that time. Source details of 169 explosions are listed in an important paper by Griggs and Press (1961) which surveys some of the outstanding seismic-nuclear problems.

A further aspect of nuclear explosions which has some problems in common with seismology is the question of the atmospheric waves produced. A valuable account of the theory of atmospheric waves from large explosions was published by Hunt, Palmer and Penney in 1960.

16.2. Source conditions in nuclear explosions.

A standard formula gives 4×10^{19} ergs as the energy released in a 1 kt explosion. On this formula, the smallest known nuclear explosions would yield between 10^{18} and 10^{19} ergs of energy; explosions of 20 kt, about 10^{21} ergs; and a 15 Mt explosion (the largest hydrogen-bomb explosion for which figures are available), 6×10^{23} ergs, i.e. about one-tenth of the energy in the largest earthquake.

In general only a small proportion of the yielded energy goes into seismic waves. The 'seismic efficiency', defined as this proportion, is greatest for underwater explosions, considerably smaller for underground explosions, still smaller for surface explosions, and smaller again for explosions above the surface. The efficiency also depends very much on conditions other than distance from the surface, for example, on the character of surrounding rocks and the size of the cavity where the explosion occurs.

As a very rough guide, Griggs and Press (1961) give the following values of the seismic efficiency of a 20 kt explosion in various conditions: 10 km altitude, 1×10^{-5}; 1 km altitude, 3×10^{-5}; surface, 1×10^{-4}; 300 m underground, 1×10^{-3}; 30 m underwater, 5×10^{-3}; 100 m underwater, 2×10^{-2}; 500 m underwater, 4×10^{-2}. They point out that a deep 25 kt underwater explosion is equivalent to a 10 Mt surface explosion. They estimate that a 1 Mt explosion could be completely contained at a depth of 1·5 km under land, and that a 10 Mt explosion could be safely contained in a deep ocean trench. They quote evidence from which they conclude that a 'clean' 1 Mt explosion could be safely conducted anywhere in the oceans below a depth of 5 km.

Latter and colleagues have estimated that an underground explosion carried out inside a large cavity may have a seismic efficiency as low as 0·003 of the value for a well-tamped explosion. They state that to realise this low efficiency, the minimum size of the cavity at 1 km depth needs to be 7×10^{10} cm^3 per kt of yield.

For the Rainier explosion (1·7 kt), the seismic efficiency has been estimated as being less than 0·01; on Latter's results, with a spherical cavity of radius 100 ft., the efficiency could have been lowered below 10^{-4}.

The symmetry at the source of an explosion results in general in a different distribution of seismic waves from that in the average earthquake. Explosions normally generate only P, SV and Rayleigh waves, though other waves are produced as the waves encounter interfaces and other places of rapid changes of velocity in the Earth. The degree of conversion to these other waves decreases with increasing wave-length. Oliver, Pomeroy and Ewing (1960), nevertheless, report some unusual recordings of Love waves from nuclear explosions. In some cases Love waves from underground explosions have been larger than Rayleigh waves, and Love waves have been identified from high-altitude explosions.

Attempts have been made to associate earthquake magnitude values with nuclear explosions. Caution is, however, required because of the differences just referred to. A statement that the magnitude of a nuclear explosion is M means that the explosion has produced P waves with amplitudes corresponding to those of an earthquake of magnitude M. With this interpretation, Griggs and Press associate magnitudes of 3, $3\frac{1}{2}$, 4, 5, $5\frac{1}{2}$, 6, $6\frac{1}{2}$, respectively, with the waves from a 20 kt explosion carried out under the various conditions stated on p. 296. Romney has proposed the empirical relation $M = 3\cdot65 + \log Y$ between the magnitude M (as estimated from seismic records) and the yield Y kt for well-tamped underground explosions at depths of order 300 m.

Nuclear explosions have had an important influence on earthquake magnitude studies. The 1946 July 24 explosion was originally assigned a magnitude of 5·5, which, on an earthquake energy-magnitude relation then in use, implied a total seismic energy of 8×10^{21} ergs, whereas the energy known from source details to have gone into seismic waves from the explosion was actually less than a thousandth of this value. This discrepancy was one of several factors which forced a drastic revision of the then used earthquake magnitude-energy formula (see § 15.7.1).

Other calculations relating to conditions near the source of nuclear explosions have been presented by Johnson and colleagues. They estimate that, in a confined underground nuclear explosion in tuff, the radius of the initial cavity produced is of the order of $50 Y^{\frac{1}{3}}$ ft.; that about half the yield goes to melting rock which is converted to glass on cooling; that collapse of the cavity produces a zone of about $10^5 Y$ tons of broken permeable material; and that radioactive products can be contained if the source depth is at least $400 Y^{\frac{1}{3}}$ ft.

16.3. Applications to the Earth's interior.

The planning of nuclear explosions for seismic purposes involves several prior considerations. First, it needs to be stressed that seismologists would require adequate precautions to be taken against danger from harmful by-products; this requirement may enforce delays, which at present cannot be estimated, in some classes of experiment. A second requirement is that seismic experiments should not interfere with experiments in other fields. (For example, one of the reasons for not pressing the 1955 proposal (§ 16.1) was the objection raised on this ground by some upper atmosphere scientists.) There are the two further important questions of cost and avoidance of political entanglements. It is possible that these two questions may admit of solution together, with wide-ranging benefits outside seismology, if nations find themselves able to channel an increasing proportion of explosion experiments towards peaceful seismological ends. There are already some signs of a trend in this direction, and seismologists for their part have devoted some attention to the best use that might be made of nuclear explosions in advancing seismology.

The calculations of Grigg and Press referred to in § 16.2 suggest that it may be reasonable to contemplate the use for seismological purposes of nuclear explosions ranging from several kt to begin with to the order of 1 Mt at some time in the (possibly distant) future.

An immediate question is that of the relative efficacies of chemical and nuclear explosions. The largest chemical explosion on which precise information is available is the 4 kt Heligoland explosion (see § 12.2.3), although reference has been made in a Soviet publication to a (presumed chemical) explosion of 9 kt in China. It has been estimated that chemical or nuclear explosions are respectively the more economical to use according as the yield is less than or greater than about 2 kt. Griggs and Press suggest that for purely seismological purposes, explosions up to a few kt should be preferably chemical unless the cost of emplacement is large compared with the cost of the explosive. Soviet seismologists have devoted much attention to the problem of deriving the maximum seismic information from chemical explosions.

In order to derive the fullest seismological advantage from a nuclear explosion, it is considered that the explosion should be preceded by a number of smaller chemical explosions in the same region. The smaller explosions would supply important local crustal knowledge and point the way to a superior planning of the nuclear experiment. This follows experience in routine explosion seismology where chemicals have been used.

With the extension from chemical to nuclear explosion seismology, the degree of experimental control that has been brought to bear in problems of the Earth's crust could be steadily extended downward into the deeper interior. With yields of order 20 kt, there is the prospect of making progress on the difficult problems of layering in the Earth's upper mantle (see § 13.1.2). The principal information would come from travel-times of P waves, but S and surface waves would be used as well. Oliver, Pomeroy and Ewing have observed waves of periods 5–50 sec from nuclear explosions and shown how the surface waves can be used to delineate regional structural differences in the Earth to improved precision. It has also been suggested that nuclear-explosion seismology should be accompanied by the use of ocean-bottom seismographs (see § 18.4).

In a nuclear explosion, many features of the source mechanism are known (see § 16.2), whereas the determination of details of the source mechanism of natural earthquakes (see § 15.7.3) is an outstanding problem in seismology on which there is at present much divided opinion. Comparisons with nuclear explosion records could help to throw light on this problem. The suggestion has also been made of carrying out suitably disposed nuclear explosions in a planned time sequence with a view to matching patterns that appear on various types of earthquake record. Such tied explosions could result in specific direction effects and in the selection of particular seismic wave modes for study.

Nuclear explosions could also be used to round out the global seismological coverage. As seen in § 15.6, the incidence of natural earthquakes is widely variable from region to region, and there are many notable gaps in knowledge of the structure below geographical regions where earthquakes are sparse. The valuable information already derived from nuclear explosions in the central Pacific is a case in point.

With the use of explosions beyond the 20 kt range, the methods could be extended to probing the Earth at depths greater than 1000 km. Very much information could be derived from explosions well short of the 10 Mt explosions which Griggs and Press state could be safely contained in a deep oceanic trench. Such explosions could probably be made to produce P waves comparable with those in the largest earthquakes, and could possibly excite observable fundamental oscillations of the whole Earth, similar to the oscillations excited by the Kamchatka and Chilean earthquakes of 1952 and 1960. With nuclear explosions, there is again the advantage that many features of the exciting mechanism would be precisely known; there is also the possibility that different types of excitation could be experimented on with consequent gains to knowledge of structural features in the outer Earth.

An explosion in an ocean trench would be in an already seismically active region and so would not contribute to the filling in of a notable global gap. Nevertheless, the waves generated could be compared with waves from natural earthquakes in the same region and so enable the latter to be more fully interpreted.

The present stage of nuclear-explosion seismology is that seismologists are making the maximum use of source data on explosions already carried out, and the account in § 16.1 gives an indication of the type of progress being made. In addition, there are signs of increasing attention being paid to seismological aspects in explosions lately planned.

16.4. Detection of nuclear explosions. Problems of the detection of nuclear explosions have lately become of considerable general importance. Apart from explosions very far above the Earth's surface, the outstanding difficulties of detection are with underwater and underground explosions, where detection rests principally on seismic methods. The problems have led to the establishment of what is virtually a new branch of seismological research.

The practical problems fall roughly under three main headings: first, to recognise that an event which could be a nuclear explosion has occurred; secondly, given that such an event has occurred, to decide whether the event is artificial or natural in origin (the natural event being normally an earthquake); thirdly, given that a nuclear explosion has occurred, to locate the source and estimate the size, etc. There is some overlapping between these three classes of problems, especially between the third and the other two. There are also subsidiary problems, for example, to distinguish between chemical and nuclear explosions (on which there has been some effort but little progress as yet).

The comparison with earthquake magnitude referred to in

§ 16.2 indicates that well-tamped 5 and 1 kt explosions 300 m underground will produce P waves comparable with those in earthquakes of magnitudes about $4\frac{1}{2}$ and $3\frac{3}{4}$, respectively. The question of recognising that such explosions have occurred therefore depends on the extent to which earthquakes of the stated magnitudes are recognised with existing world seismological coverage, on steps that might be taken to increase the coverage, and on steps to increase the present resolving power of seismographs. (Yields of 5 and 1 kt are mentioned because they appear commonly in discussions on the subject; other yields can be discussed using detail given in § 16.2.) For underground explosions not well tamped, the calculations of Johnson (§ 16.2) indicate that the magnitudes of comparable earthquakes may be very much less than the stated figures.

On the question of discriminating between natural earthquakes and nuclear explosions, several possible approaches have been considered, including the following four:

(i) With most earthquakes the mechanism at the focus is such as to produce S waves at least as prominently as P waves, whereas P waves normally predominate in the 'signature' of a nuclear explosion. Thus the observed partitioning of energy between P and S waves (and also surface waves) can be an important guide. Limitations of the method are that not all earthquakes follow the average pattern, that it is difficult to identify particular phases with many smaller earthquakes, and that there is no guarantee that new patterns of explosion records may not be evolved.

(ii) Some earthquakes give discernible patterns of anaseismic and kataseismic first onsets (see § 15.7.3), whereas the first onset with a nuclear explosion is commonly everywhere anaseismic. Limitations here are that the discrimination between anaseismic and kataseismic onsets is often doubtful for many earthquakes, and that, for the smaller events, nuclear or natural, there is the problem of determining the direction of onset against background 'noise'.

(iii) The focal depth of nuclear explosions is appreciably less than that of the average shallow natural earthquake. Here there is the severe limitation of imprecision in the determination of focal depths of most earthquakes.

(iv) The seismic regions of the world are well known, and the occurrence of an unusual event in a relatively aseismic region is accompanied by a measure of probability that the event is not of natural origin. On the other hand, many earthquakes do occur in unexpected places.

The Geneva Committee referred to in § 16.1 concluded that, with the aid of an additional special network of seismological stations, detection of underground and underwater nuclear explosions would be possible to a considerable degree. The envisaged network would consist of 100 to 110 'control posts' in continents, 20 on large and 40 on small oceanic islands, and 10 ships, each post being manned by about 30 persons. The ships and certain of the island posts would have microbarographs (to record air waves) and hydro-acoustic equipment, in addition to seismographs. Standard seismic equipment would be prescribed, and include ten short-period vertical and two short-period horizontal seismographs, and various longer-period seismographs, at all stations, with additional instruments at selected stations. On each land station, the short-period vertical instruments would be dispersed over an area of $3 \times 3 \, \mathrm{km}^2$ with a view to finer identification of detail against the ground noise (cf. § 9.9.4). The seismographs would be in continuous operation as in regular observatories.

The Geneva Committee expressed the view that the first P wave is the most important for detecting an explosion, for determining the source location and for distinguishing from a natural earthquake; and placed the main emphasis on (ii) as a means of making the discrimination. Evidence was brought to bear from the Rainier explosion (§ 16.1), the one underground explosion from which data had at the time been made generally available. Subject to the additional control posts being set up, the following principal conclusions were reached:

(a) There would be good probability of discerning seismic signals from deep underground and deep ocean nuclear explosions of 1 kt yield and more.

(b) Ninety per cent. of continental earthquakes whose signals are equivalent to 5 kt, and a small percentage of those equivalent to 1 kt, could be identified as natural events.

(c) Twenty to 100 earthquakes per year would be indistinguishable on the basis of their seismic signals from deep underground nuclear explosions of 5 kt yield.

The Geneva Report has met with a number of criticisms from seismologists, principally on the ground that it left insufficient margin for uncertainty in relation to the evidence available at the time. It was thought, for example, to have placed rather too much reliance on interpretations of first onsets from earthquakes, a topic that is one of considerable controversy among seismologists except in the case of the larger earthquakes (see § 15.7.3). There were also controversial questions on the interpretation of data from the Rainier explosion. With additional data from further underground explosions, one group of seismologists has expressed the view that the estimate in (c) of the number of indistinguishable earthquakes may need to be increased at least 10 times. Next, there is the possibility of substantially reducing the seismic efficiency of an underground explosion; if the estimates referred to in § 16.2 are sustained, it would appear that many nuclear explosions in the 1 to 5 kt range could be made to pass unnoticed. Finally, there is divided opinion on how far the signatures of nuclear explosions may be made to simulate those of natural earthquakes.

The Report has had the beneficial effect of drawing attention to some important aspects of seismology and of stimulating useful new research, especially on problems of identifying and interpreting seismic phases and of producing devices to filter out background noise interference. Summaries of research trends on these matters are to be found in work of Press, Oliver and Romney (1959) and in the *Proceedings* (1962) of a VESIAC Colloquium. Research has at the same time been carried out on such matters as the problem of lowering the seismic efficiency of nuclear explosions. While these various researches are still in their infancy, it is unwise to attempt any close prediction of the future course of events in this field. But whatever transpires, it can be said that the developments are leading to considerable advances in seismological technique and knowledge.

CHAPTER 17

EXTRA-TERRESTRIAL SEISMOLOGY

Since 1957 October 4, when the first artificial satellite invaded outer space, the application of seismic methods to the study of extra-terrestrial bodies has been increasingly discussed. At the time of writing, at least two space vehicles have carried equipment intended to be dropped on the surface of the Moon to record lunar seismic waves. Possibly quite soon, seismologists on Earth will be receiving telemetered signals conveying information from the records taken. Just as the advent of efficient seismographs late last century led to our present considerable knowledge of the Earth's interior, so will the placing of the envisaged instruments on other planets lead to much new knowledge of their interiors. Information may also be expected on many special topics, for example, in the case of the Moon, meteorite impacts.

The experiments will not merely provide knowledge of the Moon and planets directly investigated; they can be expected to have important repercussions on the theories of the Earth's interior, and to influence the course of terrestrial geophysics in a number of ways.

A good part of the present chapter will be devoted to lunar questions, since it is obvious that the main experimental effort for some time will be on the Moon. Short sections will, however, be included on Venus, Mars and other planets.

17.1. Lunar seismology

17.1.1. Some relevant data on the Moon.
Present knowledge of the interior of the Moon is comparable with, possibly slightly greater than, that of the Earth before efficient seismographs were available to record earthquakes.

The mass M', mean radius R', volume and mean density of the Moon are well determined as $7 \cdot 35 \times 10^{25}$ g, 1738 km, $2 \cdot 20 \times 10^{25}$ cm³, and $3 \cdot 34$ g/cm³, respectively. The surface value of g is 162 cm/sec².

A commonly used model for the density ρ is that of Jeffreys, in which ρ varies from $3 \cdot 28$ g/cm³ at the surface of the Moon to

3.41 g/cm^3 at the centre. This is the simplest model that allows for compression; it assumes a uniform chemical composition, absence of phase changes, and spherical symmetry. On plausible hypotheses Jeffreys gives the moment of inertia as $0.397 M'R'^2$, but there are no direct observational checks on this figure.

Jeffreys has shown that departures from a hydrostatic state are relatively marked in the Moon; the observed values of $(C' - A')/C'$, where C' and A' are the greatest and least principal moments of inertia, is 0.00063, which is about 17 times the value calculated on the assumption of hydrostatic conditions. Hence there may be some lateral variations of ρ that are comparable with the vertical variations. From data on the Moon's surface inequalities, Jeffreys has further calculated that there is a stress-difference of order 2×10^7 dyne/cm^2 at the centre.

The stress-differences in the Moon, though important in certain problems, are still small compared with the mean of the principal stresses throughout a good part of the interior, so that for broad purposes the stress in the interior can be represented in terms of pressure. Formal application of (13, (9), (10)) yields a value a little less than 5×10^{10} dyne/cm^2 for the pressure at the centre of the Moon; this pressure is reached about 150 km below the surface of the Earth.

Of various estimates that have been made of the temperature in the Moon's interior, none exceeds 2000 °C. It is therefore reasonable to assume that the temperatures in the Moon are sufficiently close to those in the outermost 150 km of the Earth to offer no special problems on seismic wave transmission.

The low value of the mean density of the Moon compared with that of the Earth, the high value of $C'/M'R'^2$, and the evidence on temperature make it strongly probable that the Moon is mainly composed of rocks like those in the region B of the Earth. There could not be a sizeable region of density comparable with that in the Earth's outer core, and it is unlikely that there is any fluid zone. A fairly convincing argument on the last point is the finding of Jeffreys that significant stress-differences persist on the Moon from the surface to the centre. Direct seismic tests on such points would, however, be of great value.

17.1.2. Problems of lunar seismology. It is to be expected that
a good part of the progress on lunar seismology will follow a course
like that of terrestrial seismology. There is likely to be the simplifying feature that background noise is less troublesome on the
Moon through the absence of atmosphere, oceans and people.

Early problems will be to determine the seismicity of the Moon,
the range of values of energies in moonquakes, whether there exist
seismically active and quiet regions as in the case of the Earth, the
variation of the frequency and intensity of moonquakes with depth,
and the extent of correlation between moonquake incidence and
observed surface features of the Moon.

When adequately precise data on arrival-times of seismic phases
have been assembled, it should be possible to construct travel-time
tables for P and S waves and to deduce the velocity variations with
depth. The results would be expected to indicate the extent of any
crustal layers, and to determine sharply whether there is any
significant core in the Moon. Evidence that S as well as P waves are
transmitted at all points of the interior would confirm the absence
of a fluid zone. Identifications of materials in the Moon could be
attempted from the inferred values of k/ρ and μ/ρ. The extent of
regional departures from spherical symmetry might be estimated
at a later stage.

Information of this type would not only be relevant to the Moon,
but would enable important restrictions to be set on Earth models.
For example, the finding of P and S velocities matching those in
the Earth at the same pressures would both verify that the Moon
consists predominantly of Earth upper-mantle material, and
strengthen the assumption that the density just below the Earth's
crust is close to $3\cdot3\,\mathrm{g/cm^3}$. There is the possibility that more direct
evidence than is now available would be provided on such questions
as whether the Moon was once ejected from the Earth (see § 13.9.3).
Definite evidence on the presence or absence of a fluid zone would
be of interest in relation to theories of the Earth's main magnetic
field. So far no lunar magnetic field appears to have been detected,
and conditions appear to be compatible with the Elsasser–Bullard
theory of the Earth's magnetism (see § 13.8.5).

A special lunar problem on which seismology may afford considerable help is that of meteorite incidence on the Moon's surface. This again bears on terrestrial geophysics, but mainly on problems of the Earth's upper atmosphere. Meteorite impacts may, moreover, cause some initial difficulty in assessing the Moon's seismicity, because of the problem of discriminating between impacts and moonquakes. There are some analogies here to the problem of discriminating between nuclear explosions and earthquakes.

In due course it may be possible to extend the methods of explosion seismology to the Moon. (This development may need to be delayed until such time as biologists are satisfied that lunar explosion experiments will not jeopardise the gathering of data in other lunar fields.) When this stage is reached, knowledge of the interior of the Moon may soon surpass that of the Earth, since relatively small explosions will be required to probe the Moon fully; also it may transpire that, because of the relatively low pressures reached in the Moon, the difficulties of unravelling the Moon's structure are less formidable than those for the Earth below a depth of 150 km. On the other hand, there could be some surprises in store.

17.1.3. Immediate practical steps. The first step towards attacking any of the problems mentioned in § 17.1.2 is to design a suitable seismometer and place it on the Moon's surface. (The term 'seismometer' seems more appropriate than 'seismograph' in the present context, in view of the instrumental procedures required.) To begin with, there would be only a single seismometer in action.

The initial requirements are for an instrument sufficiently light to be carried on present space vehicles and sufficiently robust to withstand the probably considerable impact on landing. The instrument must also be capable of functioning at the temperature of its surroundings, which may range from extreme cold to more than 100 °C. These requirements will restrict the early instruments to short-period ones (periods of the order of a second) which will register a single component of the lunar ground displacement. There must also be accompanying equipment through which the registered movements will be magnified and telemetered back to Earth. It is anticipated that, because of the relatively low background noise level, limits to the sensitivity will be set mainly by instrumental noise. For ground motions with periods in the vicinity of the instrumental period, a peak magnification of 10^5 to 10^6 is anticipated.

A further vital requirement is a power supply for sufficient length of time to ensure that information of value will be transmitted. On the assumptions that the seismicity of the Moon is comparable with that of the Earth, and that seismic wave absorption and noise level are no greater, Press, Buwalda and Neugebauer estimate that 10 to 100 moonquakes per month are likely to be recordable 'moonwide'; a single instrument would be expected to record all of these shocks, together with a large number of smaller ones at limited distances from the instrument site. On these figures, the power supply would need to last for several weeks to give any useful information on seismicity.

Lunar seismometers conforming to these requirements have already been designed, but have not as yet been successfully placed on the Moon. When the technical problems have been solved (this will not be known until a seismometer is actually placed and working), the first information to be expected will be about the noise level. It should be quickly determined whether the recorded noise is in fact predominantly instrumental. The next information is likely to be on whether there are as many moonquakes as expected, though there may be complications due to meteorite impacts. Such meagre evidence as there is points to release of accumulated strain energy in the Moon at about the same rate per unit volume as in the Earth, but this cannot be taken for granted until the evidence is more positive.

On the basis of terrestrial experience, it is possible that some phases in addition to the initial P would be identifiable on signals from a single instrument. The correlation that exists between seismic speeds and densities of common terrestrial rocks suggests that speeds close to those in the outermost 150 km of the Earth will be found for the Moon. Assuming this to be the case, it may be possible, with a single instrument, on comparing pulse arrivals from a number of moonquakes with terrestrial data, to arrive by trial and error at a rough estimate of epicentral distances. Clues might then be forthcoming on whether there are any significant lunar seismic belts analogous to those on Earth. At the same time, it needs to be noted that moonquakes may originate at all depths in the Moon, and that the question of focal depth could seriously complicate early attempts to locate epicentres.

17.1.4. Later steps. As the capacity of space vehicles increases, and as experience is gained from the initial experiments, it will become possible to place increasingly elaborate instruments on the Moon. The first step forward would be to set up a three-component seismometer which would, among other things, give detail on the directions of arriving waves, and so narrow the problem of locating foci.

When the problems of landing more delicate instruments are solved, it would be desirable to introduce seismometers of different periods and so extend the spectrum of observed lunar vibrations.

With a single seismometer of period say 6–10 sec, there is the possibility at a fairly early stage of estimating comparative focal depths by noting the relative amplitudes of surface and bodily waves. Care will of course be needed to avoid errors of earlier terrestrial seismology, such as, for example, the misidentification of L and M phases as bodily wave phases (see § 15.5.1). In fact the whole course of lunar seismology can profit from a close study of the trial and error procedures, of false tracks later abandoned, and of the fruits of successive approximation that have characterised the past 70 years of terrestrial seismological development.

Next, it should be possible to bring seismic surface wave investigations to bear as with the Earth. One of the earlier possibilities here is to separate out, on a single record of a moonquake, Rayleigh waves which have travelled distances of $\Delta + 2n\pi$, where $n = 0, 1, 2, \ldots$; with Δ unknown, group velocities can be obtained from the times taken by particular periods to travel one or more times round a great circle of the Moon. Press and colleagues, with this possibility in view, have already prepared Rayleigh wave dispersion curves for two lunar models with different crustal layering, the periods ranging from the order of 10 to 100 sec. By matching the observed dispersion against a variety of such curves, it may prove possible to eliminate many types of crustal models for the Moon and to parallel what has been accomplished for the

Earth. Ewing, Jardetzky and Press have shown that the surface-wave method can give information on layering down to a depth equal to one-third of the wave-lengths used.

When the range of recording becomes extended to periods exceeding the order of a minute, the possibility enters of registering fundamental oscillations of the whole Moon, and achieving results comparable with those realised for the Earth after the 1960 Chilean earthquakes. Preliminary calculations have already been made with this end in view. For a Moon model based mainly on the Earth Model A densities and the Jeffreys P and S velocities for the Earth, Bolt has derived the following periods for spheroidal oscillations of the Moon, the first figure in each case referring to the fundamental mode, and the second (where given) to the first higher mode: $n = 0$, 8·7 min; $n = 2$, 15·1 and 8·4 min; $n = 3$, 10·2 and 6·3 min; $n = 4$, 8·0 and 5·1 min; $n = 6$, 5·8 min. The corresponding periods for a homogeneous model with the same average properties are 8·7, 14·6, 8·0, 9·8, 6·0, 7·7, 4·8 and 5·6 min, respectively. These results show that, as with the Earth, observations of spheroidal oscillations can discriminate between certain types of Moon model. Bolt has also considered a widely different Moon model in which the density ranges from 2·60 to 4·43 g/cm³, and has extended Press's Rayleigh-wave calculations to include allowances for the curvature of the Moon. Other calculations have been made by Takeuchi.

A big increase in the precision of inferences on the internal structure of the Moon can be expected when networks of seismometers are available to provide records of moonquakes simultaneously gathered at separate locations on the Moon's surface. At this stage, it should become possible to evolve reliable travel-time tables for lunar P and S waves, and to determine the velocity distributions in the Moon to good accuracy. There may be a special problem through regional variations of structure extending to relatively greater depths than in the Earth.

On the assumption of constant P and S velocities of 8·0 and 4·6 km/sec throughout the Moon, (7, (36)) gives the P and S travel-time relations as

$$T = 434 \sin (\tfrac{1}{2}\Delta), \quad T = 756 \sin (\tfrac{1}{2}\Delta) \sec, \tag{1}$$

respectively, which could serve as trial relations to be corrected by successive approximation. Corresponding to (1), P and S waves would travel from a point of the Moon's surface to the anticentre in a little over 7, $12\frac{1}{2}$ min, respectively.

Networks of seismometers are also likely to reveal any shadow zones that exist for particular ranges of distance, and to provide auxiliary information on amplitude variation. Depending on the character of the lunar crustal structure, amplitude observations could possibly lead to finer inferences than have so far proved possible with the Earth.

At a later stage still, controlled explosion experiments can be expected, with accompanying high-precision recording of seismic waves from known sources. In addition to providing finer detail on travel-times, explosions could also be used to excite measurable fundamental oscillations of the Moon, with the advantage over the case of the Earth that much smaller energies at source would be required.

Other subjects for investigation include the extent of dust layers and lava flows, and the degree of absorption of seismic waves on the Moon. Absorption may be greater for lunar than for terrestrial seismic waves because of the lower surface gravity and the substantially lower average pressure. Press has already prepared trial amplitude tables for the Moon with the coefficient of absorption taken as zero, 10^{-4}/km and 2×10^{-3}/km, and shown that the third, but not the second, of these values would lead to severe amplitude reductions at larger Δ.

17.1.5. Meteorite impacts on the Moon. Lunar seismology can be expected to provide knowledge on the frequency of meteorite arrivals on the Moon above a certain level of impact energy, the distribution of the impacts in time, the distribution over the Moon's surface, and the distribution of energies.

An immediate question is the 'seismic efficiency' of a meteorite impact, i.e. the proportion of the original kinetic energy which goes into seismic waves (cf. § 16.2). It is reasonable to expect that the efficiency will be approximately equal to that for a shallow nuclear explosion, so that current research on the latter topic can be brought to bear. The expected periods in the seismic waves generated are between 0·01 and 1 sec; period studies may possibly assist in discriminating between meteorite impacts and moon-quakes.

Using an assessment of Harrison Brown on meteorite incidence, and data of Carder and Cloud on seismic efficiency, Press and colleagues tentatively estimate that a single seismometer with a threshold of one millimicron would record 2 to 6 meteorites per year (fewer if the coefficient of absorption exceeds 10^{-4}/km). They suggest, however, amendments to Harrison Brown's formula which could lead to a 10- or 100-fold increase in the number of recorded impacts. The existence of such uncertainty on meteorite incidence shows incidentally the advance to knowledge that may come when impacts on the Moon are instrumentally recorded.

17.2. Venus. The mass, mean radius, mean density and surface gravity value of Venus are $4·88 \times 10^{27}$ g, 6200 km, 4·9 g/cm³ and 850 cm/sec², respectively. The mass is uncertain by 0·6 % and the radius (of sub-atmospheric Venus) by at least 1 %.

Because the values of the mass and mean density of Venus and the Earth are fairly close and the two planets therefore presumably fairly similar in composition, observations of Venus may be specially important to problems of the Earth's interior. In this connection, earlier work by the writer (1949–52) has shown that one of the first problems to be solved by space vehicles near Venus will be to reduce radically the uncertainties in the mass and radius.

Evidence on the moment of inertia of Venus is so far lacking. Moments of inertia of some planets have been estimated through observations of their ellipticities (ϵ) of figure, but the figure of Venus has not so far been observed, and in any case she may rotate too slowly to show measurable oblateness. (The writer has estimated that, for Venus, $\epsilon = 1·7 \times 10^{-6} y^{-2}$, where $20y$ days is the period of rotation.) Positive information on the internal layering of Venus may therefore be expected to come almost exclusively from seismic observations.

It is confidently expected that Venus contains a core, which would be metallic and mainly fluid, like the outer core of the Earth. Confirmation of this would be a most valuable step both in respect of geophysical and geochemical problems, and in relation to problems of the Earth's magnetism (cf. § 17.1.2). No less valuable would be a determination of the Venus core radius R_v. Estimates of R_v have been made on two very different assumptions, namely, that the core and mantle are chemically distinct and that the core is a high-pressure modification of mantle material (see § 13.9.3). Direct determination of R_v might enable a sharp discrimination to be made between these assumptions, with important repercussions on theories of planetary composition.

It would also be very valuable to know whether Venus has an inner core. The writer has shown that the presence or absence of an inner core in Venus bears closely on such questions as whether the Earth and Venus have a common chemical composition, and whether the Earth's inner and outer cores are of distinct chemical composition or not. There is also the possibility of checking on Jacobs's theory that temperature plays a critical part in the solidity of the Earth's inner core.

Apart from such special questions, seismological experiments are likely to provide information on the seismicity of Venus, the detailed variation of density, incompressibility and rigidity with depth, and other properties already discussed in the case of the Earth and Moon.

Practical procedures will present rather more problems with Venus than with the Moon. The difficulties of placing equipment on Venus will be accentuated by the greater surface gravity, and there is the problem of telemetering information from a much greater distance to the Earth; the cloud cover may introduce other difficulties. Serious progress on the practical side of venusian seismology is in fact not to be expected until considerable experience has been gained from lunar experiments. Nevertheless, some theoretical investigations have been started, and there are a few useful models of Venus available, including models of the density and pressure distributions worked out by Ramsey and the writer.

17.3. Mars. The mass M'', mean radius R'', mean density and surface gravity value of Mars are $6\cdot44 \times 10^{26}$ g, 3350 km, $4\cdot1$ g/cm^3 and 380 cm/sec^2. Observations of the ellipticity of figure lead to the value $0 \cdot 386 M'' R''^2$ for the moment of inertia. The uncertainties in M'' and R'' are of the order of $0 \cdot 2$ and 1%, respectively.

Mars, like Venus, is another terrestial planet, and information similar to that for Venus would be sought in seismological research. Two special features are that a value of the moment of inertia is available as a check on estimates of the density distribution and that Mars may be less subject to internal seismic activity than the Earth and Venus. Thus meteorite impacts and artificial explosions may have to be main sources of seismic waves in Mars. The existence of a central core is less certain in Mars than in Venus, and the writer has computed an upper limit of 900 km for the radius of a core; direct testing on such matters could be very valuable. Urey suggests that Mars is probably chemically homogeneous; this too could be tested from seismic velocity data, using the writer's formula (13, (19)) and Birch's formula (13, (22)).

For models of Venus and Mars based on the Earth Model A, Bolt has computed periods of fundamental spheroidal oscillations as $51 \cdot 0$, $31 \cdot 5$ min, respectively, for $n = 2$.

17.4. Other planets. Special features of the remaining terrestrial planet, Mercury, are its proximity to the Sun and its comparatively high mean density in relation to its mass. For these reasons much interest will attach to evidence that may be gathered on the speeds of P and S waves in its interior. But seismological investigations on Mercury are not likely to be attempted for some time.

The outer planets Jupiter, Saturn, Uranus and Neptune all have much lower mean densities than the terrestrial planets, and Ramsey has shown that they consist predominantly of lighter materials such as hydrogen, methane and ammonia. They are likely to have solid surfaces at depths where appropriate pressures are reached, but the placing of seismometers on these surfaces would present entirely new problems.

It will be of some interest to know how much revision this chapter will require in say 10 years' time.

CHAPTER 18

FURTHER TOPICS

18.1. Effects of earthquakes. The effects of earthquakes are many and various, and include geological effects, effects on buildings, etc., and effects on human beings.

The geologist is specially interested in topographical changes caused by an earthquake; possible movements (vertical or horizontal) along visible fault planes; the possible production of new fault planes; the raising, lowering and tilting of earth blocks, with related effects on the distribution and flow of ground water; the production of fissures in the ground; landslides; mudflows; etc. The investigation of topographical changes is assisted by geodetical measurements, which are made systematically in a number of countries seriously affected by earthquakes. The geologist relates his observations of these various effects to his knowledge of the geological structure of the region, and of the compositions and states of aggregation of the local rock materials.

Engineers and architects investigate features of the damage caused by an earthquake to buildings, bridges, pipe-lines, railways, embankments and other man-made structures; systematic directions of fall and of rotation of columns; etc.

In the most intensely damaged region, the effects of a severe earthquake are very complicated. The most drastic effects occur chiefly in the neighbourhood of faults along which there is appreciable relative movement. Away from these faults, the effects are very dependent on the nature of the surface materials, and are as a rule more severe on soft alluvium and unconsolidated sediments than on hard rock. At some distance from the epicentre, the main damage is caused by surface waves; in mines, there is, for instance, often little damage below depths of a few hundred feet when the surface immediately above is considerably affected.

Of special importance in some earthquakes are the effects produced on the sea. We shall consider these separately in § 18.3.

Some of the effects experienced by human beings are indicated in the description of the intensity scale set out in § 18.2.1.

A further effect of some interest is the occurrence of earthquake sounds or rumblings. These sounds are generally low-pitched, and have been likened to the noise of a heavy lorry passing over a rough road or of an underground train passing through a station. The occurrence of such sounds implies the existence of corresponding significant short periods in the ground vibrations; the intensity of the sound depends on the nature of the local surface materials. Some ground motions too small to be felt are heard in this way, as when an earthquake is heard and not felt, or when it is heard before it is felt.

In severe earthquakes, individuals have sometimes reported that prior to feeling the earthquake they have seen surface earth waves approaching from a distance. In a majority of cases this is probably an illusion. In regard to other cases, it is possible that gravity waves analogous to waves in water may be set up in soft or muddy areas.

18.2. Macroseismic data. Studies of the various effects referred to in § 18.1, i.e. 'field investigations' of earthquakes, yield *macroseismic data*, which usefully supplement the data obtained from seismographs. It is sometimes possible to infer from this data features of the mechanism in the focal region of a particular earthquake. We have already referred, for example, to work of Reid (§ 15.3.1) and Wood (§ 15.3.2) in this connection. We shall now discuss the application of macroseismic data to the estimation of the position of the focus of a felt earthquake.

18.2.1. Intensity of earthquake effects. The macroseismic data reveal broad features of the variation in the intensity of an earthquake over the affected area. This 'intensity' is not capable of simple quantitative definition, and is estimated by reference to 'intensity scales' that describe the effects in qualitative terms. Efforts have sometimes been made to associate the divisions in these scales with particular accelerations of the local earth movement; but it appears that the intensity depends in a rather complicated way not only on the accelerations but also on the periods and other features of the local wave form.

Many factors go to determine the intensity at a particular point of the Earth's surface. These include the particular location of the focal region, the mechanism of the occurrence of the earthquake inside this region, the quantity of energy released, the crustal structure in the disturbed region, the distance of the point from the focus, the elastic and other properties of the surface materials adjacent to the point, and the local geological structure.

A number of different intensity scales have been set up during the past century. For many years, the most widely used was the scale set up by de Rossi and Forel in 1878. The scale now generally used is the Mercalli scale as modified by Wood and Neumann in 1931, in which the intensity is considered to be more uniformly graded. An abridged form of the modified Mercalli scale is as follows, the corresponding Rossi–Forel scale numbers being (approximately) indicated in brackets.

I. Not felt except by a few under especially favourable circumstances. (R.F., I.)

II. Felt only by a few persons at rest, especially on upper floors of buildings. Delicately suspended objects may swing. (R.F., I–II.)

III. Felt quite noticeably indoors, especially on upper floors of buildings, but many people do not recognise it as an earthquake. Standing motor cars may rock slightly. Vibration like passing of truck. Duration estimated. (R.F., III.)

IV. During the day felt indoors by many, outdoors by few. At night some awakened. Dishes, windows, doors disturbed, walls make creaking sound. Sensation like heavy truck striking building. Standing motor cars rocked noticeably. (R.F., IV–V.)

V. Felt by nearly everyone, many awakened. Some dishes, windows, etc., broken; a few instances of cracked plaster; unstable objects overturned. Disturbance of trees, poles, and other tall objects sometimes noticed. Pendulum clocks may stop. (R.F., V–VI.)

VI. Felt by all; many frightened and run outdoors. Some heavy furniture moved; a few instances of fallen plaster or damaged chimneys. Damage slight. (R.F., VI–VII.)

VII. Everybody runs outdoors. Damage negligible in buildings of good design and construction; slight to moderate in well-built ordinary structures; considerable in poorly built or badly designed structures; some chimneys broken. Noticed by persons driving motor cars. (R.F., VIII–.)

VIII. Damage slight in specially designed structures; considerable in ordinary substantial buildings, with partial collapse; great in poorly built structures. Panel walls thrown out of frame structures. Fall of chimneys, factory stacks, columns, monuments, walls. Heavy furniture overturned. Sand and mud ejected in small amounts. Changes in well water. Disturbs persons driving motor cars. (R.F., VIII+ to IX−.)

IX. Damage considerable in specially designed structures; well-designed frame structures thrown out of plumb; great in substantial buildings, with partial collapse. Buildings shifted off foundations. Ground cracked conspicuously. Underground pipes broken. (R.F., IX+.)

X. Some well-built wooden structures destroyed; most masonry and frame structures destroyed with foundations; ground badly cracked. Rails bent. Landslides considerable from river banks and steep slopes. Shifted sand and mud. Water splashed (slopped) over banks. (R.F., X−.)

XI. Few, if any, (masonry) structures remain standing. Bridges destroyed. Broad fissures in ground. Underground pipe lines completely out of service. Earth slumps and land slips in soft ground. Rails bent greatly. (R.F., X.)

XII. Damage total. Waves seen on ground surfaces. Lines of sight and level distorted. Objects thrown upward into the air. (R.F., X+.)

18.2.2. Isoseismal curves. With the use of an intensity scale it is possible to summarise the macroseismic data for an earthquake by constructing *isoseismal curves*, which are the loci of points of equal intensity. An isoseismal curve labelled (say) VIII marks the outer boundary of an area in which the intensity is VIII. If there were complete symmetry about the vertical through the earthquake's focus, the isoseismals would be a family of circles with the epicentre as centre. But because of the many unsymmetrical factors influencing the intensity, particularly the character of the local surface materials, the curves are often far from circular in shape. Moreover, an isoseismal of given intensity sometimes consists of more than the closed curve; sometimes one or more closed curves of equal intensity lie entirely outside an isoseismal of lower intensity, or inside one of higher intensity.

18.2.3. Estimation of the position of the focus. When the isoseismal curves have been constructed for an earthquake, it is immediately possible to give an estimate of the position of the

earthquake's epicentre. The most probable position of the epicentre
on the macroseismic data will be at a point inside the area enclosed
by the isoseismal of highest intensity (unless there are complications due to this isoseismal consisting of more than one closed
curve). The particular point taken will as a rule be near the centre
of this area, but the configuration of other isoseismals or special
geological considerations may be taken into account.

In some cases, it is verified from instrumental data that the
epicentre is well determined in this way. But not infrequently it
happens that the true epicentre is outside the area of greatest
intensity; this is to be expected because of the many factors influencing intensity.

It is evident that, other things being equal, the rate of diminution
of intensity with distance from the centre of the disturbed area will
be greater the shallower the focus of a given earthquake. This
suggests the possibility of inferring the focal depth from an examination of the spacings between consecutive isoseismal curves. In
some regions, this method has been usefully applied to detect
abnormal focal depths of earthquakes.

18.3. Sea disturbances due to earthquakes

18.3.1. Tsunamis.
Imamura and other Japanese seismologists
have made detailed studies of the phenomenon they call a *tsunami*,
wherein long sea waves, sometimes of great height, sweep inshore
following certain earthquakes.

The immediate cause of a tsunami is a disturbance in the adjacent
sea bed, sufficient to cause the sudden raising or lowering of a large
body of water. This disturbance may be in the focal region of an
earthquake, or may be a submarine landslide arising from an
earthquake with epicentre possibly on the land. Following the
initial disturbance to the sea surface, gravity waves travel out in all
directions, the order of the speed of travel in deep water being given
by $\sqrt{(gh)}$, where h is the sea depth; this speed may be considerable,
e.g. 100 m/sec if h is 1000 m. The amplitude at the surface does not
exceed a few metres in deep water, but the principal wave-length
may be of the order of some hundreds of kilometres; correspondingly the principal wave-period may be of the order of some tens

of minutes. On account of these features the waves are not noticed by ships well out at sea.

But when such waves approach the shallow water close to the shore, the amplitude increases, and in U- and V-shaped inlets sometimes reaches a height of the order of 20–30 m. It is in low-lying ground around such inlets that great damage is sometimes done. Frequently the wave-front in the inlet is nearly vertical as in a tidal bore, and the speed of onrush may be of the order of 10 m/sec. In some cases there are several great waves, separated by intervals of some minutes or more, and the first of these waves is not always the greatest. Frequently, the first great wave is preceded by an extraordinary recession of water from the inlet which may commence several minutes or even half an hour beforehand.

The initial disturbance causing a tsunami may be some distance from the nearest coast. In the great tsunami of 1896 June 15 which devastated the Sanriku region on the north-east coast of Japan, the place of origin was estimated to be 150–200 km from the shore. The waves from tsunamis are recorded on tide-gauges often in distant countries; the arrival-times of such waves have been used to estimate the order of the average depth of water over parts of the Pacific Ocean.

Considerable effort has lately been put into the study of tsunamis, especially since the tsunami which followed the Chilean earthquakes of 1960 May 22. This tsunami caused much damage in low-lying areas over the whole Pacific region. It produced, for example, waves of height 20 ft. in the Marquesas, 10 ft. in the Society Islands, 9 ft. in Hawaii and 8 ft. in Samoa, marked waves around the New Zealand coast and 4 ft. waves in Sydney harbour. Lomnitz reports a marked variation after the earthquake in the times of high tide at an island near Chile, and attributes this to changes in the resonance patterns of tides caused by subsidence of the continental shelf off Chile.

Cox refers to an important influence of resonance in the varying tsunami wave motion of the water in bays, on continental shelves and around islands whose dimensions are comparable with the wave-lengths. Miles and Munk have investigated the theory of wave response of harbours of assigned shape to tsunamis. Munk has drawn attention to the bearing of tsunami energy on the motion of the Moon.

Iida and Ohta have investigated tsunami amplitude and energy. Watanabe has compared the 1960 Chilean tsunami with the 1933 Sanriku tsunami, both of which damaged the Sanriku coast. Miyoshi has studied tsunamis from volcanic explosions on a Pacific Island. Lavrentyev and Savarensky have investigated the tsunami which followed the Kamchatka earthquake of 1952 November 4 and produced 20–25 ft. waves along 1000 miles of Siberian coast.

Organisations, notably in Japan, Siberia and Hawaii, have been set up to provide tsunami warning systems. Wadati, Hirono and Hisamoto have presented experience gained from the 1960 Chilean tsunami. Most data on tsunami waves comes from measurements taken in the vicinity of coasts. The gathering of much needed supplementary data from mid-ocean has become possible through the use of a gauge designed by Vitousek for the purpose.

18.3.2. Sea-quakes. P waves from an earthquake may pass through the sea following refraction through the sea floor; the speed of these waves is about $1 \cdot 5$ km/sec, the speed of sound in water. If these waves meet a ship with sufficient intensity, they give the impression that the ship has struck a submerged object, and the phenomenon is called a *sea-quake*.

18.3.3. T and Airy phases. Observatories sometimes record a phase, called the T phase, for which the corresponding ray has most of its length in a SOFAR channel in the ocean, where the wave speed is about $1 \cdot 5$ km/sec. The T phase was first noticed by Linehan in 1940 and has been recorded, for example, in California from Hawaiian earthquakes.

Pekeris in 1948 predicted, and later identified on seismograms obtained by Worzel and Ewing of explosions in shallow water, a phase which he called the Airy phase. This phase consists of a group of surface waves of period 9–11 sec which travels across an ocean at $0 \cdot 7$–$0 \cdot 8$ of the P wave speed of $1 \cdot 5$ km/sec. It corresponds to a stationary value of the group velocity for surface waves on an ocean bounded below by a rigid floor, and is observed in shallow submarine earthquakes.

18.3.4. Seismic seiches. Seiches are rhythmic motions of the water in land-locked bays or lakes, and are sometimes excited by earthquakes and by tsunamis. These oscillations may last for some hours or even for 1 or 2 days.

18.4. Ocean-bottom seismographs. Apart from limited recordings on equipment carried by ships, seismic waves are at present recorded almost wholly in land regions. Steps have lately been taken, however, to extend the recording to ocean floors. Possible procedures are to leave an appropriately designed seismograph on an ocean floor for a period of weeks or more and later collect seismograms from it, or to arrange for recorded details to be communicated as they occur, either by telemetering or cable, to the ocean surface or shore. Ewing, Press and others have designed instruments which telemeter information to a surface ship by modulation of a supersonic signal from the seismograph on the floor. Because of the relatively low noise level expected at the ocean bottom (experiments so far carried out are not definitive on the point), it is hoped to gain advantage from using seismographs of higher sensitivity than those used on land.

The use of ocean-bottom seismographs should ultimately secure a vastly improved global coverage of seismic waves and also provide much new information on oceanic regions. Stations on oceanic islands are useful but have the limitation that the island structure seriously distorts waves when the wave-lengths are of the order of the dimensions of the island or less. Ocean-bottom seismographs will enable finer details of oceanic crustal structure to be determined, and because of the relative thinness of the usual oceanic crust should enable finer seismic information to be gathered on the upper mantle. New data should be provided on focal mechanism, on the origin and propagation of microseisms, on the character of ocean-continent margins, and on such problems as whether there exist waves which are propagated only through oceanic structures and are not recordable on land.

18.5. Microseisms. An ordinary earthquake, which arises as a sudden dislocation of material within the Earth, is recognised by characteristics of the trace it leaves on a seismogram (see § 10.3).

In addition to ordinary earthquakes, seismograms at many observatories reveal the presence of additional small earth movements which are called *microseisms*. These movements attract the attention of seismologists since they sometimes complicate the problem of the accurate recording of ordinary earthquakes, and also because their form is likely to be related to features of the Earth's surface structure.

Some microseisms are purely local phenomena, for example, those due to movements of traffic or machinery, or to local wind effects and rain storms. Seismologists are mostly interested in another class of microseisms which show features that are very similar on records traced at observatories distributed over a wide area, sometimes over a whole continent. The features include the approximately simultaneous occurrence of maximum amplitudes and of marked changes in amplitudes at all the observatories concerned. These microseisms may persist for many hours at a stretch, and have more or less regular periods of from 2 to 10 or more seconds.

The largest of the earth movements associated with these microseisms are of the order of 10^{-3} cm and occur in coastal regions; in central Asia, the amplitudes rarely exceed 10^{-4} cm. The amplitudes also depend to some extent on the local geological structure. There is a fair correlation between the size of the microseisms and the occurrence of stormy weather conditions in some adjacent region.

Wiechert suggested that microseisms are generated by the action of rough surf against an extended steep coast, and this hypothesis has been followed up in some detail by Gutenberg. Tams and Jung have found a fair correlation between surf on the Norwegian coast and microseisms recorded in parts of Germany. Sezawa, Wadati and Masuda consider the action of surf to be a frequent cause of microseisms observed in Japan. Gutenberg estimated that the energy transferred from the breaking surf to the coastal ground is probably of the right order to cause the observed microseisms. Byerly has stated that a good proportion of observed microseisms at Berkeley can possibly be explained by the action of nearby surf, but that sometimes the nearby surf at Berkeley is rough when microseisms are small, and vice versa.

Gherzi noted the concurrence of large microseisms at Zi-ka-wei with cyclones far out over the ocean, and Banerji observed that in the case of a storm approaching the Indian Ocean, the largest microseisms occurred some hours before the storm reached the coastline. Subsequently, Gherzi put forward the hypothesis that microseisms are generated by atmospheric oscillations (or 'pumping') near the centre of the storm region. Whipple, Sezawa and Kanai have examined possible mechanisms of the generation of microseisms in this way.

Lee, following a detailed study of microseisms in Great Britain, has given evidence that they are essentially Rayleigh waves, and has devised means of calculating their direction of advance. Lee states that when microseisms in Europe are large, stormy weather conditions prevail over the eastern part of the North Atlantic, but that stormy conditions are not invariably accompanied by large microseisms.

In 1946 Gilmore presented an important series of data compiled by the United States Navy on the relation between microseisms and tropical storms in the region of the Caribbean Sea. Gilmore inferred that the dominant microseisms were not immediately related to the surf action.

Work of Bernard, Miche, Deacon and Longuet-Higgins has given strong support to the theory that observable microseisms are generated when large standing waves are formed at sea, the microseismic periods being half the periods of the standing waves. However, not all microseisms appear to be generated in this way. Deacon, Darbyshire and Iyer have introduced new techniques for analysing microseisms into period groups and correlating the results with storm observations.

A comprehensive survey of microseisms in Sweden was carried out by Båth; many other surveys have been made elsewhere.

Macelwane and Ramírez introduced 'tripartite' stations to study microseisms. These are sets of seismological stations up to a few kilometres apart with co-ordinated timing. In theory, one tripartite station would locate the direction of microseism advance, and two stations a storm centre. In this way it was hoped to trace the movements of large storms at sea and to forecast hurricanes. In practice, there are difficulties in securing the necessary precision.

Gilmore has sought to develop an entirely empirical method of forecasting hurricanes, based on observations of amplitude ratios at pairs of stations.

Useful summaries of recent research on microseisms have been prepared by Darbyshire and Iyer (1958), and by Carder and Eppley (1959).

Brune and Oliver (1959) have presented a summary on the general question of the seismic noise of the Earth's surface, considering periods ranging from 40 sec to less than 0·1 sec.

18.6. Seismic prospecting. The methods of seismic survey and explosion seismology have already been mentioned in chapters 9, 12 and 16. The methods had their origin in prospecting for oil and other mineral sources, and involve the artificial production and recording of seismic waves, with a view to unravelling geological structure immediately below the surface in some region. The experimental techniques have been greatly developed and the progress has led, moreover, to important advances in the recording of natural earthquakes. In addition, seismic prospecting has led to important mathematical results on the transmission of elastic waves from particular types of source and through variously complicated media.

Two basic practical methods are commonly used—the reflection and the refraction method. 'Refraction shooting' is designed to determine seismic speeds and configurations of layers in regions where the speed does not decrease with depth. Field seismographs, or other recording instruments, are set up at distances from an explosion source that are several times the depth to the lowest layer being investigated, and theory based on that of §12.1.2 is used. In 'reflection shooting', the recording instruments are close to the source, the aim being to record near-vertical reflections from the boundaries of the layer investigated. Periods of the recorded waves are commonly of the order 0·01–0·1 sec. Attention is given to such problems as isolating the sought phases from background effects including scattered waves and surface waves, and to securing adequate magnification. In these problems various filtering procedures (§9.9.4), including the use of arrays of seismographs, are brought to bear, and magnetic-tape recording is commonly employed. Ewing and Press (1956) have given a useful summary of the methods used. By suitably disposing a series of source explosions, the shapes of sloping and curved boundaries can be elucidated. Seismic methods have located thin ore bodies 20 m wide at depths of order 200 m.

The methods of seismic prospecting are also being extensively applied to problems of detecting nuclear explosions (§ 16.4).

18.6.1. Seismic determinations of ice thickness. The methods of seismic prospecting have been usefully brought to bear to determine ice thicknesses, the first experiments having been made in the Austrian Alps. In 1930, Sorge and Loewe measured thicknesses of the Greenland ice-cap, and subsequently extensive ice-thickness measurements have been made in both the Arctic and Antarctic regions. One of the most noted I.G.Y. activities was the effort made by six nations to measure Antarctic ice thicknesses, the work resulting in a 40 % increase in the estimated volume of Antarctic ice to about $4\frac{1}{2}$ million cubic miles, or 87 % of the total for the world. Summaries of the results have been prepared by Robin, and by Goodspeed and the writer.

Reflection shooting is principally used to determine the ice thickness at a given place, but is supplemented by refraction shooting to determine corrections for low velocities near the ice surface. Explosion charges commonly range from 0·1 to 3 or 4 kg in reflection shooting and are of the order of 10–20 kg in refraction shooting. Complications due to surface waves are reduced by firing shots in bore-holes up to 60 m deep. In general, it is possible to determine ice thicknesses within about 2 %.

In 1956, ice thicknesses had been determined in Antarctica on traverses totalling some 600 km, but the total length of traverses is now some 20 000 km. The results indicate that the rock surface in eastern Antarctica is mainly above sea level, while western Antarctica is more of archipelago type. This result is supported in inferences from earthquake surface-wave observations (see § 12.6). The maximum ice thickness so far found exceeds 4 km.

The values found for the P velocities in Antarctic ice range from 3·8 to 4·0 km/sec, the lower value being found in coastal regions, and the higher near the Pole of Relative Inaccessibility. The S velocity is about 1·95 km/sec. The methods have also yielded P velocities in rocks below the ice ranging from 4·7 to 6·3 km/sec.

Seismic methods have also been used to measure the thicknesses and elastic properties of floating ice in both the Arctic and Antarctic.

18.7. Model seismology. As has been seen in earlier chapters, a large part of theoretical seismology is concerned with obtaining solutions of the equations of motion of disturbances in elastic media subject to various initial and boundary conditions. Where the available mathematics is inadequate for solving complicated problems, recourse is had to model seismic experiments which yield solutions by an analogue process.

A typical procedure is to apply an impulse at a point of a physical model structure designed to represent a context of interest, and to record the ensuing displacements at various points of the model as functions of the time. The recording is made on an oscilloscope, and the scale of the model is such that the impulses can be repeated at rates of the order of 1000/sec, resulting in a steady picture like a seismogram being shown on the oscilloscope.

In practice, pains have to be taken to see that the model, with appropriate scale corrections, does represent the context sufficiently accurately. For example, if the context is a homogeneous Earth in which curvature may be neglected, it is suitable to apply an impulse at the surface of the model, and test the results against Lamb's solution for the displacements in an infinite half-space of perfectly elastic material arising from a point impulsive source at the surface. When the needed agreement is realised (which may not occur until special steps have been taken to reduce to insignificance the effects of elastic imperfections and other extraneous effects in the model), analogue solutions for impulses applied below the surface may be derived.

Model seismic experiments were carried out in Japan by Terada and Tsuboi in 1927, and have since been greatly developed by both pure and applied seismologists, for example, Kaufman, Northwood, Knopoff, Oliver, Press and Ewing. A paper by the last three (1954) contains a useful summary of the procedures.

Model seismic experiments are now applied to a great variety of topics, including for example tsunamis.

18.8. Design of earthquake-resisting structures. On account of the complicated character of earthquake waves near an epicentre, the problem of designing structures to withstand strong earth motions is a difficult one, and the measures as yet put into practice largely follow empirical lines, based on appraisals of the effects of actual earthquakes. These appraisals are assisted by the use of special 'strong motion' seismographs, which are not sensitive enough to be put out of action in a severe earthquake.

Such appraisals influence the selection of building sites in earthquake regions, of the materials used in construction and of general features of design. Special attention is paid to the use of fireproof materials since fires are often responsible for the worst disasters in earthquakes.

In many earthquake countries, a 'seismic constant' is incorporated in building codes, whereby structures are designed to withstand the horizontal forces that would arise from a steady horizontal earth acceleration of the order usually of $0 \cdot 1g$ to $0 \cdot 2g$. This 'statical method' does not touch the question of the dynamical behaviour of complicated and tall structures, and ignores many features of the actual earth motion in an earthquake. But it does lead to much reduction of earthquake damage. Even when the earth acceleration exceeds that on which the calculations are based, a structure may be undamaged because of quick reversals in the direction of the acceleration.

At present, many theoretical investigations of the dynamical behaviour of particular structures are being carried out, and are assisted by laboratory experiments on models.

In major earthquake countries, there is often a division into areas of different levels of earthquake incidence. This 'seismic zoning' is based on past seismic history and studies of local tectonic characteristics, and is taken into account in building codes. Probability considerations underlie the determination of zones, and uncertainties may be appreciable in regions where the seismic history is available for the order of only a century or so.

REFERENCES

General references

KNOTT, C. G. (1908). *The physics of earthquake phenomena.* Oxford: Clarendon Press.

WALKER, G. W. (1913). *Modern seismology.* London: Longmans Green.

DE MONTESSUS DE BALLORE, F. (1924). *La géologie sismologique.* Paris: Armand Colin.

GUTENBERG, B. (1929). Theorie der Erdbebenwellen; Beobachtungen von Erdbebenwellen; Die seismische Bodenruhe. *Handbuch der Geophysik,* 4, 1–298. Berlin.

CONRAD, V. (1932). Die zeitliche Folge der Erdbeben und bebenauslösende Ursachen. *Handbuch der Geophysik,* 4, 1007–1190. Berlin.

MACELWANE, J. B. and SOHON, F. W. (1936, 1932). *Theoretical seismology,* Parts I and II. New York: Wiley.

MACELWANE, J. B. (Editor) (1933). *Seismology. Physics of the Earth,* VI. Bull. Nat. Res. Coun., Wash., no. 90.

HECK, N. H. (1936). *Earthquakes.* Princeton: Princeton University Press.

IMAMURA, A. (1937). *Theoretical and applied seismology.* Tokyo: Maruzen.

MILNE, J. (1939). *Earthquakes and other earth movements,* rev. by A. W. Lee. London: Routledge, Kegan Paul.

BYERLY, P. (1942). *Seismology.* New York: Prentice-Hall.

JEFFREYS, H. (1950). *Earthquakes and mountains,* 2nd ed. London: Methuen.

GUTENBERG, B. (Editor) (1951). *Internal constitution of the Earth. Physics of the Earth,* VII, 2nd ed. New York: Dover.

COULOMB, J. (1952). *La constitution de la Terre.* Paris: Albin Michel.

BULLEN, K. E. (1954). *Seismology.* London: Methuen.

SAVARENSKY, E. F. and KIRNOS, D. P. (1955). *Elements of seismology and seismometry.* Moscow.

EWING, W. M., JARDETZKY, W. S. and PRESS, F. (1957). *Elastic waves in layered media.* New York: McGraw-Hill.

BENIOFF, H., EWING, M., HOWELL, B. F., Jr. and PRESS, F. (1958). *Contributions in geophysics* (in honour of Beno Gutenberg). London: Pergamon.

HEISKANEN, W. A. and VENING MEINESZ, F. A. (1958). *The Earth and its gravity field.* New York: McGraw-Hill.

RICHTER, C. F. (1958). *Elementary seismology.* San Francisco: Freeman.

GUTENBERG, B. (1959). *Physics of the Earth's interior.* New York: Academic Press.

HOWELL, B. F., Jr. (1959). *Introduction to geophysics.* New York: McGraw-Hill.

JACOBS, J. A., RUSSELL, R. D. and WILSON, J. TUZO (1959). *Physics and geology.* New York: McGraw-Hill.

JEFFREYS, Sir H. (1959). *The Earth,* 4th ed. Cambridge University Press.

MUNK, W. H. and MACDONALD, G. J. F. (1960). *The rotation of the Earth.* Cambridge University Press.

COOK, A. H. and GASKELL, T. F. (Editors) (1961). *The Earth today.* (70th birthday volume to Sir Harold Jeffreys.) London: Royal Astronomical Society.

SCHEIDEGGER, A. E. (1963). *Principles of geodynamics,* 2nd ed. Berlin: Springer-Verlag.

BATES, D. R. (Editor) (1963). *The planet Earth,* 2nd ed. London: Pergamon.

Historical (§ 1.1)

DAVISON, C. (1927). *The founders of seismology.* Cambridge University Press.

LEE, S. P. (Editor) (1956). *Chronological tabulation of Chinese earthquake records,* 2 vols. Peking: Chinese Academy of Sciences.

Elasticity theory (§§ 2.1–2.6)

JEFFREYS, H. (1930). The thermodynamics of an elastic solid. *Proc. Camb. Phil. Soc.* **26**, 101–6.

JEFFREYS, H. (1932). On plasticity and creep in solids. *Proc. Roy. Soc. A,* **138**, 283–97.

LOVE, A. E. H. (1945). *The mathematical theory of elasticity,* 4th rev. ed. Cambridge University Press.

OLDROYD, J. G. (1947). Papers on plastic flow. *Proc. Camb. Phil. Soc.* **43**, 100–5, 383–405, 521–32.

STONELEY, R. (1949). The seismological implications of aeolotropy in continental structure. *Mon. Not. R. Astr. Soc.,* Geophys. Suppl., **5**, 343–53.

GUTENBERG, B. (Editor) (1951). Colloquium on plastic flow and deformation within the Earth. (Contributions by L. H. Adams, D. Griggs, H. Benioff, E. C. Bullard, F. Birch, F. A. Vening Meinesz, B. Gutenberg, E. H. Vestine, W. Heiskanen, J. M. Burgess and others.) *Trans. Amer. Geophys. Un.* **32**, 499–543.

MURNAGHAN, F. D. (1951). *Finite deformation of an elastic solid.* New York: Wiley.

JAEGER, J. C. (1956). *Elasticity, fracture and flow.* London: Methuen.

SOKOLNIKOFF, I. S. (1956). *Mathematical theory of elasticity,* 2nd ed. New York: McGraw-Hill.

Wave theory (§§ 3.1–3.6)

LAMB, H. (1932). *Hydrodynamics,* 6th ed. Cambridge University Press.

CAGNIARD, L. (1939). *Réflexion et réfraction des ondes séismiques progressives.* Paris: Gauthier-Villars. (English trans. (1962) by FLINN, E. A. and DIX, C. H. New York: McGraw-Hill.)

JEFFREYS, Sir H. and JEFFREYS, BERTHA SWIRLES (1950). *Methods of mathematical physics,* 2nd ed. Cambridge University Press.

SCHOLTE, J. G. J. (1957). On seismic waves in a spherical Earth. *Kon. Ned. Meteorol. Inst.* **65**, 1–55.

DUVALL, G. E. (1962). Concepts of shock wave propagation. *Bull. Seismol. Soc. Amer.* **52**, 869–93.

Bodily elastic waves (§§4.1–4.7)

POISSON, S. D. (1829, 1831). Mémoire sur l'équilibre et le mouvement des corps élastiques; mémoire sur la propagation du mouvement dans les milieux élastiques. *Mem. Acad. Sci., Paris*, **8**, 623–7; **10**, 578–605.

STOKES, G. G. (1880). Propagation of an arbitrary disturbance in an elastic medium. *Cambridge Mathematical Papers*, **2**, 257–80.

OLDHAM, R. D. (1900). On the propagation of earthquake motion to great distances. *Phil. Trans.* A, **194**, 135–74.

JEFFREYS, H. (1928). The times of transmission and focal depths of large earthquakes. *Mon. Not. R. Astr. Soc.*, Geophys. Suppl., **1**, 500–21.

JEFFREYS, H. (1931). Damping in bodily seismic waves. *Mon. Not. R. Astr. Soc.*, Geophys. Suppl., **2**, 318–23.

JEFFREYS, H. (1931). On the cause of oscillatory movement in seismograms. *Mon. Not. R. Astr. Soc.*, Geophys. Suppl., **2**, 407–16.

STONELEY, R. (1937). The Mongolian earthquake of 1931 August 10. *42nd Rep., Brit. Ass. Seism. Comm.*, pp. 5–6.

BIRCH, F. (1938). The effect of pressure upon the elastic parameters of isotropic solids, according to Murnaghan's theory of finite strain. *J. Appl. Phys.* **9**, 279–88.

FU, C. Y. (1950). Problems of propagation of elastic waves. *J. Chin. Geophys. Soc.* **2**, 40–59.

STONELEY, R. (1951). Polarisation of the S-phase of seismograms. *Ann. Geofis.* **4**, 3–8.

BULLEN, K. E. (1956). Seismic wave transmission. *Encyclopedia of Physics*, **47**, 75–118. Berlin: Springer-Verlag.

JEFFREYS, Sir H. (1957). Elastic waves in a continuously stratified medium. *Mon. Not. R. Astr. Soc.*, Geophys. Suppl., **7**, 332–7.

GUTENBERG, B. (1958). Attenuation of seismic waves in the Earth's mantle. *Bull. Seismol. Soc. Amer.* **48**, 269–82.

HONDA, H. (1959). The elastic waves generated from a spherical source. *Sci. Rep. Tôhoku Univ.*, 5th ser., **11**, 178–83.

JEFFREYS, Sir H. (1961). Rock creep and tidal friction. *C.R. I.A.S.P.I.E.*, Strasbourg, **13**, 27–35.

LOMNITZ, C. (1962). Application of the logarithmic creep law to stress wave attentuation in the solid Earth. *J. Geophys. Res.* **67**, 365–8.

Surface elastic waves (§§5.1–5.9)

RAYLEIGH, LORD (STRUTT, J. W.) (1885). On waves propagated along the plane surface of an elastic solid. *Proc. Lond. Math. Soc.* **17**, 4–11.

LAMB, H. (1904). On the propagation of tremors over the surface of an elastic solid. *Phil. Trans.* A, **203**, 1–42.

LOVE, A. E. H. (1911). *Some problems of geodynamics.* Cambridge University Press.

STONELEY, R. (1924). Elastic waves at the surface of separation of two solids. *Proc. Roy. Soc.* A, **106**, 416–28.

JEFFREYS, H. (1925). On the surface waves of earthquakes. *Mon. Not. R. Astr. Soc.*, Geophys. Suppl., **1**, 282–92.

NAKANO, H. (1925). On Rayleigh wave. *Jap. J. Astr. Geophys.* **2**, 1–94.

STONELEY, R. (1926). The effect of the ocean on Rayleigh waves. *Mon. Not. R. Astr.*, Geophys. Suppl., **1**, 349–56.

JEFFREYS, H. (1928). The effect on Love waves of heterogeneity in the lower layer. *Mon. Not. R. Astr. Soc.*, Geophys. Suppl., **1**, 101–11.

STONELEY, R. and TILLOTSON, E. (1928). The effect of a double surface layer on Love waves. *Mon. Not. R. Astr. Soc.*, Geophys. Suppl., **1**, 521–7.

BYERLY, P. (1930). The dispersion of seismic waves of the Love type and the thickness of the surface layer of the Earth under the Pacific. *Beitr. Geophys.* **26**, 27–33.

JEFFREYS, H. (1931). The formation of Love waves (Querwellen) in a two-layer crust. *Beitr. Geophys.* **30**, 336–50.

LEET, L. DON (1931). Empirical investigation of surface-waves generated by distant earthquakes. *Ottawa, Dom. Observ. Publ.* **7**, 263–322.

SEZAWA, K. (1934). On the transmission of seismic waves on the bottom surface of an ocean. *Bull. Earthq. Res. Inst. Tokyo*, **9**, 115–43.

STONELEY, R. (1934). The transmission of Rayleigh waves in a heterogeneous medium. *Mon. Not. R. Astr. Soc.*, Geophys. Suppl., **3**, 222–32.

JEFFREYS, H. (1935). The surface waves of earthquakes. *Mon. Not. R. Astr. Soc.*, Geophys. Suppl., **3**, 253–61.

STONELEY, R. (1935). On the apparent velocities of earthquake waves over the surface of the Earth. *Mon. Not. R. Astr. Soc.*, Geophys. Suppl., **3**, 262–71.

SEZAWA, K. (1935). Love-waves generated from a source of a certain depth. *Bull. Earthq. Res. Inst. Tokyo*, **13**, 1–17.

SEZAWA, K. and KANAI, K. (1935). The rate of damping in seismic vibrations of a surface layer of varying density or elasticity. *Bull. Earthq. Res. Inst. Tokyo*, **13**, 484–95.

PEKERIS, C. (1935). The propagation of Rayleigh waves in heterogeneous media. *Physics*, **6**, 133–8.

COULOMB, J. (1935). *Début des ondes de Love et Rayleigh.* Paris: Livre jubilaire de Marcel Brillouin.

STONELEY, R. (1937). Love waves in a triple surface layer. *Mon. Not. R. Astr. Soc.*, Geophys. Suppl., **4**, 43–50.

SEZAWA, K. and KANAI, K. (1937). Relation between the thickness of a surface layer and the amplitudes of dispersive Rayleigh waves. *Bull. Earthq. Res. Inst. Tokyo*, **15**, 845–59.

SEZAWA, K. and KANAI, K. (1938). Anomalous dispersion of elastic surface waves. *Bull. Earthq. Res. Inst. Tokyo*, **16**, 225–33, 683–9.

WILSON, JAMES T. (1942). Surface waves in a heterogeneous medium. *Bull. Seismol. Soc. Amer.* **32**, 297–304.

SCHOLTE, J. G. (1947). The range and existence of Rayleigh and Stoneley waves. *Mon. Not. R. Astr. Soc.*, Geophys. Suppl., **5**, 120–6.

FU, C. Y. (1947). Studies on seismic waves. III. Propagation of elastic waves in the neighbourhood of a free boundary. *Geophysics*, **12**, 57–71.

WILSON, JAMES T. (1948). Increase in period of earthquake waves with distance travelled. *Bull. Seismol. Soc. Amer.* **38**, 89–93.

CALOI, P. (1948). Comportamento della onde di Rayleigh in un mezzo firmo-elastico indefinito. *Ann. Geofis.* **1**, 550–67.

VALLE, P. E. (1949). Contributo allo studio delle onde di Love. *Ann. Geofis.* **2**, 231–50, and earlier papers.

LAPWOOD, E. R. (1949). The disturbance due to a line source in a semi-infinite elastic medium. *Phil. Trans.* A, **242**, 63–100.

NEWLANDS, M. (1950). Rayleigh waves in a two-layer heterogeneous medium. *Mon. Not. R. Astr. Soc.*, Geophys. Suppl., **6**, 109–24.

PRESS, F. and EWING, M. (1950). Propagation of explosive sound in a liquid layer overlying a semi-infinite elastic solid. *Geophysics*, **15**, 426–46.

STONELEY, R. (1950). The effect of a low-velocity stratum on surface elastic waves. *Mon. Not. R. Astr. Soc.*, Geophys. Suppl., **6**, 28–35.

PRESS, F. and EWING, M. (1952). Two slow surface waves across North America. *Bull. Seismol. Soc. Amer.* **43**, 219–28.

KANAI, K. (1955). On Sezawa-waves (M_2 waves). Part II. *Bull. Earthq. Res. Inst. Tokyo*, **33**, 275–81.

STONELEY, R. (1955). Rayleigh waves in a medium with two surface layers. *Mon. Not. R. Astr. Soc.*, Geophys. Suppl., **6**, 610–15; **7**, 71–5.

EWING, W. M. and PRESS, F. (1956). Surface and guided waves. *Encyclopedia of Physics*, **47**, 119–39. Berlin: Springer-Verlag.

STONELEY, R. and HOCHSTRASSER, U. (1957, 1961). The transmission of Rayleigh waves across an ocean floor with two surface layers. Parts I and II. *Bull. Seismol. Soc. Amer.* **47**, 7–12; and *Geophys. J., R. Astr. Soc.* **4**, 197–201.

SAVARENSKY, E. F. (1959). The determination of group and phase velocities from observations. *Bull. Acad. Sci. U.S.S.R.*, Geophys. Ser. (English trans.), pp. 1102–7.

BRUNE, J. N., NAFE, J. E. and OLIVER, J. E. (1960). A simplified method for the analysis and synthesis of dispersed wave trains. *J. Geophys. Res.* **65**, 287–304.

BUCHWALD, V. T. (1961). Rayleigh waves in transversely isotropic media. *Quart. J. Mech. App. Math.* **14**, 293–317.

JEFFREYS, Sir H. (1961). Small corrections in the theory of surface waves. *Geophys. J., R. Astr. Soc.* **6**, 115–17.

PHINNEY, R. A. (1961). Propagation of leaking interface waves. *Bull. Seismol. Soc. Amer.* **51**, 527–56.

HUDSON, J. A. (1962). Love waves in a heterogeneous medium. *Geophys. J., R. Astr. Soc.* **6**, 131–47.

Reflection and refraction (§§6.1–6.7)

KNOTT, C. G. (1899). Reflexion and refraction of elastic waves, with seismological applications. *Phil. Mag.* (5), **48**, 64–97, 567–9.

WIECHERT, E. (1907). Über Erdbebenwellen. I. Theoretisches über die Ausbreitung der Erdbebenwellen. *Nachr. Ges. Wiss. Göttingen*, Math.-Phys. Klasse, pp. 415–529.

KNOTT, C. G. (1909). Seismic radiations. *Proc. Roy. Soc. Edinb.* **30**, 23–37.

JEFFREYS, H. (1926). The reflexion and refraction of elastic waves. *Mon. Not. R. Astr. Soc.*, Geophys. Suppl., **1**, 321–34.

MATUZAWA, T. and others (1928, 1929). On the forerunners of earthquake motions. *Bull. Earthq. Res. Inst. Tokyo*, **4**, 85–106; **7**, 241–60.

SLICHTER, L. B. and GABRIEL, V. G. (1933). Studies in reflected seismic waves. *Beitr. Geophys.* **38**, 228–56.

BLAKE, F. G., Jr. (1952). Spherical wave propagation in solid media. *J. Acoust. Soc. Amer.* **24**, 211–15.

GUTENBERG, B. (1952). *SV* and *SH*. *Trans. Amer. Geophys. Un.* **33**, 573–84.

JEFFREYS, Sir H. (1957). Elastic waves in a continuously stratified medium. *Mon. Not. R. Astr. Soc.*, Geophys. Suppl., **7**, 332–7.

JEFFREYS, Sir H. and LAPWOOD, E. R. (1957). The reflexion of a pulse within a sphere. *Proc. Roy. Soc.* A, **241**, 455–79.

PETRASHEN, G. N. (1957). *Results of a quantitative investigation into the dynamics of seismic waves.* Leningrad: State University Press.

V.D. WAERDEN, B. L. (1957). Reflection and refraction of seismic waves. *Shell Development Company*, pp. 1–54.

DIX, C. H. (1961). The reflected seismic pulse. *J. Geophys. Res.* **66**, 227–33.

HUDSON, J. A. (1962). The total internal reflection of *SH* waves. *Geophys. J., R. Astr. Soc.* **6**, 509–31.

Seismic ray theory (§§7.1–7.5)

HERGLOTZ, G. (1907). Über das Benndorfsche Problem der Fortpflanzungsgeschwindigkeit der Erdbebenstrahlen. *Phys. Z.* **8**, 145–7.

BATEMAN, H. (1910). The solution of the integral equation which connects the velocity of propagation of an earthquake wave in the interior of the Earth with the times which the disturbance takes to travel to different stations on the Earth's surface. *Phil. Mag.* (6), **19**, 576–87.

KNOTT, C. G. (1919). The propagation of earthquake waves through the Earth and connected problems. *Proc. Roy. Soc. Edinb.* **39**, 157–208.

JEFFREYS, H. (1926). On near earthquakes. *Mon. Not. R. Astr. Soc.*, Geophys. Suppl., **1**, 385–402.

SLICHTER, L. B. (1932). The theory of the interpretation of seismic travel-time curves in horizontal structures. *Physics*, **3**, 273–95.

JEFFREYS, H. (1934). Upward curvature in seismic travel-times. *Mon. Not. R. Astr. Soc.*, Geophys. Suppl., **3**, 201–2.

LEHMANN, I. (1937). Seismic time-curves and depth determination. *Mon. Not. R. Astr. Soc.*, Geophys. Suppl., **4**, 250–71.

BULLEN, K. E. (1945). Features of the travel-time curves of seismic rays. *Mon. Not. R. Astr. Soc.*, Geophys. Suppl., **5**, 91–8.

FU, C. Y. (1947). On seismic rays and waves. *Bull. Seismol. Soc. Amer.* **37**, 331–46.

BULLEN, K. E. (1953). Parameters of seismic rays. *J. Roy. Soc. N.S.W.* **87**, 21–3.

BULLEN, K. E. (1955). Features of seismic pP and PP rays. *Mon. Not. R. Astr. Soc.*, Geophys. Suppl., **7**, 49–59.

WILLMORE, P. L. and HODGSON, J. H. (1955). Charts for measuring azimuth and distance and for tracing seismic rays through the Earth. *Dom. Observ. Ottawa, Publ.* **16**, 405–14.

BÅTH, M. (1957). Shadow zones, travel times, and energies of longitudinal seismic waves in the presence of an asthenosphere low-velocity layer. *Trans. Amer. Geophys. Un.* **38**, 529–38.

TOLSTOY, I. (1959). Modes, rays, and travel times. *J. Geophys. Res.* **64**, 815–21.

BULLEN, K. E. (1960). A new method of deriving seismic velocity distributions from travel-time data. *Geophys. J., R. Astr. Soc.* **3**, 258–69.

BULLEN, K. E. (1961). Seismic ray theory. *Geophys. J., Roy. Astr. Soc.* **4**, 93–105.

Amplitudes of seismic waves (§§ 8.1–8.8)

GEIGER, L. and GUTENBERG, B. (1912). *Nachr. Ges. Wiss. Göttingen*, Math.-Phys. Klasse, pp. 121–206, 623–75.

WRINCH, D. and JEFFREYS, H. (1923). On the seismic waves from the Oppau explosion of 1921 September 21. *Mon. Not. R. Astr. Soc.*, Geophys. Suppl., **1**, 15–22.

JEFFREYS, H. (1926). On the amplitudes of bodily seismic waves. *Mon. Not. R. Astr. Soc.*, Geophys. Suppl. **1**, 334–48.

JEFFREYS, H. (1926). On compressional waves in two superposed layers. *Proc. Camb. Phil. Soc.* **22**, 472–81.

VALLE, P. E. (1943). Sull'energia associata alle onde sismiche SKS ed $SKKS$. *Ric. sci.* **21**, 3–9.

GUTENBERG, B. (1944). Energy ratio of reflected and refracted seismic waves. *Bull. Seismol. Soc. Amer.* **34**, 85–102.

DANA, S. W. (1945). The amplitudes of seismic waves reflected and refracted at the Earth's central core. *Bull. Seismol. Soc. Amer.* **35**, 27–35.

ERGIN, K. (1952). Observations on the recorded ground motion due to P, PcP, S and ScS. *Bull. Seismol. Soc. Amer.* **42**, 263–70.

DIX, C. H. (1955). The mechanism of generation of long waves from explosions. *Geophysics*, **20**, 87–103.

DE NOYER, J. (1958). Determination of the energy in body and surface waves. Part I. *Bull. Seismol. Soc. Amer.* **48**, 355–68.

STONELEY, R. (1958). The variation of amplitude and energy with depth in Love waves. *Contributions in geophysics*, pp. 38–43. London: Pergamon.

BULLEN, K. E. (1960). Note on cusps in seismic travel-times. *Geophys. J., R. Astr. Soc.* **3**, 354–9.

Instrumental seismology (§§ 9.1–9.9)

OMORI, F. (1901). Results of the horizontal pendulum observations of earthquakes, July 1898 to December 1899, Tokyo. *Publ. Earthq. Invest. Comm., Tokyo*, **5**, 1–82.

WIECHERT, E. (1903). Theorie der automatischen Seismographen. *Abh. Ges. Wiss. Göttingen*, Math.-Phys. Klasse, **2**, 1–128.

GALITZIN, B. (1914). *Vorlesungen über Seismometrie*. Leipzig: Teubner.

ANDERSON, J. A. and WOOD, H. O. (1925). Description and theory of the torsion seismometer. *Bull. Seismol. Soc. Amer.* **15**, 1–72.

ANDERSON, J. A., LABROUSTE, H., LACOSTE, J., NAVARO-NEUMANN, S., DE QUERVAIN, A., RÉMY, A., ROTHÉ, E., SHAW, J. J. and WOOD, H. O. (1927). État actuel des instruments séismologiques. *Bur. Centr. Séism. Internat.* A, Fasc. 4, 149 pp.

BENIOFF, H. (1932). A new vertical seismograph. *Bull. Seismol. Soc. Amer.* **22**, 155–69.

BENIOFF, H. (1935). A linear strain seismograph. *Bull. Seismol. Soc. Amer.* **25**, 283–309.

LEHMANN, I. (1949). The reliability of European seismological stations. *Geodaet. Inst. Skr.* no. 22, 66 pp.

WILLMORE, P. L. (1950). The theory and design of two types of portable seismograph. *Mon. Not. R. Astr. Soc.*, Geophys. Suppl., **6**, 129–37.

EWING, M. and PRESS, F. (1954). Mantle Rayleigh waves from the Kam chatka earthquakes of November 4, 1952. *Bull. Seismol. Soc. Amer.* **44**, 471–80.

BENIOFF, H. (1955). Earthquake seismographs and associated instruments. *Advanc. Geophys.* **2**, 219–75.

KIRNOS, D. P. (1955). Some problems of instrumental seismology. *Trans. Geophys. Inst. Acad. Sci. U.S.S.R.* **27**, 154.

COULOMB, J. (1956). Séismométrie. *Encyclopedia of physics*, **47**, 24–74. Berlin: Springer-Verlag.

GAMBURTSEV, G. A. (1957). Some new methods of seismological investigation. *Bull. Acad. Sci. U.S.S.R.*, Geophys. Ser. (English transl.), **12**, 1–8.

BENIOFF, H. (1959). Fused-quartz extensometer for secular, tidal, and seismic strains. *Bull. Geol. Soc. Amer.* **70**, 1019–32.

EWING, M., MUELLER, M., LANDISMAN, M. and SATÔ, Y. (1959). Transient analysis of earthquake and explosion arrivals. *Geofis. pur. appl.* **44**, 83–118.

PANEL ON SEISMIC IMPROVEMENT (1959). *The need for fundamental research is seismology*. U.S. Dept. of State Publ.

WILLMORE, P. L. (1959). The detection of earth movements. *Methods and techniques in geophysics*, pp. 230–76. New York: Interscience.

BENIOFF, H. (1960). Long period seismographs. *Bull. Seismol. Soc. Amer.* **50**, 1–12.

POMEROY, P. W. and SUTTON, G. H. (1960). The use of galvanometers as band-rejection filters in electromagnetic seismographs. *Bull. Seismol. Soc. Amer.* **50**, 135–51.

WILLMORE, P. L. (1961). Some properties of heavily damped electromagnetic seismographs. *Geophys. J., R. Astr. Soc.* **4**, 389–404.

Seismic phases and travel-time tables (§§ 10.1–10.9)

ZÖPPRITZ, K. (1907). Über Erdbebenwellen. II. Laufzeitkurven. *Nachr. Ges. Wiss. Göttingen*, Math.-Phys. Klasse, pp. 529–49.

GUTENBERG, B. (1914). Über Erdbebenwellen. VIIA. Beobachtungen an Registrierungen von Fernbeben in Göttingen und Folgerungen über die Konstitution des Erdkörpers. *Nachr. Ges. Wiss. Göttingen*, Math.-Phys. Klasse, pp. 1–52 and 125–76.

ANGENHEISTER, G. (1921). A study of Pacific earthquakes. *N.Z. J. Sci. Tech.* **4**, 209–31.

JEFFREYS, H. (1924). On the Radau transformation in the theory of the figure of the Earth. *Mon. Not. R. Astr. Soc.*, Geophys. Suppl., **1**, 121–4.

MOHOROVIČIĆ, A. (1925). Tables. *Bur. Centr. Séism. Internat.* A, Fasc. 3, 59 pp.

TURNER, H. H. (1926). Revised seismological tables and the Earth's liquid core. *Mon. Not. R. Astr. Soc.*, Geophys. Suppl., **1**, 425–46.

MACELWANE, J. B. (1930). The South Pacific earthquake of June 26, 1924. *Beitr. Geophys.* **28**, 165–227.

LEHMANN, I. (1930). *P'* as read from the records of the earthquake of June 16th 1929. *Beitr. Geophys.* **26**, 402–12.

LEHMANN, I. (1931). The earthquake of 22 III 1928. *Beitr. Geophys.* **28**, 151–64.

SCRASE, F. J. (1931). The reflected waves from deep focus earthquakes. *Proc. Roy. Soc.* A, **132**, 213–35.

JEFFREYS, H. (1932). An alternative to the rejection of observations. *Proc. Roy. Soc.* A, **137**, 78–87.

GUTENBERG, B. and RICHTER, C. F. (1933). Advantages of using geocentric latitude in calculating distances. *Beitr. Geophys.* **40**, 380–9.

WADATI, K. and others (1933, 1934). On the travel time of earthquake waves. *Geophys. Mag., Tokyo*, **7**, 87–153, 269–90; **8**, 187–94.

BULLEN, K. E. (1934). On the errors in calculations of epicentral distances in earthquakes. *Mon. Not. R. Astr. Soc.*, Geophys. Suppl., **3**, 190–201.

BRUNNER, G. J. (1935). *Focal depth-time-distance chart.* New York: Wiley.

JEFFREYS, H. and BULLEN, K. E. (1935). Times of transmission of earthquake waves. *Bur. Centr. Séism. Internat.* A, Fasc. **11**, 202 pp.

LEHMANN, I. (1935). Seismic time-curves for epicentral distances around 80°. *Bur. Centr. Séism. Internat.* A, **12**, 1–24.

JEFFREYS, H. (1935). On the ellipticity correction in seismology. *Mon. Not. R. Astr. Soc.*, Geophys. Suppl., **3**, 271–4.

JEFFREYS, H. (1936). On travel times in seismology. *Bur. Centr. Séism. Internat.* A, **14**, 1–86.

BULLEN, K. E. (1938). *Tables for converting geographic into geocentric angular distances.* (With introduction by H. Jeffreys.) Brit. Ass., Gray-Milne Trust, 24 pp.

JEFFREYS, H. (1938). Southern earthquakes and the core waves. *Mon. Not. R. Astr. Soc.*, Geophys. Suppl., **4**, 281–308.

GUTENBERG, B. and RICHTER, C. F. (1934, 1935, 1936, 1939). On seismic waves. *Beitr. Geophys.* **43**, 56–133; **45**, 280–360; **47**, 73–131; **54**, 94–136.

BULLEN, K. E. (1937, 1938, 1939). The ellipticity correction to travel-times of *P* and *S* earthquake waves. *Mon. Not. R. Astr. Soc.*, Geophys. Suppl., **4**, 143–57, 317–31, 332–5, 469–71; and later papers on ellipticity corrections.

MORITA, M. and YOSIMURA, Y. (1939). On seismic waves at large distances. *Geophys. Mag., Tokyo*, **13**, 163–91.

STONELEY, R. (1939). On the *L* phase of seismograms. *Mon. Not. R. Astr. Soc.*, Geophys. Suppl., **4**, 562–9.

TILLOTSON, E. (1939). *PcP* and *ScS*. *Bull. Seismol. Soc. Amer.* **29**, 345–408.

JEFFREYS, H. and BULLEN, K. E. (1940, 1958). *Seismological tables.* Brit. Ass., Gray-Milne Trust, 50 pp.

JEFFREYS, H. (1942). The times of *sP* and *sPKP*. *Mon. Not. R. Astr. Soc.*, Geophys. Suppl., **5**, 31–2.

BULLEN, K. E. (1942). The ellipticities of surfaces of equal density in the Earth's interior. *Trans. Roy. Soc. N.Z.* **72**, 141–3.

BULLEN, K. E. (1944). The Radau–Darwin approximation in the theory of the figure of the Earth. *Trans. Roy. Soc. N.Z.* **73**, 267–9.

BYERLY, P., MEI, A. I. and ROMNEY, C. (1949). Dependence on azimuth of the ampitudes of *P* and *PP*. *Bull. Seismol. Soc. Amer.* **39**, 269–84.

JEFFREYS, H. (1952). The times of *P* up to 30°. *Mon. Not. R. Astr. Soc.*, Geophys. Suppl., **6**, 348–64.

JEFFREYS, H. (1954). The times of *P* in Japanese and European earthquakes. *Mon. Not. R. Astr. Soc.*, Geophys. Suppl., **6**, 557–65.

KISHIMOTO, Y. (1954–6). Seismometric investigations of the Earth's interior. Parts I, II and III. *Mem. Coll. Sci. Kyoto*, **27**, 125–43, 243–88; **28**, 117–42.

JEFFREYS, Sir H. (1958). The times of *P* up to 30° (second paper). *Geophys. J., R. Astr. Soc.* **1**, 154–61.

KONDORSKAYA, N. V. (1959). Travel times and some dynamic characteristics of seismic waves. *Bur. Centr. Séism. Internat.* A, **20**, 113–21.

BOLT, B. A. (1960). The revision of earthquake epicentres, focal depths and origin-times using a high-speed computer. *Geophys. J., R. Astr. Soc.* **3**, 433–40.

FLINN, E. A. (1960). Local earthquake location with an electronic computer. *Bull. Seismol. Soc. Amer.* **50**, 467–70.

INTERNATIONAL SEISMOLOGICAL SUMMARY (1961). *The geocentric direction cosines of seismological observatories.* Compiled by staff of the I.S.S., 4th ed. Surrey, Kew Observatory.

Seismological observatory (§§ 11.1–11.3)

WOOD, H. O. (1942). A chronological conspectus of seismologic stations. *Bull. Seismol. Soc. Amer.* **32**, 97–159.

RICHTER, C. F. (1948). International recovery in seismology. *Sci. Mon.* **66**, 67–70.

GUTENBERG, B. (1949). Unexplained phases in seismograms. *Bull. Seismol. Soc. Amer.* **39**, 79–92.

STONELEY, R. (1951). The International Seismological Summary; an example of international co-operation in Science. *Pres. Address, Ass. Internat. de Séism., Neuvième Conf., Brussels.*

HODGSON, J. H. and others (Editors) (1929 to date). *Bibliography of seismology.* Publ. Dom. Obs. Ottawa.

INTERNATIONAL SEISMOLOGICAL SUMMARY COMMITTEE (1961). Report of Meeting, Paris, July 1961. *Int. Un. Geod. Geophys.*, I.A.S.P.I.E. Monogr. 14, 1–33.

Theory of near earthquakes (§ 12.1)

LEE, A. W. (1932). The determination of thicknesses of the continental layers from travel times of seismic waves. *Mon. Not. R. Astr. Soc.*, Geophys. Suppl., 3, 13–21.

SEZAWA, K. and KANAI, K. (1935). The effect of sharpness of discontinuities on the transmission and reflection of elastic waves. *Bull. Earthq. Res. Inst. Tokyo*, 13, 750–6.

FU, C. Y. (1950). Some problems of the propagation of elastic waves in a horizontally stratified medium. *J. Chin. Geophys. Soc.* 2, 40–59.

PRESS, F., EWING, M. and TOLSTOY, I. (1950). The Airy phase of shallow-focus submarine earthquakes. *Bull. Seismol. Soc. Amer.* 40, 111–48.

EWING, M. and PRESS, F. (1950). Crustal structure and surface-wave dispersion. *Bull. Seismol. Soc. Amer.* 40, 271–80.

STEINHART, J. S. and MEYER, R. P. (1961). *Explosion studies of continental structure.* Washington: Carnegie Inst. Publ. 622.

Near-earthquake (etc.) empirical studies (§§ 12.2–12.4)

MOHOROVIČIĆ, A. (1909). Das Beben vom 8. x. 1909. *Jb. met. Obs. Zagreb*, 9, 1–63.

CONRAD, V. (1925). Laufzeitkurven des Tauerenbebens vom 28. November, 1923. *Mitt. ErdbKomm. Wien*, 59, 23 pp.

JEFFREYS, H. (1927). On two British earthquakes. *Mon. Not. R. Astr. Soc.*, Geophys. Suppl., 1, 483–94.

WOOD, H. O. and RICHTER, C. F. (1931). A study of blasting recorded in southern California. *Bull. Seismol. Soc. Amer.* 21, 28–46.

STONELEY, R. (1931). Some near earthquakes reported in the International Seismological Summary. *Mon. Not. R. Astr. Soc.*, Geophys. Suppl., 2, 349–62.

JEFFREYS, H. (1937). On the materials and density of the Earth's crust. *Mon. Not. R. Astr. Soc.*, Geophys. Suppl., 4, 50–61.

JEFFREYS, H. (1937). A further study of near earthquakes. *Mon. Not. R. Astr. Soc.*, Geophys. Suppl., 4, 196–225.

LEET, L. DON (1938). Travel-times for New England. *Bull. Seismol. Soc. Amer.* 28, 45–56.

BULLEN, K. E. (1938). The phase S^* in New Zealand earthquakes. *N.Z. J. Sci. Tech.* 19, 519–22.

BULLEN, K. E. (1938). The Wairoa earthquake of 1932 September 15. *N.Z. J. Sci. Tech.* 20, 31 B–43 B.

BYERLY, P. (1938). The earthquake of July 6, 1934: amplitudes and first motion. *Bull. Seismol. Soc. Amer.* 28, 1–13.

BULLEN, K. E. (1939). The crustal structure of the New Zealand region as inferred from studies of earthquake waves. *Proc. Sixth Pacific Sci. Congress*, pp. 103–10.

Rozova, E. A. (1939). Contribution to the question of the deep-seated structure of the Caucasus. *Trans. Geophys. Inst. Acad. Sci. U.S.S.R.* **94**, 1–15.

Jeffreys, H. (1940). On *P* up to 20° in North America. *Bull. Seismol. Soc. Amer.* **30**, 225–34.

Gutenberg, B. (1943). Seismological evidence for roots of mountains. *Bull. Geol. Soc. Amer.* **54**, 473–98.

Byerly, P. (1946). The seismic waves from the Port Chicago explosion. *Bull. Seismol. Soc. Amer.* **36**, 331–48.

Jeffreys, H. (1947). On the Burton-on-Trent explosion of 1944 November 27. *Mon. Not. R. Astr. Soc.*, Geophys. Suppl., **5**, 99–104.

Jeffreys, H. (1947). Seismic waves in western and central Europe. *Mon. Not. R. Astr. Soc.*, Geophys. Suppl., **5**, 105–19.

Byerly, P. (1947). The periods of local earthquake waves in central California. *Bull. Seismol. Soc. Amer.* **37**, 291–7.

Mihailović, J. (1947). Caractère séismique de la côte sud de l'Adriatique yougoslave. *Bull. Acad. serbe Sci. math. nat.*

Lehmann, I. (1948). On two explosions in Danish waters in the autumn of 1946. *Geofis. pur. appl.* **12**, Fasc. 3–4, pp. 1–19.

Willmore, P. L. (1949). Seismic experiments on the North German explosions 1946 to 1947. *Phil. Trans.* A, **242**, 123–51.

Bullard, E. C. and others (1950). The granitic layer of the earth's crust. *Nature, Lond.*, **166**, 1053.

Richter, C. F. (1950). Velocities of *P* at short distances. *Bull. Seismol. Soc. Amer.* **40**, 281–89.

Valle, P. E. (1951). Sulla struttura dela crosta terrestre nel Mediterraneo centro-occidentale e nell'Adriatico. *Ann. Geofis.* **4**, 399–409; and earlier papers.

Gutenberg, B. (1951). Revised travel times in Southern California. *Bull. Seismol. Soc. Amer.* **41**, 143–64.

Research Group for Explosion Seismology, Tokyo (1951–62). Explosion-seismic observations. Papers in *Bull. Earthq. Res. Inst., Tokyo*, vols. 29–40.

Willmore, P. L., Hales, A. L. and Gane, P. G. (1952). A seismic investigation of crustal structure in the Western Transvaal. *Bull. Seismol. Soc. Amer.* **42**, 53–80.

Hodgson, J. H. (1953). A seismic survey in the Canadian Shield. *Ottawa Dom. Observ. Publ.* **16**, 113–63, 169–81.

Tatel, H. E., Adams, L. H. and Tuve, M. A. (1953). Studies of the Earth's crust using waves from explosions. *Proc. Amer. Phil. Soc.* **97**, 658–69.

Wilson, J. Tuzo (1954). The development and structure of the crust. *The Earth as a Planet*, pp. 138–214. Chicago: University Press.

Benioff, H. (1955). Seismic evidence for crustal structure and tectonic activity. *Spec. Pap. Geol. Soc. Amer.* **62**, 61–74.

Buné, V. I. and Butovskaya, E. M. (1955). Travel-time curves and the Earth's crustal structure in central Asia according to recordings of powerful explosions. *Trans. Geophys. Inst. Acad. Sci. U.S.S.R.* **157**, 142–56.

GUTENBERG, B. (1955). Channel waves in the Earth's crust. *Geophysics*, 20, 283–94.

LAPWOOD, E. R. (1955). Study of a series of Japanese earthquakes. *Mon. Not. R. Astr. Soc.*, Geophys. Suppl., 7, 135–46.

SHOR, G. G., Jr. (1955). Deep reflections from Southern California blasts. *Trans. Amer. Geophys. Un.* 36, 133–8.

TATEL, H. E. and TUVE, M. A. (1955). Seismic exploration of a continental crust. *Spec. Pap. Geol. Soc. Amer.* 62, 35–50.

VANĚK, J. (1955). Le études séismologiques en Tchechoslovaquie de 1951 à 1953. *C.R. I.A.S.P.I.E.* 11, 336–9.

BYERLY, P. (1957). Subcontinental structure in the light of seismological evidence. *Advances in geophysics*, 3, 105–52. New York: Academic Press.

EIBY, G. A. and DIBBLE, R. R. (1957). Crustal structure project. *N.Z. Dept. Sci. Indust. Res.*, Geophys. Memoir, no. 5.

CALOI, P. (1958). The crust of the Earth, from the Apennines to the Atlantic. *Z. Geophys.* 24, 65–95.

RIZNICHENKO, Y. V. (1958). Study of the structure of the Earth's crust during the IGY. *Bull. Acad. Sci. U.S.S.R.*, Geophys. Ser., 2, 1–14.

ROTHÉ, J.-P. (1958). Quelques expériences sur la structure de la croute terrestre en Europe Occidentale. *Contributions in Geophysics*, pp. 135–51. London: Pergamon.

HALES, A. L. and SACKS, I. S. (1959). Evidence for an intermediate layer from crustal structure studies in the eastern Transvaal. *Geophys. J., R. Astr. Soc.* 2, 15–33.

WOOLLARD, G. P. (1959). Crustal structure from gravity and seismic measurements. *J. Geophys. Res.* 64, 1521–44.

AOKI, H. (1960). Seismic waves in the region near explosive origin. *J. Earth Sci. Nagoya Univ.* 9, 120–73.

HALES, A. L. (1960). Seismic and gravity research on crustal structure in South Africa. *J. Geophys. Res.* 65, 2155–68.

BULLARD, E. C. and GRIGGS, D. T. (1961). The nature of the Mohorovičić discontinuity. *Geophys. J., R. Astr. Soc.* 6, 118–23.

HUNKINS, K. (1961). Seismic studies of the Arctic ocean floor. *Geology of the Arctic*, pp. 645–65. Toronto: University Press.

KOSMINSKAYA, I. P. and KRAKSHINA, R. M. (1961). On superficial reflections from the Mohorovičić discontinuity. *Bur. Centr. Séism. Internat.* A, 21, 39–54.

TRYGGVASON, E. and BÅTH, M. (1961). Upper crustal structure of Iceland. *J. Geophys. Res.* 66, 1913–26.

JEFFREYS, Sir H. (1962). Some normal earthquakes. *Geophys. J., R. Astr. Soc.* 6, 493–508.

LOMNITZ, C. (1962). On Andean structure. *J. Geophys. Res.* 67, 351–63.

Surface-wave empirical studies; oceanic and continental structure (§§ 12.5–12.6)

TAMS, E. (1921). Über die Fortpflanzungsgeschwindigkeit der seismischen Oberflächenwellen. *Zbl. Miner.* pp. 44–75.

MACELWANE, J. B. (1923). A study of the relation between the periods of elastic waves and the distance travelled by them, based upon the seismographic records of the California earthquake, January 31, 1922. *Bull. Seismol. Soc. Amer.* **13**, 13–69.

CARDER, D. S. (1934). Seismic surface waves and the crustal structure of the Pacific region. *Bull. Seismol. Soc. Amer.* **24**, 231–302.

SEZAWA, K. (1935). Rayleigh and Love waves transmitted through the Pacific Ocean and the continents. *Bull. Earthq. Res. Inst. Tokyo*, **13**, 245–9.

JEFFREYS, H. (1939). Some Japanese deep-focus earthquakes. *Mon. Not. R. Astr. Soc.*, Geophys. Suppl., **4**, 424–60.

JEFFREYS, H. (1939). Times of transmission for small distances and focal depths. *Mon. Not. R. Astr. Soc.*, Geophys. Suppl., **4**, 571–8.

BULLEN, K. E. (1939). On Rayleigh waves across the Pacific Ocean. *Mon. Not. R. Astr. Soc.*, Geophys. Suppl., **4**, 579–82.

WILSON, JAMES T. (1940). The Love waves of the South Atlantic earthquake of August 28, 1933. *Bull. Seismol. Soc. Amer.* **30**, 273–301.

DE LISLE, J. F. (1941). On dispersion of Rayleigh waves from the North Pacific earthquake of November 10, 1938. *Bull. Seismol. Soc. Amer.* **31**, 303–7.

WILSON, JAMES T. and BAYKAL, O. (1948). Crustal structure of the North Atlantic Basin as determined from Rayleigh-wave dispersion. *Bull. Seismol. Soc. Amer.* **38**, 41–53.

STONELEY, R. (1948). The continental layers of Europe. *Bull. Seismol. Soc. Amer.* **38**, 263–74.

CALOI, P., MARCELLI, L. and PANNOCCHIA, G. (1949, 1950). Papers on structure of Atlantic Ocean basin. *Ann. Geofis.* **2**, 347–58; **3**, 215–22.

ROTHÉ, J.-P. (1951). La structure de l'Atlantique. *Ann. Geofis.* **4**, 27–125.

GUTENBERG, B. (1951). Crustal layers of the continents and oceans. *Bull. Geol. Soc. Amer.* **62**, 427–40.

EWING, M. and PRESS, F. (1952). Crustal structure and surface wave dispersion, Part II. *Bull. Seismol. Soc. Amer.* **42**, 315–25.

BÅTH, M. (1954). The elastic waves Lg and Rg along Euro-Asiatic paths. *Ark. Geofys.* **2**, 295–342.

BRILLIANT, R. M. and EWING, M. (1954). Dispersion of Rayleigh waves across the United States. *Bull. Seismol. Soc. Amer.* **44**, 149–58.

BULLARD, E. C. (Editor) (1954). A discussion on the floor of the Atlantic ocean. *Proc. Roy. Soc. A*, **222**, 287–407.

EWING, M., SUTTON, G. H. and OFFICER, C. B., Jr. (1954). Seismic refraction measurements in the Atlantic ocean, Part VI. *Bull. Seismol. Soc. Amer.* **44**, 21–38.

OLIVER, J., EWING, M. and PRESS, F. (1955). Crustal structure of the Arctic regions from the Lg phase. *Bull. Geol. Soc. Amer.* **66**, 1063–74.

EWING, W. M. and PRESS, F. (1956). Structure of the Earth's crust. *Encyclopedia of Physics*, **47**, 246–57. Berlin: Springer-Verlag.

RAITT, R. W. (1956). Seismic refraction studies of the Pacific Ocean basin. *Bull. Geol. Soc. Amer.* **67**, 1623–40.

STONELEY, R. (1956). The thickness of continents. *Vistas in Astronomy,* **2**, 842–9. London: Pergamon.

HILL, M. N. (1957). Recent geophysical exploration of the ocean floor. *Phys. and Chem. of the Earth,* **2**, 129–63. London: Pergamon.

OLIVER, J. and EWING, M. (1957). Higher modes of continental Rayleigh waves. *Bull. Seismol. Soc. Amer.* **47**, 187–204.

GASKELL, T. F., HILL, M. N. and SWALLOW, J. C. (1958). Seismic measurements made by H.M.S. Challenger in the Atlantic, Pacific and Indian Oceans and in the Mediterranean Sea, 1950–53. *Phil. Trans.* A, **251**, 23–83.

OLIVER, J. and EWING, M. (1958). Normal modes of continental surface waves. *Bull. Seismol. Soc. Amer.* **48**, 33–49.

BÅTH, M. (1959). Seismic surface wave dispersion—a world-wide survey. *Geofis. pura appl.* **43**, 131–47.

EWING, M. and PRESS, F. (1959). Determination of crustal structure from phase velocity of Rayleigh waves. Part III. *Bull. Geol. Soc. Amer.* **70**, 229–44.

EVISON, F. F., INGHAM, C. E., ORR, R. H. and LE FORT, J. H. (1960). Thickness of the Earth's crust in Antarctica and the surrounding oceans. *Geophys. J., R. Astr. Soc.* **3**, 289–306. (Comment by BENTLEY, C. R. and OSTENSO, N. A. (1962). *Geophys. J., R. Astr. Soc.* **6**, 292–8.)

ARKHANGEL'SKAYA, V. M. (1960). Dispersion of surface waves and crustal structure. *Bull. Acad. Sci. U.S.S.R.,* Geophys. Ser. (English trans.), pp. 904–27.

CISTERNAS, A. (1961). Crustal structure of the Andes from Rayleigh wave dispersion. *Bull. Seismol. Soc. Amer.* **51**, 381–8.

KOGAN, S. D., PASSECHNIK, I. P. and SULTANOV, D. D. (1961). Seismic observations in Antarctica. *Bull. Acad. Sci. U.S.S.R.,* Geophys. Ser. (English trans.), pp. 146–9.

KOVACH, R. L. and PRESS, F. (1961). Rayleigh wave dispersion and crustal structure in the eastern Pacific and Indian Oceans. *Geophys. J., R. Astr. Soc.* **4**, 202–16.

KOVACH, R. L. and PRESS, F. (1961). Surface wave dispersion and crustal structure in Antarctica and the surrounding oceans. *Ann. Geofis.* **14**, 211–24.

SCHECHKOV, B. N. (1961). Structure of the Earth's crust in Eurasia from the dispersion of surface waves. *Bull. Acad. Sci. U.S.S.R.,* Geophys. Ser. (English trans.), pp. 450–3.

TRYGGVASON, E. (1961). Crustal thicknesses in Fennoscandia from phase velocities of Rayleigh waves. *Ann. Geofis.* **14**, 267–93.

OLIVER, J. (1962). A summary of observed seismic wave dispersion. *Bull. Seismol. Soc. Amer.* **52**, 81–6.

THOMSON, A. A. and EVISON, F. F. (1962). Thickness of the Earth's crust in New Zealand. *N.Z. J. Geol. Geophys.* **5**, 29–45.

TRYGGVASON, E. (1962). Crustal structure of the Iceland region from dispersion of surface waves. *Bull. Seismol. Soc. Amer.* **52**, 359–88.

Physical properties of surface layers (§12.7)

ADAMS, L. H. and WILLIAMSON, E. D. (1923). The compressibility of minerals and rocks at high pressures. *J. Franklin Inst.* **195**, 475–529.

ADAMS, L. H. and GIBSON, R. E. (1926). The compressibilities of dunite and of basalt glass, and their bearing on the composition of the Earth. *Proc. Nat. Acad. Sci., Wash.*, **12**, 275–83.

BRIDGMAN, P. W. (1931). *The physics of high pressure.* London: Bell.

ZISMAN, W. A. (1933). Young's modulus and Poisson's ratio with reference to geophysical applications. *Proc. Nat. Acad. Sci., Wash.*, **19**, 653–65.

IDE, J. M. (1936). Comparison of statically and dynamically determined Young's modulus of rocks. *Proc. Nat. Acad. Sci., Wash.*, **22**, 81–92.

GRIGGS, D. (1936). Deformation of rocks under high confining pressures. *J. Geol.* **44**, 541–77.

BIRCH, F. and DOW, R. B. (1936). Compressibility of rocks and glasses at high temperatures and pressures: seismological application. *Bull. Geol. Soc. Amer.* **47**, 1235–56.

BIRCH, F. (1938). Travel times for shear waves in a granitic layer. *Bull. Seismol. Soc. Amer.* **28**, 49–56.

BIRCH, F. and BANCROFT, D. (1938). The effect of pressure on the rigidity of rocks. *J. Geol.* **46**, 59–87, 113–41.

BIRCH, F., SCHAIRER, J. F. and SPICER, H. C. (Editors) (1942). Handbook of physical constants. *Spec. Pap. Geol. Soc. Amer.* no. 36.

BRIDGMAN, P. W. (1946). Recent work in the field of high pressures. *Rev. Mod. Phys.* **18**, no. 1, 1–93.

BRIDGMAN, P. W. (1948). The compression of 39 substances to 100,000 kg./cm.^{2}. *Proc. Amer. Acad. Arts Sci.* **76**, 55–70.

BRIDGMAN, P. W. (1949). Linear compression of 30,000 kg./cm.^{2}, including relatively incompressible substances. *Proc. Amer. Acad. Arts Sci.* **77**, 187–234.

ADAMS, L. H. (1951). Elastic properties of materials of the Earth's crust. *Internal Constitution of Earth*, 2nd ed, pp. 50–80. New York: Dover.

BIRCH, F. (1955). Physics of the crust. *Spec. Pap. Geol. Soc. Amer.* **62**, 101–17.

BIRCH, F. (1956). Interpretation of the seismic structure of the crust in the light of experimental studies of wave velocities in rocks. *Contributions in geophysics*, **1**, 158–70. London: Pergamon.

BIRCH, F. (1960–61). The velocity of compressional waves in rocks to 10 kilobars. Parts 1 and 2. *J. Geophys. Res.* **65**, 1083–1102; **66**, 2199–2224.

BOTT, M. H. P. (1961). The granitic layer. *Geophys. J., R. Astr. Soc.* **5**, 207–16.

The Mohole (§12.8)

I.A.S.P.I.E. (1958). Resolution on drilling to the Mohorovičić discontinuity. *C.R. I.A.S.P.I.E.* **12**, 210.

BULLARD, Sir EDWARD (1961). The Mohole. *Endeavour*, **20**, 188–96.

P and S velocity distributions in the Earth (§§ 13.1–13.2)

OLDHAM, R. D. (1906). Constitution of the interior of the Earth as revealed by earthquakes. *Quart. J. Geol. Soc.* **62**, 456–75.

BYERLY, P. (1926). The Montana earthquake of June 28, 1925. *Bull. Seismol. Soc. Amer.* **16**, 209–65.

LEHMANN, I. (1934). Transmission times for seismic waves for epicentral distances around 20°. *Geodaet. Inst. Skr.* **5**, 44 pp.

LEHMANN, I. (1936). *P'. Bur. Centr. Séism. Internat.* A, **14**, 3–31.

BULLEN, K. E. (1938). Composition of the Earth at a depth of 500–700 km. *Nature, Lond.*, **142**, 671.

GUTENBERG, B. and RICHTER, C. F. (1938). *P'* and the Earth's core. *Mon. Not. R. Astr. Soc.*, Geophys. Suppl., **4**, 363–72.

GUTENBERG, B. and RICHTER, C. F. (1939). New evidence for a change in physical conditions at depths near 100 kilometers. *Bull. Seismol. Soc. Amer.* **29**, 531–7.

JEFFREYS, H. (1939). The times of *P*, *S* and *SKS* and the velocities of *P* and *S*. *Mon. Not. R. Astr. Soc.*, Geophys. Suppl., **4**, 498–533.

JEFFREYS, H. (1939). The times of *PcP* and *ScS*. *Mon. Not. R. Astr. Soc.*, Geophys. Suppl., **4**, 537–47.

JEFFREYS, H. (1939). The times of the core waves. *Mon. Not. R. Astr. Soc.*, Geophys. Suppl., **4**, 548–61, 594–615.

GUTENBERG, B. (1948). On the layer of relatively low wave velocity at a depth of about 80 kilometers. *Bull. Seismol. Soc. Amer.* **38**, 121–48.

GUTENBERG, B. (1951). *PKKP, P'P'*, and the Earth's core. *Trans. Amer. Geophys. Un.* **32**, 373–90.

GUTENBERG, B. (1953). Wave velocities at depths between 50 and 600 kilometers. *Bull. Seismol. Soc. Amer.* **43**, 223–32.

LEHMANN, I. (1953). On the shadow of the Earth's core. *Bull. Seismol. Soc. Amer.* **43**, 291–306.

CALOI, P. (1954). L'astenosfera come canale-guida dell'energia sismica. *Ann. Geofis.* **7**, 491–501.

LEHMANN, I. (1955). The times of *P* and *S* in north-eastern America. *Ann. Geofis.* **8**, 351–70.

BÅTH, M. (1956). Some consequences of the existence of low-velocity layers. *Ann. geofis.* **9**, 411–50.

BULLEN, K. E. and BURKE-GAFFNEY, T. N. (1958). Diffracted seismic waves near the *PKP* caustic. *Geophys. J., R. Astr. Soc.* **1**, 9–17.

GUTENBERG, B. (1958). Caustics produced by waves through the Earth's core. *Geophys. J., R. Astr. Soc.* **1**, 238–48.

GUTENBERG, B. (1958). Wave velocities in the Earth's core. *Bull. Seismol. Soc. Amer.* **48**, 301–14.

LEHMANN, I. (1958). On amplitudes of *P* near the shadow zone. *Ann. Geofis.* **11**, 153–6.

LEHMANN, I. (1958). On phases in earthquake records at epicentral distances of 105° to 115°. *Contributions in Geophysics*, pp. 121–34. London: Pergamon.

BOLT, B. A. (1959). Travel times of *PKP* up to 145°. *Geophys. J., R. Astr. Soc.* **3**, 190–8.

GUTENBERG, B. (1959). Wave velocities below the Mohorovičić discontinuity. *Geophys. J., R. Astr. Soc.* **4**, 348–52.

KONDORSKAYA, N. V. (1959). Some results of investigation of earthquakes from Kurile-Kamchatka zone. *Studia geoph. et geod., Prague*, **3**, 360–7.

LEHMANN, I. (1959). Velocities of longitudinal waves in the upper part of the Earth's mantle. *Ann. Géophys.* **15**, 93–118.

GUTENBERG, B. (1960). *PKIKP* and pseudo-*PKIKP* phases at distances less than 140°. *Geophys. J., R. Astr. Soc.* **3**, 250–7.

GUTENBERG, B. (1960). Waves reflected at the 'surface' of the Earth: *P'P'P'P'*. *Bull. Seismol. Soc. Amer.* **50**, 71–9.

GUTENBERG, B. (1960). The shadow of the Earth's core. *J. Geophys. Res.* **65**, 1013–20.

BULLEN, K. E. (1961). Seismic travel-times and velocity distributions. *Bur. Centr. Séism. Internat.* A, **21**, 7–13.

LEHMANN, I. (1961). *S* and the structure of the upper mantle. *Geophys. J., Roy. Astr. Soc.* **4**, 124–38.

KNOPOFF, L. and GILBERT, F. (1961). Diffraction of elastic waves by the core of the Earth. *Bull. Seismol. Soc. Amer.* **51**, 35–50.

NGUYEN HAI (1961). Propagation des ondes longitudinales. *Ann. Géophys.* **17**, 60–6.

BOLT, B. A. (1962). Gutenberg's early *PKP* observations. *Nature, Lond.*, **196**, 121–4.

JEFFREYS, Sir H. (1962). Deep foci and distribution of velocity. *Geophys. J., R. Astr. Soc.* **6**, 550–2.

Density, pressure and gravity in the Earth (§§ 13.4–13.8)

RADAU, R. R. (1885). Sur la loi des densités à l'intérieur de la Terre. *C.R. Acad. Sci., Paris*, **100**, 972.

WILLIAMSON, E. D. and ADAMS, L. H. (1923). Density distribution in the Earth. *J. Wash. Acad. Sci.* **13**, 413–28.

BULLEN, K. E. (1936). The variation of density and the ellipticities of strata of equal density within the Earth. *Mon. Not. R. Astr. Soc.*, Geophys. Suppl., **3**, 395–401.

BULLEN, K. E. (1940). The problem of the Earth's density variation. *Bull. Seismol. Soc. Amer.* **30**, 235–50.

BULLEN, K. E. (1942). The density variation of the Earth's central core. *Bull. Seismol. Soc. Amer.* **32**, 19–29.

DALY, R. A. (1943). Meteorites and an earth-model. *Bull. Geol. Soc. Amer.* **54**, 401–56.

LAMBERT, W. D. and DARLING, F. W. (1951). Density, gravity, pressure and ellipticity in the interior of the Earth. *Internal Constitution of Earth*, 2nd ed., pp. 340–61. New York: Dover.

BÅTH, M. (1954). The density ratio at the boundary of the Earth's core. *Tellus*, **6**, 408–13.

BULLEN, K. E. (1956). Seismology and the broad structure of the Earth's interior. *Phys. and Chem. of the Earth*, **1**, 68–93. London: Pergamon.

BULLEN, K. E. (1956). The influence of temperature gradient and variation of composition in the mantle on the computation of density values in Earth model A. *Mon. Not. R. Astr. Soc.*, Geophys. Suppl., **7**, 214–7.

BOLT, B. A. (1957). Earth models with continuous density distribution; and homogeneous cores. *Mon. Not. R. Astr. Soc.*, Geophys. Suppl., **7**, 360–8, 372–8.

BULLARD, Sir E. C. (1957). The density within the Earth. *Verh. geol. mijnb. Genoot. Ned. Kolon.* **18**, 23–41.

HUGHES, D. S. and McQUEEN, R. G. (1958). Density of basic rocks at very high pressures. *Trans. Amer. Geophys. Un.* **39**, 959–65.

JARDETZKY, W. S. (1958). *Theories of figures of celestial bodies.* New York: Interscience.

ALTSCHULER, L. V. and KORMER, S. B. (1961). On the internal constitution of the Earth. *Bull. Acad. Sci. U.S.S.R.*, Geophys. Ser. (English trans.), pp. 18–21.

BULLEN, K. E. (1962). Earth's central density. *Nature, Lond.*, **196**, 973.

BULLEN, K. E. (1964). Rigidity and density in the Earth's core. *Nature, Lond.*, **201**, 807.

The Earth's elasticity (§§ 13.3–13.8)

JEFFREYS, H. (1926). The rigidity of the Earth's central core. *Mon. Not. R. Astr. Soc.*, Geophys. Suppl., **1**, 371–83.

BIRCH, F. (1939). The variation of seismic velocities within a simplified Earth model, in accordance with the theory of finite strain. *Bull. Seismol. Soc. Amer.* **29**, 463–79.

BULLEN, K. E. (1940). Elastic constants of the Earth's mantle. *Trans. Roy. Soc. N.Z.* **70**, 137–9.

BULLEN, K. E. (1941). The elasticity of the Earth's central core. *Trans. Roy. Soc. N.Z.* **71**, 164–6.

BULLEN, K. E. (1946). A hypothesis on compressibility at pressures of the order of a million atmospheres. *Nature, Lond.*, **157**, 405.

BIRCH, F. (1947). Finite elastic strain of cubic crystals. *Phys. Rev.* **71**, 809–24.

BULLEN, K. E. (1949). Compressibility-pressure hypothesis and the Earth's interior. *Mon. Not. R. Astr. Soc.*, Geophys. Suppl., **5**, 355–68.

RAMSEY, W. H. (1950). On the compressibility of the Earth. *Mon. Not. R. Astr. Soc.*, Geophys. Suppl., **6**, 42–9.

BULLEN, K. E. (1950). An Earth model based on a compressibility-pressure hypothesis. *Mon. Not. R. Astr. Soc.*, Geophys. Suppl., **6**, 50–9.

TAKEUCHI, H. (1950). On the earth tide in the compressible Earth of varying density and elasticity. *Trans. Amer. Geophys. Un.* **31**, 651–89.

BULLEN, K. E. (1950). Theoretical travel-times of *S* waves in the Earth's inner core. *Mon. Not. R. Astr. Soc.*, Geophys. Suppl., **6**, 125–8.

BULLEN, K. E. (1951). Theoretical amplitudes of the seismic phase *PKJKP*. *Mon. Not. R. Astr. Soc.*, Geophys. Suppl., **6**, 163–7.

BULLEN, K. E. and BURKE-GAFFNEY, T. N. (1952). Detection of *S* waves in the Earth's inner core. *Nature, Lond.*, **170**, 455.

DENSON, M. E., Jr. (1952). Longitudinal waves through the Earth's core. *Bull. Seismol. Soc. Amer.* **42**, 119–34.

BIRCH, F. (1952). Elasticity and constitution of the Earth's interior. *J. Geophys. Res.* **57**, 227–86.

UFFEN, R. J. (1953). A method of estimating the melting-point gradient in the Earth's mantle. *Trans. Amer. Geophys. Un.* **33**, 893–6.

BULLEN, K. E. (1953). The rigidity of the Earth's inner core. *Ann. Geofis.* **6**, 1–10.

SIMON, F. E. (1953). The melting point of iron at high pressures. *Nature, Lond.*, **172**, 746.

JACOBS, J. A. (1954). Temperature distribution within the Earth's core. *Nature, Lond.*, **173**, 258.

BULLEN, K. E. (1955). Physical properties of the Earth's core. *Ann. géophys.* **11**, 53–64.

MOLODENSKI, M. S. (1955). Density and elasticity within the Earth. *Trans. Geophys. Inst. Acad. Sci. U.S.S.R.*, vol. 26.

HIDE, R. (1956). The hydrodynamics of the Earth's core. *Phys. and Chem. of Earth*, **1**, 94–137. New York: McGraw-Hill.

HONDA, H., SIMA, H. and NAKAMURA, K. (1956). The *ScS* wave, the mechanism of deep earthquake and the rigidity of the Earth's core. *Sci. Rep. Tôhoku Univ.* 5th ser., **7**, 169–79.

JACOBS, J. A. (1956). The Earth's interior. *Encyclopedia of Physics*, **47**, 364–406. Berlin: Springer-Verlag.

VERHOOGEN, J. (1956). Temperatures within the Earth. *Phys. and Chem. of the Earth*, **1**, 17–43. London: Pergamon.

BULLEN, K. E. (1958). Solidity of the inner core. *Contributions in Geophysics*, pp. 113–20. London: Pergamon.

KNOPOFF, L. and MACDONALD, G. J. F. (1958). Magnetic field and the central core of the Earth. *Geophys. J., R. Astr. Soc.* **1**, 216–23.

LUBIMOVA, H. A. (1958). Thermal history of the Earth and the variable thermal conductivity of its mantle. *Geophys. J., R. Astr. Soc.* **1**, 115–34.

LUBIMOVA, H. A. (1959). On the temperature gradient in the upper layers of the Earth and on the possibility of explaining low-velocity layers. *Bull. Acad. Sci. U.S.S.R.*, Geophys. Ser. (English trans.), pp. 1300–1.

CALOI, P. (1961). Seismic waves from the outer and inner core. *Geophys. J., R. Astr. Soc.* **4**, 139–50.

HALES, A. L. (1961). A weak layer in the mantle? *Geophys. J., R. Astr. Soc.* **4**, 312–19.

The Earth's composition (§ 13.9)

ADAMS, L. H. and WILLIAMSON, E. D. (1925). The composition of the Earth's interior. *Smithson. Rep.* 1923, pp. 241–60.

ADAMS, L. H. (1931). The compressibility of fayalite and the velocity of elastic waves in peridotite with different iron-magnesium ratios. *Beitr. Geophys.* **31**, 315–21.

BERNAL, J. D. (1936). Hypothesis on 20° discontinuity. *Observatory*, **59**, 268.

JEFFREYS, H. (1937). The density distributions in the inner planets. *Mon. Not. R. Astr. Soc.*, Geophys. Suppl., **4**, 62–71.

KRONIG, R., DE BOER, J. and KORRINGA, J. (1946). On the internal constitution of the Earth. *Physica*, **12**, 245–56.

RAMSEY, W. H. (1948). On the constitution of the terrestrial planets. *Mon. Not. R. Astr. Soc.* **108**, 406–13.

RAMSEY, W. H. (1949). On the nature of the Earth's core. *Mon. Not. R. Astr. Soc.*, Geophys. Suppl., **5**, 409–26.

BULLEN, K. E. (1949). On the constitution of Venus. *Mon. Not. R. Astr. Soc.* **109**, 457–61.

BULLEN, K. E. (1949). On the constitution of Mars. *Mon. Not. R. Astr. Soc.* **109**, 688–92.

BULLEN, K. E. (1950). Venus and the Earth's inner core. *Mon. Not. R. Astr. Soc.* **110**, 256–9.

ELSASSER, W. M. (1950). The Earth's interior and geomagnetism. *Rev. Mod. Phys.* **22**, 1–35.

UREY, H. C. (1952). *The planets, their origin and development.* Yale University Press.

BULLEN, K. E. (1952). On density and compressibility at pressures up to thirty million atmospheres. *Mon. Not. R. Astr. Soc.*, Geophys. Suppl., **6**, 383–401.

BULLEN, K. E. (1952). Cores of terrestrial planets. *Nature, Lond.*, **170**, 363.

BUCHER, W. H. and others (1954). Symposium: The interior of the Earth. *Trans. Amer. Geophys. Un.* **35**, 47–98.

BULLEN, K. E. (1954). On the homogeneity, or otherwise, of the Earth's upper mantle. *Trans. Amer. Geophys. Un.* **35**, 838–41.

GOLDSCHMIDT, V. M. (1954). *Geochemistry.* Oxford University Press.

SHIMAZU, Y. (1954). Equation of state of materials composing the Earth's interior. *J. Earth Sci. Nagoya Univ.* **2**, 15–172.

VALLE, P. E. (1954). Sull'omogeneità e sullo stato di equilibrio del mantello interno della Terra. *Ann. Geofis.* **7**, 33–44.

EGYED, L. (1957). A new conception of the internal constitution of the Earth. *Geol. Rdsch.* **46**, 101–21.

MacDONALD, G. J. F. and KNOPOFF, L. (1958). The chemical composition of the outer core. *Geophys. J., R. Astr. Soc.* **1**, 284–97.

MASON, B. (1958). *Principles of geochemistry,* 2nd ed. New York: Wiley.

RINGWOOD, A. E. (1958). The constitution of the mantle—I, II and III. *Geochim. et cosmochim. Acta,* **13**, 303–21; **15**, 18–29, 195–212.

BELOUSSOV, V. V. (1960). Development of the Earth and tectogenesis. *J. Geophys. Res.* **65**, 4127–46.

KNOPOFF, L. and MacDONALD, G. J. F. (1960). An equation of state for the core of the Earth. *Geophys. J., R. Astr. Soc.* **3**, 68–77.

WADA, T. (1960). On origins of the region C and the core of the Earth. *Disaster Prev. Res. Inst., Kyoto Univ.* **38**, 1–64.

ZHARKOV, V. N. (1960). Physics of the Earth's core, I and II; Thermodynamics of the Earth's mantle. *Bull. Acad. Sci. U.S.S.R.*, Geophys. Ser. (English trans.), pp. 945–50, 1005–9, 1039–44.

BIRCH, F. (1961). Composition of the Earth's mantle. *Geophys. J., R. Astr. Soc.* 4, 295–311.

MAGNETSKY, V. A. and KHOROSHEVA, V. V. (1961). The wave guide in the mantle of the Earth and its probable physical nature. *Ann. Geofis.* 14, 87–94.

RINGWOOD, A. E. (1962). A model for the upper mantle. *J. Geophys. Res.* 67, 857–67.

BULLEN, K. E. (1963). An index of degree of chemical inhomogeneity in the Earth. *Geophys. J., R. Astr. Soc.* 7, 584–92.

BIRCH, F. (1963). *Solids under pressure.* New York: McGraw-Hill, ch. 6, 137–62.

BULLEN, K. E. (1964). New evidence on rigidity in the Earth's core. *Proc. Nat. Acad. Sci., Wash.*, 52, 38–42.

Long-period oscillations of the Earth (§§ 14.1–14.6)

HOSKINS, L. M. (1920). The strain of a gravitating sphere of variable density and elasticity. *Trans. Amer. Math. Soc.* 21, 1–43.

EWING, M. and PRESS, F. (1954). An investigation of mantle Rayleigh waves. *Bull. Seismol. Soc. Amer.* 44, 127–47.

BENIOFF, H. (1954). Progress report, seismological laboratory, Calif. Inst. of Techn., 1953. *Trans. Amer. Geophys. Un.* 35, 985.

JOBERT, N. (1956) Évaluation de la période d'oscillation d'une sphere élastique hétérogène par l'application du principe de Rayleigh. *C.R. Acad. Sci., Paris*, 243, 1230–2.

BENIOFF, H. (1958). Long waves observed in the Kamchatka earthquake of November 4, 1952. *J. Geophys. Res.* 63, 589–93.

BENIOFF, H. and PRESS, F. (1958). Progress report on long period seismographs. *Geophys. J., R. Astr. Soc.* 1, 208–15.

ALTERMAN, Z., JAROSCH, H. and PEKERIS, C. L. (1959). Oscillations of the Earth. *Proc. Roy. Soc. A*, 252, 80–95.

TAKEUCHI, H. (1959). Torsional oscillations of the Earth and some related problems. *Geophys. J., R. Astr. Soc.* 2, 89–100.

TAKEUCHI, H. (1959). A comment on the flattening of the group velocity curve of mantle Rayleigh waves with periods about 500 sec. *Bull. Seismol. Soc. Amer.* 49, 365–8.

DORMAN, J., EWING, M. and OLIVER, J. (1960). Study of shear-velocity distribution in the upper mantle by Rayleigh waves. *Bull. Seismol. Soc. Amer.* 50, 87–115.

JOBERT, N. (1960). Calcul de la dispersion des ondes de Love de grande période à la surface de la Terre. *C.R. Acad. Sci., Paris*, 250, 890–2.

NAFE, J. E. and BRUNE, J. N. (1960). Observations of phase velocity for Rayleigh waves in the period range 100–400 seconds. *Bull. Seismol. Soc. Amer.* 50, 427–39.

SATÔ, Y., LANDISMAN, M. and EWING, M. (1960). Love waves in a heterogeneous, spherical Earth, Parts 1 and 2. *J. Geophys. Res.* 65, 2395–404.

AKI, K. and PRESS, F. (1961). Upper mantle structure under oceans and continents from Rayleigh waves. *Geophys. J., R. Astr. Soc.* 5, 292–305.

ALSOP, L. E., SUTTON, G. H. and EWING, M. (1961). Free oscillations of the Earth observed on strain and pendulum seismographs. *J. Geophys. Res.* **66**, 631–41.

ALTERMAN, Z., JAROSCH, H. and PEKERIS, C. L. (1961). Propagation of Rayleigh waves in the Earth. *Geophys. J., R. Astr. Soc.* **4**, 219–41.

BACKUS, G. and GILBERT, F. (1961). The rotational splitting of the free oscillations of the Earth. *Proc. Nat. Acad. Sci., Wash.*, **47**, 362–71.

BENIOFF, H., PRESS, F. and SMITH, S. (1961). Excitation of the free oscillations of the Earth by earthquakes. *J. Geophys. Res.* **66**, 605–19.

BOGERT, B. P. (1961). An observation of free oscillations of the Earth. *J. Geophys. Res.* **66**, 643–6.

BOLT, B. A. and DORMAN, J. (1961). Phase and group velocities in a spherical, gravitating Earth. *J. Geophys. Res.* **66**, 2965–81.

BRUNE, J. N., NAFE, J. E. and ALSOP, L. E. (1961). The polar phase shift of surface waves on a sphere. *Bull. Seismol. Soc. Amer.* **51**, 247–57.

JOBERT, N. (1961). Calcul approché de la période des oscillations sphéroidales de la Terre. *Geophys. J., R. Astr. Soc.* **4**, 242–58.

KNOPOFF, L. (1961). Green's function for eigenvalue problems and the inversion of Love wave dispersion data. *Geophys. J., R. Astr. Soc.* **4**, 161–73.

NESS, N. F., HARRISON, J. C. and SLICHTER, L. B. (1961). Observations of the free oscillations of the Earth. *J. Geophys. Res.* **66**, 621–29.

PEKERIS, C. L., ALTERMAN, Z. and JAROSCH, H. (1961). Comparison of theoretical with observed values of the periods of free oscillation of the Earth. *Proc. Nat. Acad. Sci., Wash.*, **47**, 91–8.

SAVARENSKY, E. F., POPOV, I. I. and LAZAREVA, A. P. (1961). Observations of long period waves of the Chilean earthquake of 1960. *Bull. Acad. Sci. U.S.S.R.*, Geophys. Ser. (English trans.), pp. 744–54.

SLICHTER, L. B. (1961). The fundamental free mode of the Earth's inner core. *Proc. Nat. Acad. Sci., Wash.*, **47**, 186–9.

STONELEY, R. (1961). The oscillations of the Earth. *Phys. and Chem. of Earth*, **4**, 239–50. London: Pergamon.

TAKEUCHI, H. and SAITO, M. (1961). Free oscillations of the Earth. *Proc. Jap. Acad.* **37**, 33–6.

BOLT, B. A. and MARUSSI, A. (1962). Eigenvibrations of the Earth observed at Trieste. *Geophys. J., R. Astr. Soc.* **6**, 299–311.

BOLT, B. A. (1963). Recent information on the Earth's interior from studies of mantle waves and eigenvibrations. *Phys. and Chem. of Earth*, **5**, 55–119. London: Pergamon.

Earthquake energy and magnitude (§§ 15.1–15.2)

JEFFREYS, H. (1923). The Pamir earthquake of 1911 February 18, in relation to the depths of foci. *Mon. Not. R. Astr. Soc.*, Geophys. Suppl., **1**, 22–31.

JEFFREYS, H. (1927). On two British earthquakes. *Mon. Not. R. Astr. Soc.*, Geophys. Suppl., **1**, 483–94.

RICHTER, C. F. (1935). An instrumental earthquake magnitude scale. *Bull. Seismol. Soc. Amer.* **25**, 1–32.

TSUBOI, C. (1941). Isotasy and maximum earthquake energy. *Proc. Imp. Acad. Japan*, **16**, 449–54.

GUTENBERG, B. and RICHTER, C. F. (1942). Earthquake magnitude, intensity, energy and acceleration. *Bull. Seismol. Soc. Amer.* **32**, 163–91.

GUTENBERG, B. (1945). Amplitudes of surface waves and magnitudes of shallow earthquakes. *Bull. Seismol. Soc. Amer.* **35**, 3–12.

GUTENBERG, B. (1945). Magnitude determination for deep focus earthquakes. *Bull. Seismol. Soc. Amer.* **35**, 117–30.

RICHTER, C. F. (1948). History and applications of the magnitude scale. *Bur. Centr. Séism. Internat.* A, **17**, 217–24.

HONDA, H. (1951). Amplitudes of P and S, magnitude and energy of deep earthquakes. *Sci. Rep. Tôhoku Univ.* 5th ser., **3**, 138–43 and earlier papers.

BÅTH, M. (1954). The problem of earthquake magnitude determination. *Bur. Centr. Séism. Internat.* A, **19**, 1–91.

TSUBOI, C. (1956). On seismic activities in and near Japan. *Contributions in Geophysics*, pp. 87–112. London: Pergamon.

GUTENBERG, B. (1956). The energy of earthquakes. *Quart. J. Geol. Soc., Lond.*, **112**, 1–14.

BYERLY, P. and DE NOYER, J. (1958). Energy in earthquakes as computed from geodetic observations. *Contributions in Geophysics*, pp. 17–35. London: Pergamon.

KNOPOFF, L. (1958). Energy release in earthquakes. *Geophys. J., R. Astr. Soc.* **1**, 44–52.

BELOTELOV, V. L. and KONDORSKAYA, N. V. (1961). Relationship between earthquake energy and maximum velocity of the oscillations in body waves. *Bull. Acad. Sci. U.S.S.R.*, Geophys. Ser. (English trans.), pp. 22–6.

Earthquake types and distribution; focal depth and dimensions (§§ 15.3–15.6)

TURNER, H. H. (1922). On the arrival of earthquake waves at the antipodes and on the measurement of the focal depth of an earthquake. *Mon. Not. R. Astr. Soc.*, Geophys. Suppl., **1**, 1–13.

STONELEY, R. (1931). On deep-focus earthquakes. *Beitr. Geophys.* **29**, 417–35.

WADATI, K. (1928, 1929, 1931). On shallow and deep earthquakes. *Geophys. Mag., Tokyo*, **1**, 162–202; **2**, 1–36; **4**, 231–83.

SCRASE, F. J. (1932). The characteristics of a deep focus earthquake; a study of the disturbance of February 20, 1931. *Phil. Trans.* A, **231**, 207–34.

WHIPPLE, F. J. W. (1934). On the alleged tendency for great earthquakes to occur sympathetically in widely separated regions. *Mon. Not. R. Astr. Soc.*, Geophys. Suppl., **3**, 233–8.

WADATI, K. (1935). On the activity of deep-focus earthquakes in the Japan Islands and neighbourhoods. *Geophys. Mag., Tokyo*, **8**, 305–25.

STECHSCHULTE, V. C. (1936). Geological implications of deep-focus earthquakes. *Trans. Amer. Geophys. Un.*, Rep. 17th Ann. Meeting, Seismology, pp. 81–3.

LEITH, A. and SHARPE, J. A. (1936). Deep-focus earthquakes and their geological significance. *J. Geol.* **44**, 877–917.

BRUNNER, G. J. (1938). The deep earthquake of May 26, 1932 near the Kermadec Islands. *Beitr. Geophys.* **53**, 1–64.

JEFFREYS, H. (1939). Deep focus earthquakes. *Ergebn. Kosm. Phys.* **4**, 75–105.

KONING, L. P. G. (1941). On the mechanism of deep-focus earthquakes. *Beitr. Geophys.* **58**, 159–97.

JEFFREYS, H. (1942). The deep earthquake of 1934 June 29. *Mon. Not. R. Astr. Soc.*, Geophys. Suppl., **5**, 33–6.

VENING MEINESZ, F. A. (1946). Deep-focus and intermediate earthquakes in the East Indies. *Proc. K. Akad. Wet. Amst.* **49**, 5–14.

GUTENBERG, B. and RICHTER, C. F. (1948). Deep focus earthquakes in the Mediterranean region. *Geofis. pur. appl.* **12**, Fasc. 3–4.

BENIOFF, H. (1951). Earthquakes and rock creep. Part I. Creep characteristics of rocks and the origin of aftershocks. *Bull. Seismol. Soc. Amer.* **41**, 31–62.

KONING, L. P. G. (1952). Earthquakes in relation to their geographical distribution, depth and magnitude. *Proc. K. Akad. Wet. Amst.* B, **55**, 60–77, 174–206, 263–92.

RITSEMA, A. R. (1952). Over diepe aardbevingen in de Indische Archipel. Doctorate thesis, *Univ. of Utrecht*, 132 pp.

BULLEN, K. E. (1953). On strain energy and strength in the Earth's upper mantle. *Trans. Amer. Geophys. Un.* **34**, 107–9.

NISHIMURA, E. (1953). On some destructive earthquakes measured at a great distance. *Disaster Prev. Res. Inst., Kyoto Univ.*, **6**, 1–16.

GUTENBERG, B. and RICHTER, C. F. (1954). *Seismicity of the Earth and associated phenomena*, 2nd. ed. Princeton: University Press.

WILLIAMS, H. (1954). Problems and progress in volcanology. *Quart. J. Geol. Soc., Lond.*, **109**, 311–32.

RITSEMA, A. R. (1954). A statistical study of the seismicity of the Earth. *Met. and Geophys. Serv., Indonesia*, Verh. 46.

PETERSCHMITT, E. (1956). Quelques données nouvelles sur les séismes profonds de la mer Tyrrhenienne. *Ann. Geofis.* **9**, 305–34.

HOPE, E. R. (1958). Review of *Chronological tabulation of Chinese earthquake records* (Chin. Acad. of Sci., 1956). *Bull. Seismol. Soc. Amer.* **48**, 194–8.

ROTHÉ, J.-P. (1958). *Séismes et volcans*, 3rd ed. Paris: Que sais-je?

MEI SHI-YUN (1960). The seismic activity of China. *Bull. Acad. Sci. U.S.S.R.*, Geophys. Ser. (English trans.), pp. 254–64.

Conditions near the focus (§15.7)

REID, H. F. (1911). The elastic-rebound theory of earthquakes. *Bull. Dep. Geol. Univ. Calif.* **6**, 413–44.

NAKANO, H. (1923). Notes on the nature of forces which give rise to earthquake motions. *Seismol. Bull., Centr. Meteor. Obs. of Japan*, **1**, 92–120.

BYERLY, P. (1926). The Montana earthquake of June 28, 1925. *Bull. Seismol. Soc. Amer.* **16**, 209–65.

WHIPPLE, F. J. W. (1930). The great Siberian meteor and the waves, seismic and aerial, which it produced. *Quart. J. R. Met. Soc.* **56**, 287–304.

BRIDGMAN, P. W. (1936). Shearing phenomena at high-pressure of possible importance for geology. *J. Geol.* **44**, 653–69.

KAWASUMI, H. (1937). An historical sketch of the development of knowledge concerning the initial movement of an earthquake. *Bur. Centr. Séism. Internat.* A, **15** (ii), 258–330.

TSUBOI, C. (1941). Secular deformations of the base line rhombus at Mitaka in relation to seismic activities in its vicinity. *Bull. Earthq. Res. Inst. Tokyo*, **19**, 559–78.

LOUDERBACK, G. D. (1942). Faults and earthquakes. *Bull. Seismol. Soc. Amer.* **32**, 305–30.

WOOD, H. O. (1947). Earthquakes in southern California with geologic relations. I and II. *Bull. Seismol. Soc. Amer.* **37**, 107–57, 217–58.

BYERLY, P. and EVERNDEN, J. F. (1950). First motion in earthquakes recorded at Berkeley. *Bull. Seismol. Soc. Amer.* **40**, 291–8.

WILSON, J. TUZO (1950). On the growth of continents. *Proc. Roy. Soc. Tasm.* pp. 85–111.

ANDERSON, E. M. (1951). *The dynamics of faulting*, 2nd ed. Edinburgh: Oliver and Boyd.

HODGSON, J. H. and MILNE, W. G. (1951). Direction of faulting in certain earthquakes of the North Pacific. *Bull. Seismol. Soc. Amer.* **41**, 221–42.

HONDA, H. and MASATUKA, A. (1952). On the mechanisms of the earthquakes and the stresses producing them in Japan and its vicinity. *Sci. Rep. Tôhoku Univ.*, 5th ser., **4**, 42–60.

BULLEN, K. E. (1953). On strain energy and strength in the Earth's upper mantle. *Trans. Amer. Geophys. Un.* **34**, 107–9.

BENIOFF, H. (1954). Orogenesis and deep crustal structure. *Bull. Geol. Soc. Amer.* **65**, 385–400.

BENIOFF, H. (1955). Seismic evidence for crustal structure and tectonic activity. *Spec. Pap. Geol. Soc. Amer.* **62**, 61–73.

BULLEN, K. E. (1955). On the size of the strained region prior to an extreme earthquake. *Bull. Seismol. Soc. Amer.* **45**, 43–6.

BYERLY, P. (1955). Nature of faulting as deduced from seismograms. *Spec. Pap. Geol. Soc. Amer.* **62**, 75–86.

SCHEIDEGGER, A. E. (1956). Forces in the Earth's crust. *Encyclopedia of physics*, **47**, 258–87. Berlin: Springer-Verlag.

TSUBOI, C. (1956). Earthquake energy, earthquake volume, aftershock area, and strength of the Earth's crust. *J. Phys. Earth*, **4**, 63–6.

HODGSON, J. H. (1957). Nature of faulting in large earthquakes. *Bull. Geol. Soc. Amer.* **68**, 611–43.

KEILIS-BOROK, V. I. (1957). The determination of earthquake mechanism using both longitudinal and transverse waves. *Ann. geofis.* **10**, 105–28.

HODGSON, J. H. (Editor) (1959). The mechanics of faulting, with special reference to the fault-plane work. (A symposium.) *Ottawa Dom. Obs. Publ.* **20**, no. 2.

HONDA, H. (1959). The mechanism of earthquakes. *Sci. Rep. Tôhoku Univ.*, 5th ser., **9** (Suppl.), 1–46.

SCHEIDEGGER, A. E. (1959). Statistical analysis of recent fault-plane solutions of earthquakes. *Bull. Seismol. Soc. Amer.* **49**, 337–47.

AKI, K. (1960). Further study of the mechanisms of circum-Pacific earthquakes from Rayleigh waves. *J. Geophys Res.* **65**, 4165–72.

KNOPOFF, L. and GILBERT, F. (1960). First motions from seismic sources. *Bull. Seismol. Soc. Amer.* **50**, 117–34.

BALAKINA, L. M., SAVARENSKY, E. F. and VVEDENSKAYA, A. V. (1961). On determination of earthquake mechanism. *Phys. and Chem. of the Earth*, **4**, 211–38. London: Pergamon.

HONDA, H. (1962). Earthquake mechanism and seismic waves. *J. of Phys. of the Earth, Tokyo*, x, 1–97.

SCHOLTE, J. G. J. and RITSEMA, A. R. (1962). The mechanism at the focus of an earthquake—Parts I, II and III. *Bull. Seismol. Soc. Amer.* **52**, 711–66.

STAUDER, W. (1962, 1963). *S*-wave studies of earthquakes of the North Pacific, Parts I and II. Kamchatka. *Bull. Seismol. Soc. Amer.* **52**, 527–50; **53**, 59–77.

Foreshocks, etc.; periodicities; prediction (§§ 15.8–15.9)

WOOD, H. O. and GUTENBERG, B. (1935). Earthquake prediction. *Science*, **82**, 219–20.

MACELWANE, J. B. (1936). Forecasting earthquakes. *Bull. Seismol. Soc. Amer.* **36**, 1–4.

JEFFREYS, H. (1938). Aftershocks and periodicity in earthquakes. *Beitr. Geophys.* **53**, 111–39.

DAVISON, C. (1938). *Studies on the periodicity of earthquakes.* (Reviewed by R. Stoneley, *Bull. Seismol. Soc. Amer.* **29**, 559–62. 1939.) London: Murby.

SASSA, K. and NISHIMURA, E. (1956). On phenomena forerunning earthquakes. *Bur. Centr. Séism. Internat.* A, **19**, 277–85.

BÅTH, M. and BENIOFF, H. (1958). Aftershock sequence of the Kamchatka earthquake of November 4, 1952. *Bull. Seismol. Soc. Amer.* **48**, 1–15.

Seismology and nuclear explosions (§§ 16.1–16.4)

GUTENBERG, B. (1946). Interpretation of records obtained from the New Mexico atomic bomb test. *Bull. Seismol. Soc. Amer.* **36**, 327–9.

GUTENBERG, B. and RICHTER, C. F. (1946). Seismic waves from atomic bomb tests. *Trans. Amer. Geophys. Un.* **27**, 776.

LEET, L. DON (1946). Earth motion from the atomic bomb test. *Amer. Sci.* **34**, 198–211.

BULLEN, K. E. (1948). The Bikini bomb and the seismology of the Pacific region. *Nature, Lond.*, **161**, 62.

GUTENBERG, B. (1953). Travel times of longitudinal waves from surface foci. *Proc. Nat. Acad. Sci., Wash.*, **39**, 849–53.

BURKE-GAFFNEY, T. N. and BULLEN, K. E. (1957, 1958). Seismological and related aspects of the 1954 hydrogen bomb explosions. *Aust. J. Phys.* **10**, 130–6; **11**, 318–21.

RITSEMA, A. R. (1957). On the seismic records of nuclear test explosions. *Madjalah II mu Alam untuk Indonesia*, **113**, 123–7.

BULLEN, K. E. (1958). Seismology in our atomic age. *C.R. I.A.S.P.I.E.* **12**, 19–35.

BOLT, B. A., DOYLE, H. A. and SUTTON, D. J. (1958). Seismic observations from the 1946 atomic explosions in Australia. *Geophys J., R. Astr. Soc.* **1**, 135–45.

CARDER, D. S. and BAILEY, L. F. (1958). Seismic wave travel times from nuclear explosions. *Bull. Seismol. Soc. Amer.* **48**, 377–98.

LABROUSTE, I. (1958). Enregistrement séismique d'explosions nucléaires. *C.R. Acad. Sci., Paris*, **247**, 321–3.

OLIVER, J. and EWING, M. (1958). Seismic surface waves at Palisades from explosions in Nevada and the Marshall Islands. *Proc. Nat. Acad. Sci., Wash.*, **44**, 780–5.

CARDER, D. S. and CLOUD, W. K. (1959). Surface waves from large underground explosions. *J. Geophys. Res.* **64**, 1471–87.

GROSSLING, B. F. (1959). Seismic waves from the underground explosion in Nevada. *Bull. Seismol. Soc. Amer.* **49**, 11–32.

JOHNSON, G. W., HIGGINS, G. H. and VIOLET, C. E. (1959). Underground nuclear explosions. *J. Geophys. Res.* **64**, 1457–70.

PRESS, F., OLIVER, J. and ROMNEY, C. (1959). The need for fundamental research in seismology. *Trans. Amer. Geophys. Un.* **40**, 213–21.

ROMNEY, C. (1959). Amplitudes of seismic body waves from underground nuclear explosions. *J. Geophys. Res.* **64**, 1489–98.

HUNT, J. N., PALMER, R. and PENNEY, Sir W. (1960). Atmospheric waves caused by large explosions. *Phil. Trans. A*, **252**, 275–315.

KOGAN, S. D. (1960). Travel times of longitudinal and transverse waves from nuclear explosions in the Marshall Islands. *Bull. Acad. Sci. U.S.S.R.*, Geophys. Ser. (English trans.), pp. 246–53.

OLIVER, J., POMEROY, P. and EWING, M. (1960). Long-period seismic waves from nuclear explosions and various environments. *Science*, **131**, 1804–5.

RIZNICHENKO, J. V. (1960). On seismic magnitudes of underground nuclear explosions. *Trans. Inst. Phys. Earth, Acad. Sci. U.S.S.R.* **15**.

ROTHÉ, J.-P. (1960). La séismicité du globe. *Nucleus, Paris*, **6**, 1–10.

WILLIS, D. E. and WILSON, JAMES T. (1960). Maximum vertical ground displacement of seismic waves generated by explosive blasts. *Bull. Seismol. Soc. Amer.* **50**, 455–9.

GRIGGS, D. T. and PRESS, F. (1961). Probing the Earth with nuclear explosions. *J. Geophys. Res.* **66**, 237–58.

KOGAN, S. D. (1961). Travel times of body waves from a surface focus. *Bur. Centr. Séism. Internat. A*, **21**, 15–21.

LATTER, A. L., LE LEVIER, R. E., MARTINELLI, E. A. and McMILLAN, W. G. (1961). Method of concealing nuclear explosions. *J. Geophys. Res.* **66**, 943–6.

CARPENTER, E. E., SAVILL, R. A. and WRIGHT, J. K. (1962). The dependence of seismic signal amplitudes on the size of underground explosions. *Geophys. J., R. Astr. Soc.* **6**, 426–49.

VESIAC REPORT (1962). Proceedings of colloquium on detection of underground nuclear explosions. *Spec. pap., Univ. of Michigan*, 477 pp.

THIRLAWAY, H. I. S. (1962). A summary of research in the United Kingdom on the detection of underground nuclear explosions. *VESIAC Colloquium*, pp. 259–83.

CARDER, D. S. and others (1962). The Gnome explosion. *Bull. Seismol. Soc. Amer.* **52**, 977–1077.

LEHMANN, I. (1962). The travel times of the longitudinal waves of the Logan and Blanca atomic explosions. *Bull. Seismol. Soc. Amer.* **52**, 519–26.

JEFFREYS, Sir H. (1962). Travel times from Pacific explosions. *Geophys. J., R. Astr. Soc.* **7**, 212–19.

POMEROY, P. W. (1963). Long period seismic waves from large, near-surface nuclear explosions. *Bull. Seismol. Soc. Amer.* **53**, 109–49.

Extra-terrestrial seismology (§§ 17.1–17.4)

JEFFREYS, H. (1937). The density distributions in the inner planets. *Mon. Not. R. Astr. Soc.*, Geophys. Suppl., **4**, 62–71.

BULLEN, K. E. (1951). Origin of the Moon. *Nature, Lond.*, **167**, 29.

BULLEN, K. E. and Low, A. H. (1952). Planetary models of terrestrial type. *Mon. Not. R. Astr. Soc.* **112**, 637–40.

DATTA, A. N. (1954). On the energy required to form the Moon. *Mon. Not. R. Astr. Soc.*, Geophys. Suppl., **6**, 535–9.

JEFFREYS, H. (1954). Dynamics of the Earth-Moon system. *The Earth as a Planet*, pp. 42–56. Chicago: University Press.

UREY, H. C., ELSASSER, W. M. and ROCHESTER, M. G. (1959). Note on the internal structure of the Moon. *Astrophys. J.* **129**, 842–8.

BROWN, HARRISON (1960). The density and mass distribution of meteoritic bodies in the neighbourhood of the Earth's orbit. *J. Geophys. Res.* **65**, 1679–83.

PRESS, F., BUWALDA, P. and NEUGEBAUER, M. (1960). A lunar seismic experiment. *J. Geophys. Res.* **65**, 3097–105.

BOLT, B. A. (1961). Theoretical phase velocities for a lunar experiment. *J. Geophys. Res.* **66**, 3513–18.

TAKEUCHI, H., SAITO, M. and KOBAYASHI, N. (1961). Free oscillations of the Moon. *J. Geophys. Res.* **66**, 3895–8.

UREY, H. C. and KOPAL, Z. (Editors) (1961). *The Moon, its physics and astronomy.* London: Academic Press.

JOBERT, G. (1962). Nonhydrostatical stresses in a gravitating planet. *J. Geophys. Res.* **67**, 1579–85.

LEHNER, F. E. and others (1962). A seismograph for lunar experiments. *J. Geophys. Res.* **67**, 4779–94.

Macroseismic data (§§ 18.1–18.2)

SIEBERG, A. (1930). Die Erdbeben; Erdbebengeographie. *Handb. Geophys.* **4**, 527–1005. Berlin.

WOOD, H. O. and NEUMANN, F. (1931). Modified Mercalli intensity scale of 1931. *Bull. Seismol. Soc. Amer.* **21**, 277–83.

FREEMAN, J. R. (1932). *Earthquake damage and earthquake insurance.* New York: McGraw-Hill.

BENIOFF, H. (1934). The physical evaluation of seismic destructiveness. *Bull. Seismol. Soc. Amer.* **24**, 398–403.

STEINBRUGGE, K. V. and MORAN, D. F. (1954). An engineering study of the southern California earthquake of July 21, 1952, and its aftershocks. *Bull. Seismol. Soc. Amer.* **44**, 201–462.

RICHTER, C. F. (1959). Seismic regionalization. *Bull. Seismol. Soc. Amer.* **49**, 123–62.

RIZNICHENKO, J. V. (1959), On quantitative determination and mapping of seismic activity. *Ann. Geofis.* **12**, 227–38.

Sea effects of earthquakes, etc. (§§ 18.3–18.4)

GUTENBERG, B. (1939). Tsunamis and earthquakes. *Bull. Seismol. Soc. Amer.* **29**, 517–26.

LINEHAN, D. (1940). Earthquakes in the West Indian region. *Trans. Amer. Geophys. Un.* **21**, 229–32.

HECK, N. H. (1947). List of seismic sea waves. *Bull. Seismol. Soc. Amer.* **37**, 269–86.

PEKERIS, C. L. (1948). Theory of propagation of explosive sounds in shallow water. *Geol. Soc. Amer. Mem.* **27**.

WORZEL, J. L. and EWING, M. (1948). Explosive sounds in shallow water. *Geol. Soc. Amer. Mem.* **27**.

OMER, G. C., Jr. and HALL, H. H. (1949). The scattering of a tsunami by a cylindrical island. *Bull. Seismol. Soc. Amer.* **39**, 257–60.

PRESS, F., EWING, M. and TOLSTOY, I. (1950). The Airy phase of shallow-focus submarine earthquakes. *Bull. Seismol. Soc. Amer.* **40**, 111–48.

BYERLY, P. and HERRICK, C. (1954). *T* phases from Hawaiian earthquakes. *Bull. Seismol. Soc. Amer.* **44**, 113–21.

IIDA, K. (1956). Earthquakes accompanied by tsunamis occurring under the sea off the islands of Japan. *J. Earth Sci. Nagoya Univ.* **4**, 1–43.

GALANOPOULOS, A. G. (1960). Tsunamis observed on the coasts of Greece from antiquity to the present time. *Ann. Geofis.* **13**, 369–86.

EATON, J. P., RICHTER, D. H. and AULT, W. U. (1961). The tsunami of May 23, 1960, on the Island of Hawaii. *Bull. Seismol. Soc. Amer.* **51**, 135–58.

EWING, J. and EWING, M. (1961). A telemetering ocean-bottom seismograph. *J. Geophys. Res.* **66**, 3863–78.

KATÔ, Y. and others (1961). The Chile tsunami of 1960 observed along the coast of Japan. *Sci. Rep. Tôhoku Univ.*, 5th ser., **13**, 107–25.

NAKAMURA, K. and EMURA, K. (1961). Maximum water height at bay head in case of tsunami invasion. *Sci. Rep. Tôhoku Univ.*, 5th ser., **13**, 32–42.

I.A.S.P.I.E. (1962). Report on tsunami meetings. *I.U.G.G. Chronicle*, **41**, 2–16.

Microseisms (§18.5)

GHERZI, E. (1923, 1928). Étude sur les microséismes. *Notes de Sismologie, Obs. de Zi-ka-wei,* **5,** 1–16; **8,** 1–12.

BANERJI, S. K. (1930). Microseisms associated with disturbed weather in the Indian Seas. *Phil. Trans.* A, **229,** 287–328.

GUTENBERG, B. (1931). Microseisms in North America. *Bull. Seismol. Soc. Amer.* **21,** 1–24.

WHIPPLE, F. J. W. and LEE, A. W. (1935). Notes on the theory of micro-seisms. *Mon. Not. R. Astr. Soc.,* Geophys. Suppl., **3,** 287–97.

LEE, A. W. (1935). On the direction of approach of microseismic waves. *Proc. Roy. Soc.* A, **149,** 183–99.

WADATI, K. and MASUDA, K. (1935). On pulsatoric oscillations of the ground. *Geophys. Mag., Tokyo,* **9,** 299–340.

SEZAWA, K. and KANAI, K. (1939). Microseisms caused by transmission of atmospheric disturbances. *Bull. Earthq. Res. Inst., Tokyo,* **17,** 190–207.

RAMÍREZ, J. E. (1940). An experimental investigation of the nature and origin of microseisms at St Louis, Missouri. *Bull. Seismol. Soc. Amer.* **30,** 35–84, 139–78.

BERNARD, P. (1941). Étude sur l'agitation microséismique et ses variations. *Ann. Inst. Phys. Globe Mét.* **19,** 1–77.

BYERLY, P. (1942). Microseisms at Berkeley and surf on near-by coasts. *Bull. Seismol. Soc. Amer.* **32,** 277–82.

MICHE, M. (1944). Mouvements ondulatoires de la mer en profondeur constante ou decroissante. *Ann. Ponts Chauss.* **144,** 25–87, 131–64, 270–92, 396–406.

DEACON, G. E. R. (1947). Relations between sea-waves and microseisms. *Nature, Lond.,* **160,** 419–21.

California Institute of Technology, Seismological Laboratory (B. Gutenberg) (1949). *Bibliography on microseisms.* Contr. 523, Div. Geol. Sci., 63 pp.

LONGUET-HIGGINS, M. S. (1950). A theory of the origin of microseisms. *Phil. Trans.* A, **243,** 1–35.

BÅTH, M. (1951). The distribution of microseismic energy, with special reference to Scandinavia. *Ark. Geofys.* **1,** 359–93.

CALOI, P. (1951). Sull'origine dei microsismi con particolare riguardo all'alto Adriatico. *Ann. Geofis.* **4,** 525–77.

WILSON, JAMES T. and PRESS, F. (Editors) (1953). Symposium on micro-seisms. *U.S. Nat. Res. Council, Publ.* 306.

COULOMB, J. (1956). L'agitation microséismique. *Encyclopedia of Physics,* **47,** 140–52. Berlin: Springer-Verlag.

OLIVER, J. and EWING, M. (1957). Microseisms in the 11- to 18-second period range. *Bull. Seismol. Soc. Amer.* **47,** 111–27.

MITRA, M. (1957). Rayleigh waves in a multi-layered medium with applica-tions to microseisms. *Mon. Not. R. Astr. Soc.,* Geophys. Suppl., **7,** 324–31.

DARBYSHIRE, J. and IYER, H. M. (1958). Some recent developments in the study of microseisms in Great Britain and the United States. *Geophys. J., R. Astr. Soc.* **1,** 180–4.

GUTENBERG, B. (1958). Microseisms. *Advanc. Geophys.* **5,** 53–92.

BRUNE, J. N. and OLIVER, J. (1959). The seismic noise of the Earth's surface. *Bull. Seismol. Soc. Amer.* **49**, 349–53.

CARDER, D. S. and EPPLEY, R. A. (1959). The microseismic program of the U.S. Navy: a terminal report. *U.S. Coast and Geod. Survey Publ.*, pp. 1–196.

HATHERTON, T. (1960). Microseisms at Scott base. *Geophys. J., R. Astr. Soc.* **3**, 381–405.

FRANTTI, G. E., WILLIS, D. E. and WILSON, JAMES T. (1962). The spectrum of seismic noise. *Bull. Seismol. Soc. Amer.* **52**, 123–32.

OLIVER, J. (1962). A worldwide storm of microseisms with periods of about 27 seconds. *Bull. Seismol. Soc. Amer.* **52**, 507–18.

Seismic prospecting; ice-thicknesses (§ 18.6)

SORGE, E. (1930). Die ersten Dickenmessungen des grönländischen Inlandeises. *Z. Geophys.* **6**, 22.

EDGE, A. BROUGHTON and LABY, T. H. (1931). *The principles and practice of geophysical surveying.* Cambridge University Press.

EWING, M., CRARY, A. P. and THORNE, A. M. (1934). Propagation of elastic waves in ice. Parts I and II. *Physics,* **5**, 165–8, 181–4.

BULLARD, E. C., GASKELL, T. F., HARLAND, W. B. and KERR-GRANT, C. (1946). Seismic investigations on the palaeozoic floor of East England. *Phil. Trans.* A, **239**, 29–94.

ROTHÉ, E. and ROTHÉ, J.-P. (1950). *Prospection géophysique,* Tome I. Paris: Gauthier-Villars.

PRESS, F. and EWING, M. (1951). Progapation of elastic waves in a floating ice sheet. *Trans. Amer. Geophys. Un.* **32**, 673–8.

DIX, C. H. (1952). *Seismic prospecting for oil.* New York: Harper.

EWING, W. M. and PRESS, F. (1956). Seismic prospecting. *Encyclopedia of Physics,* **47**, 153–68. Berlin: Springer-Verlag.

ROBIN, G. DE Q. (1958). *Seismic shooting and related investigations.* Scientific results, Vol. 5, Norwegian–British–Swedish Antarctic Expedition, 1949–52, pp. 1–134.

HUNKINS, K. (1960). Seismic studies of sea ice. *J. Geophys. Res.* **65**, 3459–72.

WHITE, J. E. and PRESS, F. (1960). Geophysical research and progress in exploration. *Geophysics,* **25**, 168–80.

WILLMORE, P. L. and BANCROFT, A. M. (1960). The time term approach to refraction seismology. *Geophys. J., R. Astr. Soc.* **3**, 419–33.

OLIVER, J., CRARY, A. P. and COTELL, R. (1961). Elastic waves in Arctic pack ice. *Trans. Amer. Geophys. Un.* **34**, 282–91.

HATHERTON, T. and EVISON, F. F. (1962). A special mechanism for some Antarctic earthquakes. *N.Z. J. Geol. Geophys.* **5**, 864–73.

ROBIN, G. DE Q. (1963). Wave propagation through fields of pack ice. *Phil. Trans.* A, **255**, 313–39.

BULLEN, K. E. and GOODSPEED, M. J. (1964). Seismic investigations of Antarctic structure. *Annals of I.G.Y.* xxx, 218–64.

Model seismology (§ 18.7)

TERADA, T. and TSUBOI, C. (1927). Experimental studies on elastic waves. Parts I and II. *Bull. Earthq. Res. Inst., Tokyo*, **3**, 55–65; **4**, 9–20.

KAUFMAN, S. and ROEVER, W. L. (1951). Laboratory studies of transient elastic waves. *Proc. Third World Petrol. Congr. (The Hague)*, **1**, 537–45.

NORTHWOOD, T. D. and ANDERSON, D. V. (1953). Model seismology. *Bull. Seismol. Soc. Amer.* **43**, 239–46.

OLIVER, J., PRESS, F. and EWING, M. (1954). Two-dimensional model seismology. *Geophysics*, **19**, 202–19.

KATÔ, Y. and TAKAGI, A. (1955–6). Model seismology, parts I, II and III; Seismic model studies, parts 1 and 2. *Sci. Repts. Tôhoku Univ.*, 5th ser., **7**, 35–44, 180–9, 64–85.

OLIVER, J. (1956). Body waves in layered seismic models. *Earthquake Notes*, **27**, 29–31. Eastern Section, Seismol. Soc. Amer.

RIZNICHENKO, I. V. and SHAMINA, O. G. (1960). Multiple reflected and transmitted waves. *Bull. Acad. Sci. U.S.S.R.*, Geophys. Ser. (English trans.), pp. 1129–39.

LAVERGNE, M. (1961). Recherches expérimentales sur modèles sismiques: problèmes de diffraction et de réfraction. *Bur. Centr. Séism. Internat.* A, **21**, 99–125.

RIZNICHENKO, I. V. (1961). Elastic waves with generalized velocity in two-dimensional bimorphic models. *Bull. Acad. Sci. U.S.S.R.*, Geophys. Ser. (English trans.), pp. 321–34.

Design of earthquake-resisting structures (§ 18.8)

HECK, N. H. and NEUMANN, F. (1933). Destructive earthquake motions measured for first time. *Engng News Rec.* **110**, 804–7.

CARDER, D. S. (1936). Vibration observations. *Spec. Publ. U.S. Cst Geod. Surv.* no. 201, pp. 49–106.

SEZAWA, K. and KANAI, K. (1936). Energy dissipation in seismic vibrations of an eight-storied structure. *Bull. Earthq. Res. Inst., Tokyo*, **14**, 514–24.

SEZAWA, K. and KANAI, K. (1937). Model experiment confirmations of a dynamic method of minimising the seismic vibrations of a structure. *Bull. Earthq. Res. Inst., Tokyo*, **15**, 598–613.

KANAI, K. (1938). Three-dimensional vibrations of a framed structure. *Bull. Earthq. Res. Inst., Tokyo*, **16**, 538–49.

KANAI, K. (1939). Model experiments confirming the dissipation phenomena (scattering) in the seismic vibration of a structure. *Bull. Earthq. Res. Inst., Tokyo*, **17**, 37–48.

PATTERSON, W. D. (1940). Determination of ground periods. *Bull. Seismol. Soc. Amer.* **30**, 129–38.

HOUSNER, G. W. (1949). Current practice in the design of structures to resist earthquakes. *Bull. Seismol. Soc. Amer.* **39**, 169–79.

HOUSNER, G. W. (1955). Properties of strong ground motion earthquakes. *Bull. Seismol. Soc. Amer.* **45**, 197–218.

HOUSNER, G. W. (1959). Behaviour of structures during earthquakes. *Proc. Amer. Soc. Civ. Eng.* **85**, 107.

SCIENCE COUNCIL OF JAPAN (1960). *Proceedings of Second World Conference on Earthquake Engineering.* Vols. I–III, Tokyo.

HUDSON, D. E. (1962). Some problems in the application of spectrum techniques to strong-motion earthquake analysis. *Bull. Seismol. Soc. Amer.* **52**, 417–30.

TANABASHI, R., KOBORI, T. and KANETA, K. (1962). Nonlinear torsional vibration of structures due to an earthquake. *Bull. Disaster Prev. Res. Inst.* **56**, 1–40.

HOUSNER, G. W. and others (1963). An engineering report on the Chilean earthquakes of May 1960. *Bull. Seismol. Soc. Amer.* **53**, 219–480

INDEX

Italic figures denote an entry in the list of references

Double surface layers, waves in, 95–6
Dow, R. B., *344*
Doyle, H. A., *356*
Drum rotation, 141, 184
Dummy suffix, 9
Dunite, 214–15, 245–6
Duvall, G. E., *330*
Dynamical magnification, 144

Earth, as vibrating continuous system, 51–3, 250–65
— central core of, 3, 168–70, 171, 217–18, 220–3, 241–4, 247–9, 256, 264–5
— central density, 232, 238, 242, 265
— chemical inhomogeneity in, 230, 237, 240–2
— composition of, 213–15, 230, 244–9, 313
— compressibility of, 233, 238, 240–4
— crust of, 79, 193–216
— deep interior of, 217–49, 263–5, 297–300, 304, 313
— density distribution of, 214–15, 226–32, 238, 240–2
— discontinuities within, 201–2, 217–23, 244–9
— elasticity of, 212–15, 233, 238
— ellipticity of, 163–4, 173–5, 179–80, 239–40
— gravity anomalies, 244
— gravity variation, 234, 238
— imperfections in elasticity of, 82–3
— inner core of, 169–70, 220–1, 242–4, 248–9, 265, 313
— magnetism of, 244, 306, 313
— mantle of, 168, 218, 225, 240–1, 244–6, 256, 260, 264, 313
— mass of, 226
— mean density of, 226
— model, 109, 125, 154, 172, 174, 176, 217, 224, 226–7, 231–9, 251, 256–7, 263–5, 284
— moment of inertia of, 226, 230–2, 239
— outer core of, 169–70, 221, 225, 247–9
— poles of, 180, 225
— pressure distribution in, 235, 238
— regions, subcrustal, 4, 222
— rigidity of, 225–6, 233, 238, 242–4
— solidity of, 225, 242–4
— strength of, 280–3
— symmetry of, 163, 224

— temperature (gradient) in, 227–9, 243
— tidal effects, 225, 250, 256, 288
— velocity (*P* and *S*) distributions in, 119–22, 201–7, 223–5, 241–2, 259
Earth motion, acceleration of, 147, 148, 316, 328
— — amplitudes of, 80, 125–36, 148, 156, 166, 256, 264, 267–70
— — components of, 137
— — general, 145–6
— — impulsive, 144–5, 150
— — inferred from seismograms, 146–7
— — oscillatory character of, 77–80
— — periods of, 148–9, 257–63, 316
— — simple harmonic, 143–4, 150
Earthquake acceleration, 147, 148, 316, 328
— aftershocks, 286–7, 288, 290
— amplitude, 80, 97–8, 125–36, 156, 166, 185–6, 210, 217, 219, 220, 267–70, 271, 276
— appraisals of, 1, 317–19, 328
— 'average', 172, 173
— belts, 278
— bodily waves, theory of, 73–84
— catalogues, 1, 190, 278
— causes of, 273–4
— deep-focus, 53, 177–8, 185, 209, 212, 275–7, 278–9, 281
— destructive, 272, 287, 290, 318, 328
— direction of first movement in, 187, 283–4, 303
— distant, 148
— distribution, 277–9
— effects, 1, 315–22
— energy of, 266–70, 271–3, 278–9, 280–1
— epicentre, 154, 190, 318–19
— field investigations of, 273, 316–19
— focal depth of, 154, 164–6, 177–8, 189, 269, 275–7, 278–9, 281, 301
— focal region of, 153–4, 274–7, 280–1, 295, 316–17, 318–19
— focus, 154, 275, 277
— foreshock, 287
— frequency, 271–3
— magnitude, 270–3, 288, 296–7, 300–1
— major, 272, 277–9, 280–1, 288–90, 296–7
— multiple, 78, 287
— near, 134, 148, 155, 164, 193–207, 267–8
— normal, 158, 185, 271, 275, 277–9